Quantitative Techniques for
Marketing Decisions

4.95

Quantitative Techniques for Marketing Decisions

MARVIN A. JOLSON, D.B.A.
University of Maryland

RICHARD T. HISE, D.B.A.
Shippensburg State College

THE MACMILLAN COMPANY • *New York*
Collier-Macmillan Limited • *London*

THE MACMILLAN COMPANY
866 Third Avenue, New York, New York 10022

COLLIER–MACMILLAN CANADA, LTD., Toronto, Ontario

Library of Congress catalog card number: 72-190155

Printing: 1 2 3 4 5 6 7 8   Year: 3 4 5 6 7 8 9 0

To Betty and Carol
. . . Our Optimal Decisions

Preface

Marketing students are often "shook up" by the mere mention of the expression "quantitative methods." They regret that the material is required. They perceive statistical and mathematical methods as being a combination of black magic and mental jujitsu. Obviously, many university faculty members have failed to change or reduce the students' negative reactions at a classroom level. It is normal for most people to shrink from anticipated danger especially when they face an unknown opponent that has the reputation of being a "student killer."

Two approaches are open to the teacher:

1. He can minimize the amount of resistance to be expected.
2. He can, tacitly acknowledging that some subjects are more difficult than others, give the student confidence in his ability to overcome this obstacle by mastering the material, building a much-needed foundation for future studies, and getting a good grade.

It is unlikely that a student can be persuaded that he will meet with *no* resistance. After all, the very potent student feedback system negates this possibility.

The second approach means giving the student new weapons—weapons he never before had available. A man who anticipates an argument with a tiger will approach his ordeal with much more confidence if he has a well-oiled, large-caliber rifle he can trust. It is the authors' wish that this text be such a weapon.

The first two marketing courses encountered by business school students are typically titled "Principles of Marketing" and "Marketing Management," respectively. Such courses tend to be descriptive in nature, reinforcing the impression that descriptive ability is important in business and perhaps, conversely, that an analytical approach is not. However, as new-found opportunities for rapid quantitative analysis shorten the decision-making cycle and increase the competitive demand for managerial excellence, course designs are beginning to change. In one direction, marketing management courses are bursting out into the field of applied mathematics, including probability sampling, operations research, and marketing research. Few schools intend to continue a purely descriptive format. Most universities are in the process of integrating the descriptive and analytical components of marketing management into a useful blend of intuition and science.

This text is intended, ideally, as a three-to-four-week section of a full-semester undergraduate course in marketing management. The descriptive material has already been presented during both the "principles" and "management" courses. Once the student has been exposed to the relationships connecting the firm's objectives with the multifaceted controllable and uncontrollable characteristics of the marketing environment, he is ready to concentrate on problem solving.

We have assumed as prerequisites a reasonable grasp of college algebra, probability theory, and matrix algebra. The scope of the book is intentionally limited. The authors prefer not to introduce the student to a large number of quantitative tools which can be used to solve an infinite number of marketing problems. In fact, following a summary of the familiar framework of decision theory, four and *only four* quantitative tools are covered, all in detail, so that the student may learn to use them and to appreciate their strengths and weaknesses in attacking and solving marketing problems. These are:

1. Bayesian analysis.
2. Simulation and the Markov process.
3. Linear programming.
4. Differential calculus.

In each chapter, illustrative examples are given and solved problems dominate the text. The examples and assigned exercises are in many cases based upon actual corporate situations. The student hopefully will develop a knack of "thinking situationally." Too often, students learn how to use mathematical and statistical tools in an ordered sequence with the result that they look for a problem to fit a given tool rather than seeking an effective tool to solve a current problem.

Our objective of simplicity obviously points this text in the direction of undergraduate marketing students. Although it is designed to be used as a supplementary text in a basic marketing management course, the material may be easily adopted as part of undergraduate or graduate courses in "Marketing Research," "Operations Research," or "Quantitative Methods in Marketing." Moreover, it is geared to serve those who, in their capacity as decision makers in their firm, seek to apply the more useful quantitative tools.

MARVIN A. JOLSON
RICHARD T. HISE

Contents

CHAPTER 3 *Simulation as a Marketing Tool*   71

CHAPTER 4 *Linear Programming for Marketing Decisions*   117

Quantitative Techniques for Marketing Decisions

CHAPTER 1

A Framework for Marketing Decisions

Until recently most marketing executives made their decisions almost completely on intuition or chance. Perhaps this explains the use of such terms in the marketing literature as "judgment," "insight," "wisdom," "hunch," or "seat-of-the-pants management." These expressions contrast with the notions of "precision," "scientific management," and "dependence on data" that characterize quantitative techniques. The growing use of quantitative methods in marketing does not mean that the marketing manager's experience, know-how, or past success patterns are no longer important in the realm of marketing management. In fact, many subfunctions of marketing emphasize the need for intuition and common sense. Examples include the sizing up of a prospect, the design of an ethical sales presentation, and the selection of an appropriate common carrier.

1.1 Are Quantitative Methods Practical?

Since most undergraduate marketing students are not budding market researchers and even fewer are potential doctoral candidates, the question of the *why* of quantitative methods in undergraduate marketing courses is posed. Is it merely fashionable for the new graduate to bandy about such "sophisticated" terms as linear programming, Markov chains, optimization models, Bayesian analysis, factor analysis, or multiple correlation? Is one's first boss impressed by such verbal glibness? Put directly, when and under what circumstances will the new graduate be required to use any of the quantitative tools that he carries in his newly acquired black bag?

Several of the quantitative models mentioned previously have received multiple plaudits for their accomplishments. Yet when evaluated against the spectrum of practical marketing problems, the use of marketing models, particularly mathematical models, has been quite limited. Perhaps, then, it is the promise of *potential* quantitative applications in marketing, rather than *actual* applications, which has triggered the acceleration of quantitative emphasis for marketing students. Is it that marketing faculties are not practical enough—or that marketing practitioners are not academic enough? In all fairness the answer seems to be: a little bit of each. For example, in the marketing classroom, the problems surrounding sales management and personal selling are often viewed with a jaundiced eye as to their academic respectability. On the other hand, it is not uncommon for most marketing managers to merely assume away critical marketing variables. For instance, demand is assumed; consumer behavior is taken as given; promotional effects are treated as knowns; competitive strategies and reactions are viewed as automatic processes; market share and sales potential are treated as known quantities.[1] To some degree, then, the business schools have produced a steady flow of quantitative techniques that have seldom been applied in practical marketing situations but have furnished impressive manuscripts for esoteric journals that have not been understandable by marketing executives.

Perhaps, however, the failing lies with marketing management. Perhaps, in fact, when business is good, as in a sellers' market, these failings and others are swept under the rug of complacency. Many companies whose well-known products generate virtual monopolies have seemingly ignored all the right things to do, including modern technology in various functional areas. Yet sales do not seem to drop off. Recently a Canadian sales manager criticized such a company.

> That damn company mistreats its salesmen, uses deceptive sales methods, is making a poorer product, is raising prices . . . and still sales are holding up. The company is so well known that you can hit it, kick it, spit on it, and pour cold water on it. But nothing can hurt it. The product still sells.

Such comments and other negative word-of-mouth publicity have done much to blur the image of business for the young graduate. Consequently, it is not surprising that our young marketing people feel that industry has little desire for the sophisticated, bright, college-trained person; i.e., the skills of our new graduates are not likely to be used quickly enough in many of the marketing jobs now offered by industry.

On the other hand, such perceptions on the part of the business-school graduate may be ill founded. Consider the following caption in a recent recruiting ad for MBA graduates:

WE'RE LOOKING FOR A BRIGHT YOUNG GUY WITH HIS MASTER'S WHO DOESN'T WANT TO BE TREATED LIKE A BRIGHT YOUNG GUY WITH HIS MASTER'S

The body of the full-page ad includes "We figure you've had enough school for a while. So we'll give you a chance to stub your toe. We'll show you the ropes but we won't tie you down." The implication is that the bright, young executive-to-be welcomes a track to run on but doesn't want a groove to

[1] Eugene J. Kelley and William Lazer, *Managerial Marketing—Perspectives and Viewpoints* (Homewood, Ill.: Richard D. Irwin, Inc., 1967), p. 247.

confine him. The above copy is merely one of a growing number of indications that management no longer believes in the pragmatist–intellectual dichotomy shown in Table 1–1.[2]

TABLE 1–1. Differences in Attitudes and Inclinations

A: Pragmatic	B: Intellectual
* Joiners: loyal to a church, a company, a community	* Nonjoiners: loyal to a discipline or an art
* Accept hierarchy of power	* Accept hierarchy of intellect or talent
* Accept the fact that power comes from seniority in organization	* Accept power stemming from intellectual attainment, not seniority
* Seek praise from superiors in power	* Seek praise from high priests of discipline
* Prefer life of action to life of reflection	
* Uneasy with abstractions; prefer the concrete	* Prefer ideas and words to life of action
* See government as an organization, a vast bureaucracy	* Prefer abstractions to the concrete and the detailed
* Often solve problems intuitively or judgmentally	* See government as "The People"
	* Tend to think analytically and conceptually

SOURCE: John S. Fielden, "The Right Young People for Business," *Harvard Business Review* (March–April 1966), Exhibit I, p. 77. Reproduced with permission of Harvard Business Review.

This is because seat-of-the-pants, reactive managerial styles are already on the wane, and increased emphasis is being placed on "scientific" analysis and planning. Experience is still invaluable (if it is up to date), but it must be used with greater discipline. Analysis is now more rigorous, and computer techniques permit more alternatives to be analyzed in greater depth. Therefore, business needs some of the column B values (Table 1–1) to blend with the column A values. Industry desperately requires some A/B newcomers to blend with the pure A types who are no longer adequate within today's spectrum of decision requirements.[3] For example, in the marketing area alone, increasing use of Bayesian decision theory is evidence of management's desire to recruit graduates skilled in quantitative methods who can in turn help to create a genuine A/B atmosphere within the firm.

1.2   Major Areas of Application of Quantitative Tools

Such a proposed combination of theory and practice clearly punctuates this text's purpose of attempting to bridge the chasm that exists between

[2] Table 1–1 was reproduced from the article by John S. Fielden, "The Right Young People for Business," *Harvard Business Review* (March–April 1966), p. 77.

[3] *Ibid.* Also see Robert F. Vandell, "Management Evolution in the Quantitative World," *Harvard Business Review* (January–February 1970), p. 87.

mathematically oriented tools and their application to practical marketing problem areas. Although the marketing-mix controllable variables have been broadly divided into four categories (product, price, place, and promotion decisions), the subsections of these four major areas have been estimated to approximate some 150 to 200 elements. It is beyond the scope of this treatment to illustrate the application of the huge number of analytical tools that will aid management in selecting optimal strategies in all these subsections.

Instead, we have first examined the applications of quantitative methods in marketing since 1955 to determine those areas where the most successful applications have taken place. The major applications have occurred in the areas of (1) new products, (2) pricing, (3) physical distribution, (4) advertising, and (5) sales-force management.

1.3   Objectives of the Text

Next we have selected only a few quantitative techniques for inclusion in this text. These are (1) Bayesian analysis, (2) simulation and the Markov process, (3) linear programming, and (4) differential calculus. The purpose of this book is to introduce the major concepts underlying these approaches and to describe and illustrate their relevance to the analysis of those marketing problems which lie within the confines of the strategic areas previously listed. Succinctly put, the subject of this text is decision making, which involves quantitative techniques that are and/or can be important in helping the decision maker to make better marketing decisions. The criteria for selecting *these* four tools to the exclusion of all others are

1. General applicability potential in the marketing area.
2. Comprehension level of the student.
3. Our ability to generate appropriate practice problems.
4. Usefulness in developing a conceptual framework that will develop a background for understanding more complex models.

1.4   Organization of the Text

The balance of Chapter 1 provides a general framework within which the content of succeeding chapters can be placed. Specifically Chapter 1 deals with decision frameworks and conditions with heavy emphasis upon the high degree of uncertainty that is associated with the outcomes of marketing decisions. A special (and highly practical) case of uncertainty is partial ignorance of the probabilities of the various states of nature. Bayesian decision theory has been developed to deal with these types of problems, which are developed in Chapter 2.

Simulation and Markov processes, the subject of Chapter 3, deals with a sequence of events that are generated by a probabilistic process over time. Although our coverage will emphasize applications in analyzing customer brand-shifting behavior, other practical uses of these techniques, including sales-force turnover, will be investigated. Chapter 4 concentrates on linear programming; however, unlike most texts, the conventional departmental production example is omitted in favor of situations that specifically interest the marketing manager.

Finally, Chapter 5 develops the set of optimization techniques that are based on the differential calculus. This chapter limits its applications to optimization of differentiable functions of no more than two independent decision variables, which in turn will train the student to deal with even more variables.

When dealing with statistical or mathematical processes that may be new to the reader, the text seemingly is quite redundant. The authors want the student to understand each step in a process so that the method may be applied in a situation yet unencountered. We believe in *understanding* steps, not *memorizing* steps. We are very opposed to the memorization of formulas. These can be looked up in a manual by the marketing manager. For the most part, therefore, formulas (including "the rule of Bayes") are de-emphasized.

Hopefully, this text will accomplish two diverse goals. First, the authors will strive to use quantitative analysis as a means of better structuring and organizing a student's thought processes. Second, a desirable yield will be the reader's ability to plug in the appropriate technique to solve an existing marketing problem.

1.5   Marketing Management Function

A fundamental task of the modern marketing leader is to formulate and implement a never-ending series of yearly, monthly, weekly, daily, and even hourly decision strategies in order to accomplish a given marketing goal or objective.

However, before the marketing manager can select the "best" action from the array of available alternatives, certain preliminary steps must first be considered. Initially, the feasibility of the expressed goal must be examined. The marketing manager cannot arbitrarily establish an objective of "$3 million dollars of profit" or "$10 million dollars of sales" or "a 30 per cent share of the market." Numerous external and internal resistances and constraints must be reckoned with. Many of these constraints are not controllable or easily influenced by the marketing manager. If the resistances to be encountered are too formidable, the objective may require modification to a more realistic level. Then, after establishing reasonably attainable targets, the marketing manager may select an appropriate combination of controllable variables (i.e., product, price, promotion, and place strategies), which hopefully will accomplish the established goal. This selection and manipulation of the variable factors of the marketing mix can be accomplished in an infinite number of ways.

The selection of the optimal strategies by the firm is further complicated by the differing and sometimes conflicting objectives of the key entities in the marketing system. Although objectives among firms vary, marketing managers and classical economists are generally in agreement that for a firm, the main objective is to maximize profits; for a customer, to maximize utility or satisfaction; and for a community, to maximize welfare or benefit.

1.6   Sequence of the Marketing Decision

Figure 1–1 helps the reader to conceptualize the totality of the marketing manager's problem and to understand the relationship of the various elements of the marketing mix with the environmental factors, corporate objectives, and marketing goals. Also, a logical sequence for marketing management activities is included.

The flow chart (Figure 1–1) starts with an examination of external uncontrollable factors as they affect the firm under consideration. It is not difficult to understand that these external environmental forces both assist and impede existing marketing programs. For example, ecology forces have compelled automakers to modify their production processes, to raise prices, and to emphasize new antipollution features in their advertising appeals. Improved transportation technology has led to a reduction of the average inventory level for some firms. Increasing government pressures in response to consumerism have increased the cancellation rate of contracts sold by door-to-door sellers, forcing some of these firms to shift to mail-order or in-store marketing. The banning of cyclamates had a serious marketing impact upon the processors of dietary foods.

Obviously all possible external events cannot be anticipated. However, a preliminary inquiry into these real and fancied influences may serve to stimulate thinking to clarify poorly articulated problem parameters and to compel decision makers to give due weight to factors that may have been overlooked or previously dismissed as insignificant.

Next, in keeping with the growing emergence of the marketing concept, the marketing staff must be constantly aware of its customers' needs, desires, and requirements and the environmental factors that affect them. The firm cannot restrict its "customer orientation" to its immediate customer. For example, the manufacturer of consumer products must plan its marketing programs after a careful consideration of wholesaler, retailer, and consumer wants and expectations. Such a customer focus demands the coordination

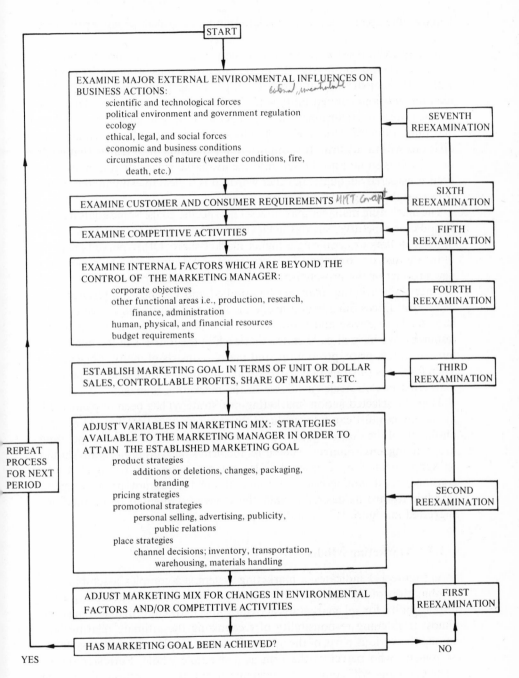

FIGURE 1–1.   Sequence of Marketing Management Activities.

and teaming up of all marketing-related activities so as to produce profitable results.

Management must keep abreast of competitive offerings, pricing, promotional effort, and so on. Also the marketing group must of necessity operate within the constraints imposed by top management, including budget requirements and compatibility with the firm's overall objectives. To assure an integrated effort, the marketing manager must be familiar with weaknesses and limitations of personnel, techniques, and policies of other functional divisions within the firm. It is important for the student to realize that goals or objectives should not be set until the available means or resources have been considered adequate. In other words, it is logical to estimate the inputs before establishing a desired output.

The marketing manager may now set his specific goals. Some goals may be periodic or repetitive, such as achieving a specific sales volume in terms of units or dollars or acquiring a higher market share. Other pursuits may be of the unique, or "one-time," variety, such as the launching of a completely new product or the proselytism of a rival sales manager.

Once the marketing manager has studied and weighed the physical and behavioral forces outside and inside his firm and developed realistic goals, he is ready to devise and install a mix of procedures that fit his available resources. We have already stated that each of the four P's in the marketing mix—product, price, promotion, and place—consists of many subelements. Therefore, it is obvious that there are at least tens of thousands of possible marketing-mix strategies available to the marketing manager.

After the selected action (marketing-mix strategy) has been implemented, management must carefully evaluate the progress over time toward accomplishment of the desired goal(s). It is evident that the marketer is operating in a dynamic environment. Therefore, the firm's marketing program should be supplemented by empirical tests and measurements to check trade, consumer, and competitors' response. If the firm is not progressing on schedule toward its desired results, the series of sequential reexaminations suggested in Figure 1–1 should take place.

1.7 Marketing Model

As Figure 1–1 indicates, a marketing system is a complex assemblage or combination of activities, institutions, and operations. In accepting total responsibility for all marketing activities, the marketing manager has the almost frightening responsibility of recognizing the intimate relationships among the various parts of the system. Referring to the view of the systems' proponent, who perceives the firm as a dynamic whole, Forrester states: "The company will come to be recognized not as a collection of separate functions, but as a system in which the flows of information, materials, manpower, capital equipment, and money set up forces that determine the basic tendencies toward growth, fluctuation, and decline."[4]

Figure 1–1 is a model that translates the described marketing relationship into a series of sequential blocks. It is known as a logical flow model. In general, a model is anything that shows the relations and interrelations of actions and reactions—of cause and effect—in operational situations. A model is a shorthand representation, an abstraction of an actual object or real situation. Other examples of models are road maps, circuit diagrams of television sets, a firm's balance sheet or income statement, a drawing of a simple demand curve, or a mathematical equation.

1.8   The Construction of Marketing Models

The flow chart of Figure 1–1 was developed by the *abstractions* approach. In essence, a real-world situation has been perceived and converted into a model. In abstraction, the model builder perceives certain logical conceptual relationships among the variables or factors in a marketing situation. Once he is able to state or list these relationships, he may quantify them by use of available records, experiments, or simulation. He may then derive a mathematical model that can be applied in a live situation.[5]

For example, suppose a sales manager for Avon Cosmetics Company observes through experience and analysis of data that unit sales increase in direct proportion to the number of salesladies in the field. Once the productivity per salesperson has been determined, the relationship may be quantified and expressed in terms of a linear equation, i.e.,

$$Q = KN$$

where Q = number of sales in units
K = unit sales/month/salesperson
N = number of active salespeople

Such a model has been developed for door-to-door sales organizations and it has proved to be quite useful for planning lead requirements, new branch-office needs, and recruiting policies.[6]

Another process of model building is by *realization*. In this case, the model starts with a consideration of a logically consistent conceptual system. Then some aspect of the real world can be viewed as the model of the system. It is

[4] Jay W. Forrester, "Industrial Dynamics," *Harvard Business Review*, Vol. 36, No. 4 (July–August 1958), p. 52.

[5] For a more detailed description of the abstraction and realization approaches to model building, see William Lazer, "The Role of Models in Marketing," *Journal of Marketing*, Vol. 26 (April 1962), pp. 9–14.

[6] Marvin A. Jolson, "How Important Is Sales Force Size?" *Business Studies*, North Texas State University, Vol. 10 (Spring 1971), pp. 31–40.

a process of going from the logical system to the real world.[7] The Markov process to be discussed in Chapter 3 is developed in this way. This model studies the present market shares of the various firms in an industry and what has happened through some transition time. By starting with this model, the decision maker may isolate the direction and degree of change in brand loyalty that is currently taking place. If things are not going well, the model may provide useful clues as to recommended changes in the firm's marketing strategies.

1.9   Types of Marketing Models

Marketing models may be categorized and dichotomized in many ways, depending upon the dimensions and distinguishing characteristics that are used as criteria for classification. Two examples are offered.

DESCRIPTIVE AND NORMATIVE MODELS. A descriptive model describes how a system works without making value judgments about the phenomenon being studied and without attempting to select the best strategy from a list of alternatives. The flow chart of Figure 1–1, the accounting model, the Markov brand-switching, and simulation models are descriptive in purpose.

NORMATIVE DECISION MODEL. Normative decision model is a term often applied to the choice principles that *ought* to be used. The normative model is prescriptive in that it assists management in selecting the optimal action. Succeeding chapters covering Bayesian statistics, differential calculus, and linear programming will offer applications of normative or prescriptive models.

DETERMINISTIC AND STOCHASTIC MODELS. Many quantitative techniques assume that the data required by a model are known with certainty. The linear-programming examples offer a neat set of objective functions and constraints. The decision maker knows precisely the amount of profit contribution resulting from a sales presentation or an advertising insertion. Promotional costs are known exactly and the input data include such information as the length of time required to deliver a sales presentation. The differential calculus chapter (Chapter 5) assumes that precise mathematical relationships between demand and its determinants—price, advertising, and so on—can be derived. Fixed and variable costs are known with certainty. Such models and techniques are *deterministic*.

There are, however, many applications that may be more appropriately handled by use of *stochastic* models. Stochastic is synonymous with "chance," "random," or "probabilistic." The Markov process and the Monte Carlo method are stochastic tools that are used to make conditional predictions

[7] C. H. Coombs, H. Raiffa, and R. M. Throll, "Some Views on Mathematical Models and Measurement Theory," in R. M. Throll, C. H. Coombs, and R. L. Davis (Eds.), *Decision Processes* (New York: John Wiley & Sons, Inc., 1954), pp. 20–21.

about brand share, customer-service requirements, and other sought-after information. Bayesian analysis is largely stochastic in nature because of the assumption that the marketing manager can state probability distributions to describe the elements of uncertainty in the model. However, since the input data include precisely stated payoff values for each strategy/event combination, the Bayesian model also takes on a deterministic dimension.

Although the authors have no intention of minimizing the usefulness of deterministic approaches, many authors are finding it useful to introduce stochastic versions of deterministic models.[8]

OTHER CLASSIFICATIONS OF MODELS.   Marketing models may also be classified as mathematical or nonmathematical, according to the degree of abstraction, according to the types of equations used, goal oriented or systems oriented, static or dynamic, and others.

1.10   Certainty and the Marketing Decision

Our introductory remarks have hinted at, and succeeding examples will reinforce, the fact that marketing decisions are most often made in the context of insufficient information about processes that are dynamic, most often stochastic, nonlinear, interactive, and downright difficult.[9] We have suggested that the decision maker has various possible strategies available to him and that he has certain specific goals he is trying to achieve. If he could predict with certainty the state of the uncontrollable elements, he would have little difficulty in arriving at an optimal decision.

For example, suppose a resort-hotel manager is contemplating a gala July 4 weekend that would include exhibitions by golfers Jack Nicklaus, Lee Trevino, and Arnold Palmer; tennis star Arthur Ashe; and entertainers Johnny Cash and Barbra Streisand. The manager would be delighted to invest the required $100,000 to invite all six celebrities if he knew the weather would be perfect over the weekend. With perfect weather, the hotel would be filled to capacity, ensuring handsome profits. If, however, the July 4 weather turns out to be variable, the hotel's profits will be minimal. Finally, it is anticipated that a rainy weekend will discourage patronage, resulting in a heavy financial setback for the hotel. The manager determines that he has three practical alternatives—(1) invite all six performers, (2) invite only Cash and Streisand, or (3) do not invite any big-name performers. Which of the three strategies should be selected?

We have assumed that the strategies and states of nature (weather conditions) can each be summarized in three possibilities. We also assume that

---

[8] After the reader has completed the linear-programming chapter in this text he may enjoy a treatment of the stochastic linear-programming model. See Harvey M. Wagner, *Principles of Management Science* (Englewood Cliffs, N.J.: Prentice-Hall, Inc., 1970), pp. 351–356.

[9] Philip Kotler, *Marketing Management: Analysis, Planning and Control* (Englewood Cliffs, N.J.: Prentice-Hall, Inc., 1967), p. vii.

the decision maker is in a position to quantify the profit consequence for each strategy/weather combination. All this information can be summarized in a payoff matrix. A matrix is nothing more than a two-dimensional array of numbers arranged in rows and columns. We shall use the rows to represent available strategies and the columns to represent relevant states of nature. The entry at the intersection of each row and column is the *payoff* or specific outcome that occurs with a given state of nature and the use of a particular strategy.

	Weather Conditions		
Strategy	N_1: Perfect	N_2: Variable	N_3: Rain
S_1: Invite all performers	$340,000	$30,000	−$110,000
S_2: Invite Cash and Streisand	180,000	60,000	−40,000
S_3: Invite none	−40,000	−70,000	−10,000

Obviously, if the hotel manager received a private message from heaven that guaranteed perfect weather, he would invite all six performers and enjoy $340,000 in profits; if he was certain of variable weather, the best payoff would be the $60,000 consequence of inviting Cash and Streisand; however, if rain were guaranteed, the best alternative would be to invite none of the celebrities and limit the hotel's losses to $10,000. The absence of an oracular communications network makes such an approach unworkable in practice.

1.11   Risk and the Marketing Decision

A more logical tactic would be to investigate the likelihood of each possible weather condition by examining weather data in the resort hotel area for previous July 4 weekends.

Suppose weather records for the past 30 seasons indicate that the weather was perfect 9 times, variable 15 times, and rainy 6 times. It would then be logical to assign historical probabilities to each possible weather event for the season being investigated: i.e., the probability of perfect weather is .30 (9/30), the probability of variable weather is .50 (15/30), and the probability of rain is .20 (6/30). The payoff matrix could then be revised as follows:

	N_1: .30	N_2: .50	N_3: .20	EV
S_1	$340,000	$30,000	$−110,000	$95,000
S_2	180,000	60,000	−40,000	76,000
S_3	−40,000	−70,000	−10,000	−49,000

The final column (EV) of the matrix represents the calculated expected values of each strategy such that the expected value of strategy 1 (S_1) is

$$EV(S_1) = 340,000(.30) + 30,000(.50) + (-110,000)(.20) = 95,000$$

Similarly,

$$EV(S_2) = 180,000(.30) + 60,000(.50) + (-40,000)(.20) = 76,000$$

$$EV(S_3) = -40,000(.30) + (-70,000)(.50) + (-10,000)(.20) = -49,000$$

Therefore, if the maximization of expected profitability is the optimizing criterion of choice, the hotel manager would select and implement S_1; i.e., he would invite all the performers.

It may be noted that the expected value of a strategy is the weighted average of all the conditional values of the strategy; i.e., the sum of each payoff value is weighted by its probability of occurrence.

To sum up the examples of decision making under *certainty* and under *risk*, we may say that certainty infers that the marketing manager knows which state of nature will occur; *risk* infers that the marketing manager knows the probability of occurrence of each of the various states of nature $(N_1, N_2, N_3, \ldots, N_i)$, so that he can calculate expected values of the strategies $(S_1, S_2, S_3, \ldots, S_j)$ to determine the optimal action. Knowledge of probabilities means that long-run frequency data or historical evidence are available. Such historical evidence exists in the case of weather conditions, defect rates of a production process, inventory movement, direct-mail response, and other recurring situations.

1.12   Uncertainty and the Marketing Decision

However, in practice the marketing manager can seldom rely on historical frequencies alone because of the preponderance of behavioral variables. There is no evidence on file which will tell us, for example, the probability that our firm's common stock will rise five points in the next five months, the probability that our star salesman will join a competitor within two years, the probability that a newly offered product will generate 12 million dollars in revenue over the next year, the probability that firms will be required to pay minimum wages to outside salesmen, or the probability that a competitor will follow our price rise.

Since most of the marketing planner's problems seem to involve decisions under uncertainty, the major focus of this text will be in that area. Several criteria for dealing with uncertainty will be treated in this chapter. The important Bayesian method will be treated fully in Chapter 2.

1.13   Criterion of Pessimism

This criterion was first introduced by Abraham Wald and is also known as the *maximin* or *Wald criterion*. Wald's attitude was that if the decision maker doesn't know anything about the probability of occurrence of the various states of nature, he should protect himself against the worst.

For an example, let us study the decision problem of a burglar-alarm firm which is considering the installation of a central-station alarm reporting center which will require an immediate investment of $200,000. The other possible actions are to lease the central-station services of a competitor or to continue to use the firm's present method of automatic police-dialing equipment. The firm has the objective of achieving the maximum net profit over the next five years. Assume also that only three relevant states of nature can occur: increased crime rate, reduced crime rate, no change in crime rate. These states of nature are *mutually exclusive* in that if one state occurs the other two cannot occur, and *collectively exhaustive* in that no other state of nature other than the three mentioned can occur.

The firm's management is able to quantify its net profits for each strategy/state of nature combination so that the payoff matrix reflects the firm's profitability in tens of thousands of dollars:

	N_1: Increased Crime	N_2: Decreased Crime	N_3: No Change in Crime Rate
S_1: Install central station	170	−15	30
S_2: Lease central station	100	10	70
S_3: Use police dialers	80	20	50

According to Wald, *the decision rule is to list the worst payoff for each strategy and then to select the best of these worst payoffs.* If he selects S_1, the worst payoff that could occur would be -15; if he selects S_2, the worst payoff would be 10; the worst outcome following the use of S_3 would be 20. The three strategies and their worst payoffs are

Strategy	Worst Payoff
1	−15
2	10
3	20

The best of the above three payoffs is 20, which would suggest use of strategy 3. This decision maker may not be a complete pessimist; he may merely be conservative or a person who feels unlucky.

1.14   Criterion of Regret

This criterion, suggested by Leonard Savage, is sometimes called the "hard-loser's criterion." Savage argues that after the strategy has been selected and a state of nature occurs, the decision maker may regret that he didn't choose a different strategy. The amount of regret may be measured by the difference between his actual payoff and the payoff that would have taken place if the true state of nature had been known.

In the burglar-alarm example of Section 1.13, suppose strategy 3 were actually selected and then the rate of crime increased. The decision maker would have selected S_1 if he had known that state of nature N_1 would take place. Thus the opportunity loss of $170 - 80 = 90$ measures his regret. If N_2 took place, there would be no regret since 20 is the largest payoff possible. If N_3 turned out to be the state of nature, the regret would be $70 - 50 = 20$.

Therefore, the procedure is to construct a new regret matrix by setting the best payoff under each state of nature equal to zero and inserting the regret values in all other cells. The new regret matrix looks like this:

	N_1	N_2	N_3
S_1	0	35	40
S_2	70	10	0
S_3	90	0	20

Now Savage proposes to apply the criterion of pessimism (Wald) to the regret matrix. The worst that can happen for each of the strategies is

Strategy	Worst Regret
1	40
2	70
3	90

The decision maker now chooses the strategy reflecting least regret, i.e., strategy 1.

This criterion is quite practical in that most people who make wrong decisions, including managers and consumers, experience a form of remorse or regret which one seeks to minimize.

1.15   Criterion of Rationality

This criterion, which is also known as the *Laplace criterion*, permits the decision maker to convert the decision problem under uncertainty into a decision problem under risk. The rationale is that if we don't know the probabilities with which the various states of nature will occur, we can assume that each state of nature is equally likely to occur.

In the burglar-alarm example we thus say that $p(N_1) = p(N_2) = p(N_3) = \frac{1}{3}$. Then we calculate the expected payoff for each strategy and select the strategy with the optimal payoff. For example,

Strategy	Expected Payoff
1	$\frac{1}{3}(170) + \frac{1}{3}(-15) + \frac{1}{3}(30) = 61.7$
2	$\frac{1}{3}(100) + \frac{1}{3}(10) + \frac{1}{3}(70) = 60.0$
3	$\frac{1}{3}(80) + \frac{1}{3}(20) + \frac{1}{3}(50) = 50.0$

Strategy 1 is therefore selected.

Marketing analysts argue that most alternative marketing events are not equally likely to occur. A competitor's reaction to a firm's product improvement is hardly analogous to the toss of a coin. These arguments are in essence objecting to the use of all three decision criteria on the grounds that the decision maker is rarely completely ignorant about the likelihood of occurrence of the various states of nature. The very fact that the decision maker's personal knowledge and overall experience should be considered in assessing probabilities is the cornerstone of the Bayesian approach.

1.16   Criterion of Optimism

Hurwicz takes a step toward the Bayesian approach by suggesting that the optimistic decision maker should assign a probability called the *coefficient of optimism* (k) to the best possible payoff for each strategy. $1 - k$ will be assigned to the worst payoff for each strategy. *The criterion of optimism* suggests the calculation of the weighted average of the best and worst payoffs for each strategy.

Suppose that the decision maker in our example is fairly optimistic and establishes a coefficient of optimism (k) equal to .70.

Strategy	Best Payoff: $k = .70$	Worst Payoff $1 - k = .30$	Expected Payoff
1	170	-15	$170(.70) - 15(.30) = 114.5$
2	100	10	$100(.70) + 10(.30) = 73$
3	80	20	$80(.70) + 20(.30) = 62$

This criterion dictates the selection of S_1. If the decision maker is a complete optimist, $k = 1$ and he would be using the *maximax* criterion, i.e., selection of the strategy corresponding to the best payoff in the entire matrix. A coefficient of optimism equal to zero leads to the *criterion of pessimism*.

It may seem that both the *criterion of rationality* and the *criterion of optimism* represent attempts to convert a decision problem under uncertainty to one under risk.

1.17   Summary of Decision Criteria

The comparison of decisions and description of the various decision makers in the present illustration are as follows:

Criterion	Selected Strategy	Type of Decision Maker
Pessimism	Use police dialers	Cautious
Regret	Install central station	Bad loser
Rationality	Install central station	Rational
Optimism	Install central station	Adventurous
Maximax	Install central station	Speculator or optimist

In this example, four of the five illustrated criteria called for the use of S_1 (install central station). This is true because of the specific nature of the present problem, where an increase in crime will produce greater profits than for any other state of nature regardless of strategy employed. There are, however, many cases where each criterion of choice will suggest a different strategy. The exercises at the end of the chapter will further illustrate the possibility of disagreement among the criteria.

1.18   Decision Tree Analysis

The *decision-tree model* may frequently be used as an alternative to the payoff matrix. In fact, the decision tree may be preferred to the payoff matrix when the decision problem is more complex. First, let us use the decision tree to solve the decision problem under risk described in Section 1.11. The payoff matrix developed by the resort hotel manager is as follows:

| Strategy | Weather Conditions | | |
	N_1: Perfect, $P = .30$	N_2: Variable, $P = .50$	N_3: Rain, $P = .20$
S_1: Invite all performers	$340,000	$30,000	$ − 110,000
S_2: Invite Cash and Striesand	180,000	60,000	− 40,000
S_3: Invite none	− 40,000	− 70,000	− 10,000

Let us examine the portion of the decision tree that illustrates strategy 1 (invite all performers). If S_1 is employed, three possible events can take place: perfect weather, variable weather, or rain. Each event has a different probability of occurrence and will result in a different consequence or payoff:

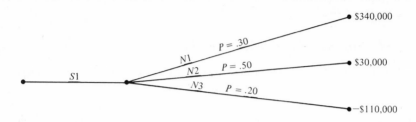

Strategies 2 and 3 may be pictured in the same way along with their events and consequences. The entire decision tree is shown in Figure 1–2(I).

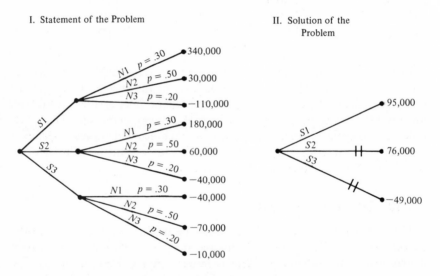

FIGURE 1–2.   An Example of Decision-tree Analysis.

Analysis starts at the right-hand side of the decision tree. First the expected consequences for the event fork following S_1 are calculated; i.e., $EV(S_1) = 340{,}000(.30) + 30{,}000(.50) - 110{,}000(.20) = \$95{,}000$. The event forks following S_2 and S_3 are similarly treated. In Figure 1–2 (II), these expected values replace the actual event forks and their consequences. Since the payoff of \$95,000 associated with strategy 1 is greater than the payoffs of \$76,000 and −\$49,000, the S_2 and S_3 branches are blocked off with vertical hash marks (—||—) and S_1 is the optimal act.

There are many situations in which decision-tree analysis provides a neat solution whereas a payoff-matrix approach is practically useless. For example, a manufacturing firm that is presently earning $200,000 per year has become disenchanted with its vice president for marketing and is concerned that its earnings will not grow if he is not replaced. The firm has three immediate options:

1. Use an executive search firm to locate a replacement.
2. Hire a replacement by use of classified ads.
3. Retain the present vice president.

The executive search firm indicates a 40 per cent probability that they will be able to find a suitable replacement. The costs of the two recruiting methods, the probability of the replacement's success by each method, and the resultant effects on profits are as follows:

	Cost	Probability of Replacement's Success	Effect on Profits (recruiting costs not included)
Executive search firm	$20,000	.8	Successful man (+ $200,000) Unsuccessful man (− $50,000)
Classified-ad campaign	$5,000	.6	Successful man (+ $100,000) Unsuccessful man (− $100,000)
Retain present employee	None	—	None

If the executive search firm cannot find a replacement, the firm can either use classified ads or do nothing. The manufacturing firm is certain that classified advertising will produce a replacement. List the three options in order of preference.

The first step is to state the problem in decision-tree form as shown in Figure 1–3.

The terminal consequences of Figure 1–3 were developed as follows:

1. *Retain present employee option:* Present earnings will remain at the present $200,000 level.
2. *Use search-firm option:* If a man is found and he is successful, the firm's profits will increase by $200,000. After the search-firm's fee of $20,000 is subtracted, the net profit increase will be $180,000, which when added to the present $200,000 earnings yields new earnings of $380,000. If the search-firm's recruit is not successful on the job, the firm's earnings will drop by $50,000 and, after the $20,000 fee is paid, the new earnings

will be $130,000, i.e., 200 − 50 − 20. If the search firm fails to find a man and the firm then decides to retain its present employee, the earnings will be reduced by the amount of the fee, $200,000 − 20,000 = $180,000. However, following the failure of the search firm to locate a man, the firm could hire a man by use of classified ads. If this man is successful, gross earnings will increase by $100,000 and when the search-firm's fee of $20,000 and the $5,000 ad cost are deducted, the firm's total earnings will be $275,000 (200 + 100 − 20 − 5). If the man hired by ads fails on the job, new earnings will total 200 − 100 − 20 − 5 = $75,000.

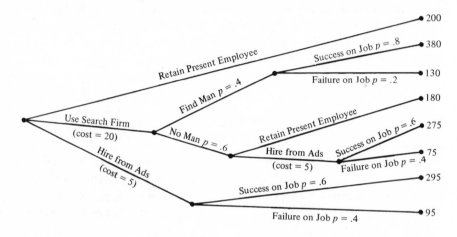

FIGURE 1–3.   Decision Tree (recruitment problem). Note: terminal values' or consequences are expressed in thousands of dollars of earnings.

3. *Classified-ad option:* If the ad approach is used initially, a successful man will increase profits to $295,000; an unsuccessful man will reduce profits to $95,000. The calculations are as follows:

$$200 − 5 + 100 = 295$$

$$200 − 5 − 100 = 95$$

Once the terminal values have been computed, the analyst should begin his solution by working from the right-hand edge of Figure 1–3. Starting at the top branch, he should attempt to replace event forks by their expected values. The first group of events to be replaced is the group attesting to success or failure on the job. For example, starting at the top and reading down, 380 with a probability of .8 and 130 with a probability of .2 may be replaced by its expected value of 330; i.e., 380(.8) + 130(.2). Similarly,

−275(.6) + 75(.4) = 195. Finally, 295(.6) + 95(.4) = 215. Following this first reduction the tree diagram will look like this:

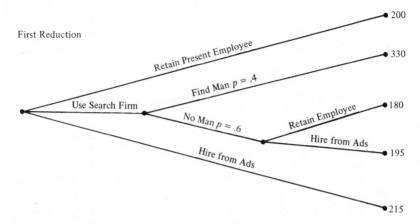

First Reduction

It will be noted that the first reduction differs from Figure 1–3 only in the respect that the expected values of the event (success–fail) have replaced the original terminal values.

Scrutiny of the right-hand edge of the decision tree following the first reduction reveals no additional expected values that can be calculated. However, suppose the search firm is used and no man is found. The company can either retain the employee (profits = 180) or hire from ads (profits = 195). Obviously the latter option will be chosen, and the second tree-diagram reduction will reflect this choice:

Second Reduction

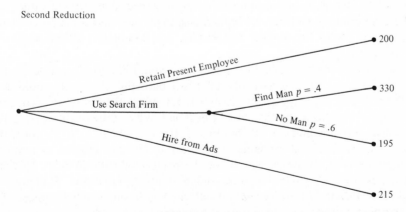

Again, examination of the right-hand side of the second reduction indicates an opportunity to replace a fork by its expected value:

$$330(.4) + 195(.6) = 249$$

The third and final tree-diagram reduction includes this replacement and yields the final solution:

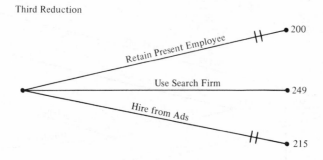

Third Reduction

Since the maximization of expected profits is the optimizing criterion, and since the option "use search firm" yields the largest expected profits of $249,000, the other two options are blocked off. The firm should initially use the search firm. If the search firm fails to locate a man, the firm should use classified ads (see first-reduction tree diagram). The decision sequence is thus defined.

1.19   Utility and Attitudes Toward Risk

In our formulation of the decision problem, we have suggested that the marketing decision maker attempts to employ the strategy that will best accomplish a given goal, objective, or degree of effectiveness or satisfaction. In most of the examples the desired accomplishment has been expressed in monetary terms. In attempting to optimize expected monetary values, we have ignored the fact that all individuals, managers, and firms do not have the same utility for money. Specifically, decision-maker attitudes toward risk may vary.

One of the authors asked a student if he would like to place a bet on the toss of a coin. The professor offered 4 to 1 odds that the result would be a "head." The student readily accepted but when the professor proposed stakes of $400 to $100, the student declined. Why? Obviously because the student was unwilling or unable to risk the loss of $100. No doubt if the professor had offered the same proposition to Howard Hughes or to a Las Vegas gambler, the wager would have been accepted without delay. Howard Hughes and the student possess different utility functions. Therefore, it appears logical that utility could be adopted by businessmen as a means for incorporating risk attitudes toward alternative outcomes.

Refer again to the recruitment problem shown in Figure 1–3. Suppose that the manufacturer is in the process of seeking acquisition by a larger firm who would call off negotiations if the manufacturer's earnings dropped below

$200,000. The manufacturer would now have only one option—to retain the present employee. Why? The answer is that the use of the search firm might lead to profit consequences of $130,000, $180,000, or as low as $75,000. The direct use of classified ads could result in a reduction of profits to the $95,000 level.

On the other hand, another manufacturer faced with the same decision situation might be willing to risk a substantial drop in earnings in exchange for the opportunity to push earnings up to the $380,000 level. His strategy would be to use the executive search firm.

The point of this discussion is that several decision makers faced with the same array of natural payoff measures in terms of money, market share, rate of return on investment, and so on, may view the problem differently. The natural measure may not be coincident with the utility the decision maker receives from the degree of achievement of his objective. Therefore, it is correct to say that utility governs the decision problem, not the natural measure.[10]

Utility is a subjective notion and it is difficult, in fact often impossible, to compare the utilities of different people. For this reason, future chapters will refer exclusively to the more familiar numerical payoffs, usually in terms of money values. The reader should remember, however, that in practice some effort should be made to substitute utility for money data.

1.20 Types of Information Inputs

It should be clear to the reader that it would be difficult if not impossible to quantify marketing decision making without an organized flow of internally generated data and externally gathered information. The development of the electronic computer has provided the means to collect such information and to analyze it fast enough to be useful. Even though all examples in this text can be solved by manual methods, larger-scale problems will require computer assistance.

The types of information available for management's use may be represented by a trichotomy consisting of *knowledge, opinion,* and *speculation.*[11] Figure 1–4 attempts to relate these information categories with the classes of decision problems we have discussed so far. When the available information is highly confirmed, the information can be called *knowledge.* At the other extreme is information called *speculation*—there is little or no evidential backing. In between is a broad area of material for which there is some basis for belief but which is not sufficiently confirmed to warrant being called

[10] David W. Miller and Martin K. Starr, *Executive Decisions and Operations Research* (Englewood Cliffs, N.J.: Prentice-Hall, Inc., 1960), pp. 63–64.

[11] Norman C. Dalkey, Memorandum RM-5888-PR, a report prepared for the United States Air Force Project Rand (Santa Monica: The Rand Corporation, June 1969), pp. 2–5. A portion of the discussion in this section is based on Dalkey's thesis.

knowledge. Dalkey calls this middling area *opinion*, which in turn serves as the foundation for stochastic models, probabilistic approaches, and the Bayesian decision-making method.

The dividing lines between the information types are quite vague and the three-way split masks the large differences that exist within types. However, Figure 1–4 offers advantages over the common tendency to dismiss whatever is not knowledge as mere speculation.

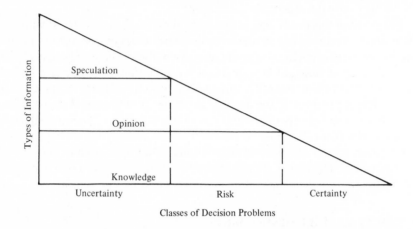

FIGURE 1–4.   Spectrum of Information Inputs.

The prototype of knowledge may be found in the systematized experimentally confirmed propositions of the natural sciences. The marketing manager's use of knowledge for generating probabilities for decisions under risk has already been demonstrated. There are those marketing managers who insist that most marketing decisions under uncertainty involve more than a dash of speculative information, quite a sprinkling of opinion, and little or no factual knowledge. However, Figure 1–4 shows that the high degree of uncertainty associated with the outcomes of marketing decisions is a result of a mixture of all three types of information input. The chapters to follow will logically reinforce the latter conclusion.

1.21   A Systematic Study of the Future

The success of the enterprise in terms of customers, products, channels, and prices represents short-range objectives, in contrast to the long-range plan for continuing in business 15 or 20 years hence. Marketing decisions are rooted in a widespread alarm that aimless actions today can lead only to conflict and chaos, to daily firefighting rather than fire prevention.

The appropriate goal of scientific decision making is nothing less than to help mold and manipulate the firm's future rather than merely fatalistically accept it. It is the authors' opinion that the firm's future can indeed be changed or guided by knowledge gained and appropriate actions taken today.

EXERCISES

1. Precisely what is meant by expected value?

2. Since the descriptive model suggests no value judgment about whether the marketing activity whose nature it reflects is good or bad, what is the purpose of using such a model?

3. Bernoulli proposed that the utility of dollars could be represented by the logarithm of the dollars. Justify such a conclusion.

4. Offer an example of a set of company strategies which are geared to maximize current profits but which have the effect of undermining the firm's future.

5. A discount appliance chain faces a difficult financial problem and will be forced out of business if its assets are reduced by more than $3,000. Their marketing manager is considering the purchase of 6,000 new but unproved Hayakawa television sets. Based on the experience of a competitor, historical probabilities are assigned to all possible defect rates of the sets. The payoffs in the following matrix represent asset increases or decreases (in thousands of dollars):

	Defect Rates		
	$N_1: 5\%$, $P = .10$	$N_2: 10\%$, $P = .40$	$N_3: 15\%$, $P = .50$
S_1: Purchase TV sets	30	10	−4
S_2: Do not purchase TV sets	0	0	0

What strategy will the marketing manager use?

6. Using the data of the previous problem, assume that no historical evidence is available pertaining to the probabilities of the various defect rates of Hayakawa TV sets. Determine the optimal strategy by use of the following decision criteria: pessimism, regret, rationality, optimism ($k = .9$), and maximax.

7. In terms of utility analysis, what is the rationale for self-insurance?

8. A firm has present assets of $12 million. Suppose that the firm has the opportunity to make an advertising investment of $2 million which will either raise the assets to $20 million (if successful) or reduce the assets to $4 million (if unsuccessful). What is the minimum probability of success for which the investment would be recommended?

9. A firm is considering three candidate products in order to select an addition to its line. Minimization of unit costs of the new product is the optimizing criterion. The possible states of new product demand are expressed in the following matrix, which shows unit costs in dollars as payoff measures:

	N_1	N_2	N_3	N_4	N_5
Add product A	4	7	10	1	6
Add product B	4	2	8	2	3
Add product C	9	4	3	2	7

(a) If the firm is sure that the demand level will be N_3, what strategy should be chosen?
(b) What would be the maximax choice?
(c) What would be the result if we used the criterion of regret?
(d) Assume a coefficient of optimism of .80. Which will be chosen? If the coefficient of optimism dropped to .70, would the choice of strategy change?
(e) What would be the choice if we used the Laplace criterion?

10. Assume the following payoff matrix, including historical probabilities of occurrence of the states of nature:

	N_1: .8	N_2: .2
S_1	16	1
S_2	0	10
S_3	18	-2
S_4	-12	5

(a) If the cell values represent values of utility, select the strategy that will maximize expected utility.
(b) Assume that the decision maker lacks confidence in the probability estimates and wishes to conduct *sensitivity analysis*; i.e., he wishes to determine how incorrect the probability estimates have to be in order that the strategy calculated in part (a) would be wrong.

11. An international marketer of religious objects is contemplating the opening of a distribution center in Israel. However, he is concerned about his ability to recruit qualified Israeli salesmen. His decision is also dependent upon future Israeli–Arab tensions. Construct a payoff matrix that describes his problem and discuss your plan for arriving at a solution.

12. The Bunky McFarland Company has developed and patented a unique process for manufacturing ornamental candles. The firm can either sell the patent, produce and market the product at once, or test the marketability of the product in the Boston area. The following information is available:

GROSS MARGIN IN THOUSANDS OF DOLLARS

Good Market	Fair Market	Poor Market
400	100	10

MARKETING COSTS IN THOUSANDS OF DOLLARS

Test Marketing	Promotion
15	50

SALE OF PATENT IN THOUSANDS OF DOLLARS

Without test marketing	30
Following favorable test	60
Following unfavorable test	10

PROBABILITY OF TEST-MARKET RESULTS

Favorable Test	Unfavorable Test
.60	.40

PROBABILITY OF MARKET RECEPTION

	Good	Fair	Poor
Without test	.30	.40	.30
Following favorable test	.60	.30	.10
Following unfavorable test	.10	.30	.60

What should be the initial strategy of the firm?

REFERENCES

ALDERSON, WROE, and GREEN, PAUL E., *Planning and Problem Solving in Marketing* (Homewood, Ill.: Richard D. Irwin, Inc., 1964).

DARDEN, WILLIAM R., and LAMONE, RUDOLPH P., *Marketing Management and the Decision Sciences: Theory and Applications* (Boston: Allyn and Bacon, Inc., 1971).

DONNELLY, JAMES H., JR., and IVANCEVICH, JOHN M., *Analysis for Marketing Decisions* (Homewood, Ill.: Richard D. Irwin, Inc., 1970).

KING, WILLIAM R., *Quantitative Analysis for Marketing Management* (New York: McGraw-Hill Book Company, 1969).

MILLER, DAVID W., and STARR, MARTIN K., *Executive Decisions and Operations Research* (Englewood Cliffs, N.J.: Prentice-Hall, Inc., 1965).

SHUCHMAN, ABE, *Scientific Decision Making in Business* (New York: Holt, Rinehart and Winston, Inc., 1963).

CHAPTER 2

The Application of Bayesian Decision Theory

In Chapter 1 marketing decision problems under risk, certainty, and un-certainty were discussed. Chapter 2 will focus entirely upon the case of uncertainty.

2.1 Subjective and Objective Probability

It is appropriate to briefly review the case of *decision making under risk*. In this situation the decision maker *knows* the probability of occurrence of each of the possible states of nature. These probabilities may be called *objective probabilities* since their values were determined by analysis of the long-run relative frequency of occurrence of the events. The resort-hotel manager in Chapter 1 assigned a probability of .2 to the state of nature "rain on the 4th of July" merely because historical data were available to show that in the pertinent resort area, it had rained on July 4 six times during the past 30 years. Therefore, $\frac{6}{30} = .2$. The objective probability of .2 was assigned based on the history of the event "rain on July 4" and predicted upon "what has happened in the past will no doubt happen in the future." This is a logical assumption when the decision area involves such variables as weather conditions, failure rates of electrical-component parts, the outcome of a roll of the dice, and so on.

However, the marketing executive is most often required to make a new, original, or unique decision such as pricing a product that has never been marketed before or running an advertisement that has never appeared before. The states of nature are no longer historically oriented. In the case of the advertising innovation the relevant states of nature may be

N_1: Chief competitor does nothing.
N_2: Chief competitor runs a similar ad.
N_3: Chief competitor runs a larger, more expensive, more elaborate ad than our own.

Since the advertisement has not appeared before, the chief competitor has never responded before. No long-run ratio of occurrence is available; therefore, no frequency rates can be computed.

Thus the preponderance of behaviorally oriented, external uncontrollables in the marketing environment and the scarcity of the marketing department's background of experience that can be described as identical enough to the current problem often precludes the assignment of *objective probabilities* to the occurrence of the relevant states of nature. Faced with such unknowns, the marketer can make a reasoned choice among alternative actions only when he can make a human judgment about the relative likelihood of occurrence of each perceived state of nature. The marketing decision maker must therefore assume the role of a personalist who cannot consider the long-run relative frequency of a repetitive event but instead must assign *subjective probabilities* to an array of mutually exclusive and collectively exhaustive states of nature.

This subjective or personalistic view of probability is the cornerstone of the Bayesian approach to decision making. Unlike the objectivist, the personalist is not at all concerned with the relative frequency of occurrence of a given event over a long period of time. He is solely concerned with the likelihood that the event in question will occur *once* and *only once*.

In summary, the Bayesian approach admits the assignment of probabilities to unique as well as repetitive events (states of nature). In some cases the probability assignments will be based on more or less "public" experience in the sense that most people would assign the same or nearly the same probability to the event.[1] For example, a travel agency located near the University of Maryland was asked to assess the probability that a charter 727 jet ski flight would be completely sold out if the trip were scheduled during the Christmas vacation. Even though an identical trip had never taken place in the past, the travel agency assigned a subjective probability of .80[2] to the event "the plane would be fully sold out." When four other travel organizations in the same area were asked the same question, the probability estimates spanned the range from .70 to .95. The mean estimate was .81.

However, in the majority of marketing situations, there are so few comparable data available that several decision makers, all confronted with the same question, may disagree vehemently in their probability estimates. For example, a decision maker when asked to assign probabilities to various competitive reactions to the advertising innovation might say:

$$\text{``}p(N_1) = .2; p(N_2) = .3; p(N_3) = .5\text{''}$$

Another decision maker might look at the proposition differently, i.e.,

$$\text{``}p(N_1) = .8; p(N_2) = 2; p(N_3) = 0\text{''}$$

Because subjective probabilities are often based on personal experience, hunch, or intuition, there are those who attach a nonscientific or non-

[1] Paul E. Green and Donald S. Tull, *Research for Marketing Decisions* (Englewood Cliffs, N.J.: Prentice-Hall, Inc., 1966), p. 58.

[2] This is the same as saying that the odds are 4:1 in favor of the event (i.e., a probability of .8 for the event and a probability of .2 against the event).

systematic label to decision making which is based on subjective probabilities alone (prior analysis). The solution lies in gathering additional evidence which can in turn be used to modify or revise the original, prior, or subjective probabilities. This segment of Bayesian theory is known as posterior analysis and will be discussed in a later section of this chapter.

2.2   Partial Versus Complete Ignorance

It was stated previously that this chapter was to concentrate entirely upon "decision making under uncertainty." Seemingly the case of uncertainty was treated in depth in Chapter 1 when the Wald, Hurwicz, Savage, and Laplace criteria were discussed. What further contributions can be made by the Bayesian approach?

When the previous criteria were discussed in Chapter 1, it was assumed that the decision maker was operating at the *speculation level* of the spectrum of inputs (see Figure 1–4). In other words, it was assumed in most cases that the decision maker was *totally ignorant* regarding the set of probabilities to be associated with the various states of nature.

From a practical point of view, this is seldom the case. Usually, the decision maker is operating at the *opinion level* rather than the speculation level of the spectrum of inputs. This means that the marketing manager is not *totally ignorant*. He is *partially ignorant*. He usually possesses some information about states of nature, even though that information may be based only on personal experiences, extrapolation from similar situations, an educated guess, and so on. This case of partial ignorance is still classified under the broad category of "decision making under uncertainty."[3]

2.3   How Prior Probabilities Are Assigned

The notion of "partial ignorance" is analogous to "partial knowledge," and partial knowledge is the rationale for assigning subjective (prior) probabilities to the various states of nature.

The assignment of prior probabilities to the states of nature with or without the benefit of historical data can be accomplished through many varieties of individual and group opinion measurement. The procedures differ in the number of judges employed and the degree of anonymity surrounding individual responses. Thus the procedures available for probability determination range from the judgments of the decision maker himself to some form of brainstorming session. The procedure actually followed is a function of the time available, the importance of the decision, the number of judges eligible, and the relative merit placed on the alternative procedures by the decision maker.

[3] Green and Tull, *op. cit.*, p. 93.

Unfortunately, the precise techniques for assigning prior probabilities have not drawn much attention in the marketing literature nor been examined searchingly as critical factors in the Bayesian models. To illustrate the lightness of treatment of the methodology for assigning prior probabilities, the following excerpts from prominent marketing texts are offered:

> *Based on his experience* in the market place in dealing with his competitor, the marketing manager is able to assign probabilities to the two potential competitor actions. He believes there is a .4 probability that the competitor will do nothing and a .6 probability that the competitor will lower the price of a substitute product.[4]

> The company *consults a team of experienced sales managers* to obtain estimates of the likelihood of each sales response to each combination of price and advertising it is considering.[5]

> Suppose that the marketing executive, *based on his business judgment and personal knowledge* of the new region feels that the chances assigned to the occurrence of the state of nature N_1 against N_2 are .4 and .6 respectively.[6]

The preceding criticism is surely not an admonishment of the cited published materials or their authors. We are merely sympathetic to the student who asks: "Assuming no background or historical data are available, thus negating the use of objective prior probabilities, how does the decision maker select specific subjective probability values such as .1 or .6?"

Green offered a specific suggestion in his core study of the Everclear Plastics Co.[7] The objective was the determination of pricing policy for an industrial product. In this case, a search for possible courses of action indicated that four pricing alternatives covered the range of strategies under consideration. Introductory sessions were held with the firm's sales managers to develop a set of states of nature large enough to represent an adequate description of the real problem, yet small enough to be comprehended by the participating sales personnel. Next, separate interview sessions were held with two groups of the firm's sales personnel; subjective probabilities regarding the occurrence of alternative states of nature were developed in these sessions. A final session was held with all contributing personnel in attendance where each projection and/or subjective probability was discussed in detail.

There are those who would much prefer this method of pooling the minds of key people in the firm to "one man's intuitive opinion." However, various

---

[4] James H. Donnelly, Jr., and John M. Ivancevich, *Analysis for Marketing Decisions* (Homewood, Ill.: Richard D. Irwin, Inc., 1970), p. 63.

[5] Frederick D. Sturdivant *et al.*, *Managerial Analysis in Marketing* (Glenview, Ill.: Scott, Foresman and Company, 1970), p. 480.

[6] Wroe Alderson and Paul E. Green, *Planning and Problem Solving in Marketing* (Homewood, Ill.: Richard D. Irwin, Inc., 1964), p. 110.

[7] Paul E. Green, "Bayesian Decision Theory in Pricing Strategy," *Journal of Marketing* (January 1963), pp. 5–14.

research projects have disclosed serious difficulties with direct confrontation and person-to-person interaction.[8] Among the most serious are

1. *Influence of dominant individuals.* For example, the group opinion is highly influenced by the people who talk the most. There is very little correlation between pressure of speech and knowledge.
2. *Noise.* This refers to semantic as well as auditory noise. Much of the communication in a discussion group has to do with individual and group interests rather than with problem solving. This kind of verbal exchange, although it may appear to be problem oriented, is often irrelevant or biasing.
3. *Group pressure for conformity.* It can be dramatically illustrated that group pressure can trigger major distortions of individual judgment. Experiments at the Rand Corporation have demonstrated that after face-to-face discussion, the group response is more often less accurate than a simple median of individual estimates without discussion.[9]

The next section will introduce an unproved but promising method of overcoming the disadvantages of pooling individual opinions of experts by face-to-face discussions. First, it is appropriate to summarize the most widely used methods of assigning prior probabilities. These are

1. Use of historical data if they are available.
2. Experience or intuition of a single decision maker.
3. Face-to-face discussion to obtain a composite opinion of key people in the firm.
4. The *private* pooling of group opinion (i.e., without face-to-face discussion).

2.4   Delphi Process

The Delphi process[10] is a systematic and somewhat scientific method of accomplishing method 4 in Section 2.3.

[8] See H. H. Kelly and J. W. Thebaut, "Experimental Studies of Group Problem Solving and Process," Gardner Lendzey (ed.), *Handbook of Social Psychology*, Vol. II (Reading, Mass.: Addison-Wesley Publishing Company, 1954) and S. E. Asch, "Effects of Group Pressure upon the Modification and Distortion of Judgments," Eleanor E. MacCoby *et al.* (eds.), *Readings in Social Psychology*, 3rd ed. (New York: Holt, Rinehart and Winston, 1958).

[9] Norman C. Dalkey, *The Delphi Method: An Experimental Study of Group Opinion*, A Report Prepared for the United States Air Force Project Rand (Santa Monica, Calif.: The Rand Corporation, June 1969), p. 14.

[10] A portion of this section was developed by use of the following references: Norman C. Dalkey and O. Helmer, *An Experimental Application of the Delphi Method to the Use of Experts*, The RAND Corporation Rm 727, July 1962; T. Gordon and O. Helmer, *Report on a Long-range Forecasting Study*, The RAND Corporation, p-2982, September 1962; Olaf Helmer, *Analyses of the Future*, The RAND Corporation, March 1967, p. 8.

The Delphi technique is a method of eliciting and refining group judgment. It is based upon the rationale that two heads are better than one in situations where exact knowledge is not available. More generally, the method assumes that *n* heads are better than one, for the technique utilizes a panel of experts with repeated measurement and controlled feedback. Delphi replaces direct confrontation and debate by a carefully planned, orderly program of sequential individual interrogations usually conducted by questionnaires.

The process has three salient features: (1) anonymity, (2) controlled feedback, and (3) group response. Anonymity, effected by the use of questionnaires or other formal communication channels such as on-line computer systems, is a way of reducing the effect of dominant individuals. Controlled feedback serves to reduce noise by conducting the experiment in a series of rounds between which the judges are notified of the previous rounds' results. Group response ensures that the final response takes into consideration the opinion of every member of the panel.

A convenient measure of group consensus, applicable especially whenever the solicited judgments can be cast in numerical form, is the median. Aside from being independent of a particular metric, it has the intuitively appealing quality that it can be viewed as the outcome of a democratic voting process, in the sense that half the panel considers the correct answer to lie on each side of the median.

Within the three features there can be a considerable amount of variation, particularly with the controlled feedback system. The results returned to the respondents may consist only of the median response of the previous round. On the other extreme, the 25th, 50th, and 75th percentiles may be returned in addition to a list of reasons, given by the respondents, for their particular response. The result of this feedback is to emphasize and encourage informed judgment, and eliminate the pressure to conform to the opinions of prestigious judges.

The basic theory upon which the Delphi method is based is twofold: (1) that with repeated measurement the range of responses will decrease and converge toward the midrange of the distribution, and (2) that the total group response, or median, will successively move toward the correct or true answer. The basic characteristics and features of Delphi can be maintained, yet the panel size and feedback system can be varied extensively to satisfy a wide range of decision-making restrictions. Of course, the validity and reliability of the method for obtaining subjective judgments and its merit must be judged against alternatives available.

The Delphi technique has been employed sparingly since its inception with application almost exclusively in the areas of technological and environmental forecasting. However, a recent experiment[11] was conducted at the

[11] Marvin A. Jolson and Gerald L. Rossow, "The Delphi Process in Marketing Decision Making," *Journal of Marketing Research* (November 1971), pp. 443–448.

Pace Computing Corporation of Arlington, Va., to investigate the usefulness of the Delphi technique as a generator of the various prior probabilities to be assigned to various levels of anticipated demand for a company's product. The decision to be made concerned the advisability of opening up a company branch in New York City.

With the assistance of Pace, a payoff table was constructed for different levels of class instruction. The payoff table is shown as Table 2–1. The payoff cell values are expressed in dollars of monthly profit contribution.

TABLE 2–1. Monthly Payoff Matrix ($) for Various Levels of Demand for Class Instruction

Strategy	Number of Classes Demanded				
	0	1–3	4–6	7–9	10–12
Branch	(7,200)	(3,800)	1,300	6,400	11,500
No branch	0	1,100	2,900	4,700	6,500

After three rounds of iteration and feedback, the round 3 probability medians were used as the prior probability values in computing the expected value of each strategy. Table 2–2 shows the results for all three rounds. Generally speaking, the changes in probability estimates tended to be in the

TABLE 2–2. Adjusted Probability Estimates for All Rounds

Rounds	Probability Medians for Various Levels of Demand					
	0	1–3	4–6	7–9	10–12	Total
Round 1	.07	.20	.33	.27	.13	1.0
Round 2	.05	.18	.31	.31	.15	1.0
Round 3	0	.16	.36	.36	.12	1.0

same direction; i.e., the distribution of individual responses progressively converged.

The Delphi process is compatible with Bayesian theory objectives in that it does indeed combine *intuition* and *science*.

2.5 Prior Analysis

It has been shown that the prior probabilities of the relevant array of states of nature may be generated by several methods. The marketing decision maker is now in a position to prepare a completed table of conditional payoffs. The previous example of the decision problem facing the Pace Computing Corporation will be used to illustrate the use of prior analysis only. The pertinent facts of the situation will be repeated.

The company was faced with the problem of whether to open a branch in the New York City area. The decision to be made depended upon the degree of demand for the firm's product, i.e., the number of classes demanded per month. The company determined that the range of class demand could realistically vary from zero classes to 12 classes per month. Accordingly, the firm calculated the dollar values of profit contribution for each strategy/ demand combination. The firm decided to use the prior probability values generated by the Delphi process. Table 2–1 may now be modified to include the prior probabilities which have been assigned to the five states of nature. The completed collection of input data is shown by Table 2–3.

TABLE 2–3. Completed Monthly Payoff Matrix ($) for Various Levels of Demand for Class Instruction

	Demand for Classes [N_i]				
	0	1–3	4–6	7–9	10–12
	Prior Probabilities [$p(N_i)$]				
Strategy	0	.16	.36	.36	.12
S_1: Open branch	(7,200)	(3,800)	1,300	6,400	11,500
S_2: No branch	0	1,100	2,900	4,700	6,500

If the decision maker was required to choose *now* between the two strategies "Open branch (S_1)" or "Do not open branch (S_2)," he would merely calculate the expected money value for each course of action and choose the strategy which leads to the larger expected or weighted average payoff. The expected value of S_1 is

$$E(S_1) = 0(-7,200) + .16(-3,800) + .36(1,300) + .36(6,400) + .12(11,500)$$

$$= \$3,544$$

The expected value of S_2 is

$$E(S_2) = 0(0) + .16(1,100) + .36(2,900) + .36(4,700) + .12(6,500) = \$3,692$$

Therefore, strategy S_2 (Do not open branch) is preferred.

To summarize the case of prior analysis, it has been assumed that the decision maker is in a position to list a relevant set of mutually exclusive and collectively exhaustive strategies and discrete states of nature. In addition, he can calculate the dollar payoff of each strategy/state of nature combination.

Finally, he can express his beliefs—expressed as numerical probabilities—about the likelihood that each state of nature will occur. He will then select the course of action that leads to the optimal expected payoff, which in this example is the larger expected monthly profit contribution in dollars.

It has been inferred during this discussion of prior analysis that the decision-maker's choices of action are restricted to two strategies:

S_1: Open branch

S_2: Do not open branch

One other strategy is available:

S_3: Delay a terminal decision until additional data and information have been gathered and analyzed

The selection of S_3 represents a procedure for revising the prior probabilities on the basis of new, more objective information. These new, revised, or posterior probabilities may be substituted for the original prior probabilities so that new expected payoff values may be calculated for each strategy. This process of collecting additional information *before* choosing the terminal strategy underlies the *posterior analysis* procedure.

2.6 Marginal, Conditional, and Joint Probabilities

So as to establish the foundation for a discussion of posterior analysis, it is appropriate at this time to review and clarify the relationships among the notions of conditional, marginal, and joint probabilities.

A *marginal* probability is an *unconditional* or a *prior* probability. These three terms can be considered to be synonymous and are often used interchangeably. The derivation of the term "marginal" will be shown later in this section. The term "prior" is assigned inasmuch as the probability of occurrence of the event is determined *in advance* of any experiment, research or trial and therefore is "unconditional." A marginal probability may be assigned as a result of logic or intuition or may be determined empirically as a result of historical observations. Thus marginal probabilities may be either subjective or objective. For example, as an objective approach, the marginal probability of drawing an ace from a fair deck of cards is $\frac{4}{52} = \frac{1}{13}$. This may be expressed: $p(A) = \frac{1}{13}$.

A *conditional* probability implies that certain additional information must be considered before the assignment of a numerical probability value. Put another way, conditional probability means that an event of a certain class will occur under the condition that it belongs to a specified subclass of the whole class. For example, suppose Mr. Jones draws a card from a deck of cards, observes that the drawn card is a spade, and then asks, "What is the probability that this same card is an ace?" The relevant population of cards has been reduced from 52 cards (the entire deck) to 13 cards (the number of spades in the deck). Therefore, the conditional probability of "Ace" given that the drawn card has been identified as a "spade" is $\frac{1}{13}$. This is expressed

$$P(A|S) = \frac{1}{13}$$

The vertical line between the A and S means "given the occurrence of."

The probability that two or more events will *all* occur is called the *joint* probability of those events. During the discussion of conditional probability we discussed a sequence of two events:

> *First*—The event "Spade was drawn"
> *Second*—The event "Ace given that the drawn card is a spade"
> The first event is a marginal probability, $p(S)$
> The second event is a conditional probability, $p(A|S)$

The question then arises: What is the probability of drawing the ace of spades from a deck of cards? We may quickly respond that there is only one such card in the deck; therefore, the probability of the drawn card being both an ace and a spade is $\frac{1}{52}$. A less intuitive approach is to multiply the probability of the two events, i.e., *joint = marginal × conditional*:

$$p(S, A|S) = p(S) \times p(A|S) = \frac{1}{4} \times \frac{1}{13} = \frac{1}{52}$$

We may therefore define joint probability as the product of the marginal and conditional probabilities, i.e., $J = MC$.

The following table illustrates the absolute values of aces and spades in a deck of cards. Note that $\tilde{A}$ (A tilde) means "no ace," and $\tilde{S}$ means "no spade."

	S	$\tilde{S}$	
A	1	3	4
$\tilde{A}$	12	36	48
	13	39	52

The columns sum the number of spades and nonspades. The rows sum the number of aces and nonaces.

By dividing each value in the above chart by 52 (the total population of cards), we may develop a chart of relative values:

	S	$\tilde{S}$	
A	$\frac{1}{52}$	$\frac{3}{52}$	$\frac{4}{52}$
$\tilde{A}$	$\frac{12}{52}$	$\frac{36}{52}$	$\frac{48}{52}$
	$\frac{13}{52}$	$\frac{39}{52}$	1.0

Note that the *marginal* probabilities are given in the *margins*, the joint probabilities are contained within the cells of the matrix, and the conditional probabilities may be determined by the $J = MC$ formula (in this case $C = J/M$). To pluck a few values:

$$p(A) = \tfrac{4}{52} = \tfrac{1}{13}$$

$$p(\tilde{S}) = \tfrac{39}{52} = \tfrac{3}{4}$$

$$p(\tilde{A}, S) = \tfrac{12}{52} = \tfrac{3}{13}$$

$$p(\tilde{A}|\tilde{S}) = \tfrac{36}{52}/\tfrac{39}{52} = \tfrac{36}{39}$$

The student may determine the values of

$$p(\tilde{A}); p(\tilde{S}|\tilde{A}); p(A, \tilde{S})^{12}$$

(See footnote 12 for the answers to this exercise.)

2.7 Probability Relationships—A Problem Situation

Consider the following problem: A storm-window company operating nationwide acquires leads for salesmen by using direct-response coupons in *Playboy, Harper's,* and *TV Guide* magazines. The firm received 6,000 leads during 1969, with 50 per cent of the total from *TV Guide* and 40 per cent of the total from *Playboy.* Twenty per cent of the *Harper's* leads converted into sales, whereas the conversion ratios for *Playboy* and *TV Guide* were 10 and 4 per cent respectively. A market researcher contacts Mrs. Wm. Parker, who explains that she mailed in a magazine coupon from one of the three publications, was contacted by a salesman, but did not buy. What is the probability that Mrs. Parker clipped a coupon from *TV Guide*?

Discussion: The steps in the solution are as follows:

1. As in the case of the playing cards a table of absolute values may be constructed. All given values are inserted in the appropriate cells or margins:

	S	$\tilde{S}$	
Playboy	240		2,400
TV Guide	120		3,000
Harper's			
			6,000

---

[12] The answers are $\tfrac{12}{13}; \tfrac{3}{4}; \tfrac{3}{52}$.

S indicates the number of consumers who were sold; $\tilde{S}$ indicates the number of consumers who were not sold. Since 50 per cent of the leads were received from *TV Guide* and 40 per cent from *Playboy* the total number of leads received from each of these two publications are 3,000 and 2,400, respectively. Since the conversion ratio of *Playboy* leads was 10 per cent, 240 of the 2,400 *Playboy* leads were converted into sales. The *TV Guide* sales were similarly determined.

2. The missing cell and margin values may now be plugged in to yield a completed table:

	S	$\tilde{S}$	
Playboy	240	2,160	2,400
TV Guide	120	2,880	3,000
Harper's	120	480	600
	480	5,520	6,000

Since 5,400 of the 6,000 leads were received from *Playboy* and *TV Guide*, the remaining 600 obviously came from *Harper's*. Twenty per cent of these 600 leads were converted to provide 120 sales from *Harper's* leads. The remaining cell and margin values were easily derived by vertical or horizontal addition.

3. The problem indicates that Mrs. Parker did not buy ($\tilde{S}$) and questions the likelihood that she clipped a *TV Guide* coupon, i.e.,

$$P(\text{TV}|\tilde{S})$$

This is the conditional probability of *TV Guide* given the fact she did not buy. Since 5,520 people did not buy and 2,880 of these nonbuyers sent in a *TV Guide* coupon,

$$P(\text{TV}|\tilde{S}) = \frac{2,880}{5,520} = .52$$

The problem can be observed another way; i.e., conditional probability = joint probability/marginal probability.

Joint probability of *TV Guide* and no sale is $P(\text{TV}, \tilde{S}) = 2,880/6,000$. Marginal probability of no sale is $P(\tilde{S}) = 5,520/6,000$. Therefore,

$$C = \frac{J}{M} = \frac{2,880}{6,000} \Big/ \frac{5,520}{6,000} = \frac{2,880}{5,520} = .52$$

Therefore, if we know that Mrs. Parker did not buy, the probability is .52 that the source of her inquiry was *TV Guide*.

However, if we may change the problem for a moment, suppose that we were interested in knowing the probability that Mrs. Parker had clipped a *TV Guide* lead without having been informed as to whether she did or did not purchase. We would now be seeking the unconditional or marginal probability that Mrs. Parker had sent in a *TV Guide* lead, i.e.,

$$P(\text{TV}) = 3,000/6,000 = .50.$$

Therefore, the additional knowledge that Mrs. Parker did not buy in effect enables us to revise and improve our prior estimate from .50 to .52.

2.8   Bernoulli Process and the Binomial Distribution[13]

The output of many random processes encountered in practical marketing problems can be described in terms of a number of *distinct trials* each of which has one or the other of *just two possible results*, such as good–defective, successful–unsuccessful, sale–no sale, or, more generally, success–failure.

In such processes, the same probability is assigned to a success on *every* future trial and will continue to be assigned regardless of the outcomes of any future trials. Such trials are known as *Bernoulli trials with fixed probability.* Such an assumption is logical only if both of the following statements are true:

1. There is absolutely *no pattern* to the occurrences of successes and failures; successes tend to occur with exactly the same frequency in the first as in the last part of a long run; successes tend to be followed by failures exactly as frequently as failures are followed by failures; and so on. (*Stability*)
2. The long-run fraction of successes is *known with certainty*, so that experience with early trials in a sequence will not lead us to change our minds about the value of this fraction. (*Independence*)

These statements truly apply to certain physical processes such as tossing a true coin. They are considerably less realistic when dealing with behavioral situations in marketing. Obviously in tossing a coin, the probability of "head" on the tenth toss is $\frac{1}{2}$ even if the previous nine tosses resulted in "tail." However, suppose that a salesman delivers unsuccessful sales presentations to nine consecutive consumers who have sent in leads from *Harper's Magazine* (conversion ratio = .20). Such a salesman may be discouraged by nine consecutive failures such that his probability of success on the tenth presentation may be considerably less than .20. A coin will not become tired or discouraged; a salesman may. Therefore, the former process is *stable* and the

---

[13] Much of the material in this section was taken from Robert Schlaifer, *Probability and Statistics for Business Decisions* (New York: McGraw-Hill Book Company, 1959), pp. 174–200, 388–339.

individual tosses are independent; the latter process is *not stable* and the individual sales presentations are *not independent*. The decision maker must be aware that a real process can seldom be *exactly* represented by a Bernoulli model. Yet such an assumption is not far-fetched enough to negate its usefulness.

We may now illustrate the binomial probability distribution by considering the probability of S successes in N Bernoulli trials, where the probability of success is P on any one trial. For example, our magazine lead illustration indicates the probability that a single *Harper's* magazine lead will be converted into a sale to be .20. Therefore, $P = .20$. To repeat, the value of P is a state of nature that was developed after observing the rate of conversion of many hundreds or thousands of *Harper's* leads over a period of time. Suppose that an average salesman worked three *Harper's* leads, two of which he sold. What is the probability of such a result; i.e., what is the probability of two successes in three (assumed Bernoulli) trials where the probability of success is .20 on any one trial?

1. Assuming that the first two leads were sold and the third was not sold:
    (a) The probability of selling the first lead is .20.
    (b) The probability of selling the second lead is .20.
    (c) The probability of not selling the third lead is .80.
2. Therefore, $P(S, S, \tilde{S}) = .20 \times .20 \times .80 = .032$.
3. However, since two sales out of three leads can occur in three different orders the above results must be multiplied by 3: $.032 \times 3 = .096$.
4. We must conclude, therefore, that if an average salesman is given three *Harper's* leads, the probability that he will convert *exactly* two leads into sales is .096. Since the probability of selling all three leads is $P(S, S, S) = .20 \times .20 \times .20 = .008$, the probability of selling two or more leads is $.096 + .008 = .104$.

When N is larger than 3 or 4, the student would be wise to refer to the binomial distribution tables, Appendix A.

2.9   Posterior Analysis—Example 1

We may now proceed with a description of the statistical procedures to be used when the decision maker wishes to revise or modify his previously assigned prior probabilities.

Consider the following marketing problem, which is related to the previous discussion involving the conversion of magazine coupon responses into sales. The vice president for sales of the storm-window company is considering a new five-year contractual agreement with the publishers of a new magazine, *The Modern Consumer*. Since the agreement will involve the insertion of four full-page ads per year totalling almost $300,000 in expenditures over the five-year period, the sales manager is very cautious about his decision. He is particularly concerned about the rate at which leads will convert into sales (conversion rate).

Since his firm has never advertised in *The Modern Consumer* no historical evidence is available. However, the decision maker feels that the demographic characteristics of the publication's audience are somewhat similar to those of *Harper's*. He constructs a payoff table as shown in Table 2–4.

TABLE 2–4. Conditional Payoff Matrix for *The Modern Consumer* Magazine (Annual Cash Flows in Thousands of Dollars)

	Potential Conversion Rates				
	$N_1:.05$	$N_2:.10$	$N_3:.15$	$N_4:.20$	$N_5:.25$
	Prior Probabilities				
Strategies	.05	.30	.50	.10	.05
S_1: Sign contract	-40	-10	20	40	60
S_2: Do not sign contract	0	0	0	0	0

The reader will note that the possible conversion rates (states of nature) consist of five discrete values, .05, .10, .15, .20, and .25. These values are collectively exhaustive because of the assumption that the true conversion ratio cannot assure any other value. The payoff values (-40, -10, 20, 40, and 60) associated with S_1 represent the positive or negative dollar cash-flow values associated with the interaction of S_1 and the various N values (states of nature). The series of zeros associated with S_2 means that if the contract is not signed, no additional cash flows would take place.

Note that the sales manager and his staff based on experience, intuition, pooling of opinions, or some other method of generating subjective probabilities assign prior probabilities to the occurrence of the several potential conversion rates.

If the decision maker decided not to gather any additional information and had to choose *now* between strategies S_1 and S_2, he would calculate the expected money value for each act and select that act which would lead to the largest expected cash flow in thousands of dollars. The expected value of S_2 is zero. The expected value of S_1 is $-40(.05) - 10(.30) + 20(.50) + 40(.10) + 60(.05) = \$12,000$. Therefore, strategy S_1 would be selected.

Presume, however, that the sales manager is somewhat skeptical about the distribution of prior probabilities which has been generated. Before contracting with the magazine publisher he prefers to gather and analyze some additional information which will tell him whether the selected prior probabilities should be modified, altered, or revised.

He arranges with the publisher to test his advertisement by running it in 1 per cent of the magazine copies to be distributed in a chosen city the following month. The ad appears and nineteen leads are returned. The returned leads are issued to four average salesmen and the result is two sales. How would the original probabilities be revised now that the leads have been sampled and 2 of the 19 leads have been converted into sales? The analysis of the problem is carried out in Table 2–5.

TABLE 2–5. Calculation of Posterior Probabilities

(1)	(2)	(3)	(4)	(5)
		Conditional	$(2) \times (3)$	
Conversion Rate	Prior	Probability	Joint	Posterior
(State of Nature)	Probability	of the Sample	Probability	Probability
P	$P(P)$	$P(s = 2 \mid n = 19, P)$	$P(s = 2, P)$	$P(P \mid s = 2)$
.05	.05	.179	.00895	.039
.10	.30	.285	.08550	.362
.15	.50	.243	.12150	.514
.20	.10	.154	.01540	.066
.25	.05	.080	.00400	.019
	1.0		.23535	1.0

The posterior probabilities in Column 5, Table 2–5, may now be substituted for the prior probabilities in column 2 and the revised expected value of S_1 may be calculated:

$$-40(.039) - 10(.362) + 20(.514) + 40(.066) + 60(.019) = \$8,800$$

The selection of strategy S_1 (sign contract) is supported by the additional evidence of the test even though the expected dollar cash-flow anticipation is $8,800 rather than $12,000.

So that the reader may fully comprehend the five columns of Table 2–5 the following explanation is offered:

Column 1 lists the given exhaustive possible states of nature i.e., the rates of conversion of leads into sales.

Column 2 lists the subjective probabilities of occurrence of the various states of nature listed in column 1. These are called *prior* probabilities since they were generated prior to the receipt of the test results. The total of this column must *always* be equal to 1.

Column 3 may be constructed after the appropriate sample results have been obtained; i.e., 19 leads have been sampled and of these 19 leads, 2 were

sold. We show in column 3 how likely this observed sample result is, given
the five discrete states of nature. Put another way we ask: What is the probability of 2 sales given the first condition that the lead conversion ratio is
5 per cent? Expressed in terms of a conditional probability, we are seeking
$P(s = 2|N = 19, P = .05)$. The result (.1787) may be read directly from
bionomial probability distribution tables (Appendix A) or may be calculated
by use of the binomial probability distribution formula.[14] The remaining
conditional probabilities in column 3 may be obtained by use of the values
$P = .10, .15, .20, .25$, respectively.

If the sample size is small, i.e., $N = 3$, $s = 1$, the computation is quite
simple: Assume that $P(S) = .05$; then $P(S, \tilde{S}, \tilde{S}) = .05 \times .95 \times .95 = .045$.
However, since there are two other orders in which 1 success in 3 trials can
occur, $.045 \times 3$ possible orders $= .135$. This result can be verified by reference
to Appendix A.

Column 4 consists of the joint probabilities which may be obtained by
multiplying the marginal (prior) probability by the conditional probability,
i.e., column 2 by column 3. For example, $.05 \times .179 = .00895$. The total of
column 4 (total of all joint probabilities) yields another marginal probability, which is the marginal probability of getting one particular test event
(two sales).

Column 5 represents the new conditional probabilities, i.e., the revised or
posterior probabilities and is obtained by dividing each value of column 4 by
the total of column 4 (normalizing). We are, in fact, using the relationship
that conditional probability equals joint probability divided by marginal
probability.

In the event the reader experiences any confusion in following the columnar
explanations, he should refresh his memory by reviewing Section 2.6. It may
be noted that the total of column 5, as in the case of column 2, must *always*
be equal to 1. It will also be observed that column 5 is the reverse of column 3:
column 3 gives the probability of a specific sample result given a discrete
state of nature; column 5 gives the probability of a discrete state of nature
given a specific sample result.

---

[14] $p(s) = \binom{n}{s} p^s (1 - p)^{n-s}$, where $\binom{n}{s}$ denotes the number of possible orders in which s

successes can occur in n trials and

$$\binom{n}{s} = \frac{n!}{s!(n - s)!}$$

For example, in the case of state of nature, $p = .05$:

$$p(s = 2) = \binom{19}{2} \times .05^2 (1 - .05)^{19-2} = .179$$

This is what the posterior probability is intended to convey, the probability of a particular state of nature after the decision maker has had an opportunity to consider a specific sample or research result.

2.10　Bayes' Theorem

We may summarize the technique of posterior analysis by use of Bayes' theorem. To calculate the posterior probability of any one state of nature, say N_1, after observing a particular sample or research results, say Z_1:

1. Multiply the prior probability of N_1, i.e., $p(N_1)$, by the conditional probability of the sample result, i.e., $p(Z_1|N_1)$, to yield the joint probability of N_1 and the sample result. The result is $p(N_1) \cdot p(Z_1|N_1)$.
2. Repeat step 1 for all states of nature and calculate the sum of the joint probability column to yield

$$\sum_{j=1}^{n} p(N_j) \cdot p(Z_1|N_j)$$

3. Divide the result of step 1 by the result of step 2 to give the probability of N_1 given the observed sample result:

$$P(N_1|Z_1) = \frac{p(N_1) \cdot p(Z_1|N_1)}{\sum_{j=1}^{n} p(N_j) \cdot p(Z_1|N_j)}$$

4. The above formula is nothing more than a short-hand account of the procedure for calculating the posterior probability. Memorization of the formula is unnecessary. However, a discussion of the Bayesian method would be incomplete without at least a general formulation of Bayes' theorem.

2.11　Posterior Analysis—Example 2

In many marketing problems, the Bernoulli model discussed in Section 2.8 is not appropriate, owing to the absence of a random experiment having only two possible outcomes: success–failure, sale–no sale, and so on. States of nature may not always be expressed by rates, percentages, or proportions.

Consider a distribution problem where the marketing manager is undecided as to whether the firm should continue to distribute its line of carpeting by use of sales agents or whether the company should develop a captive sales force. Because of the different cost structures of the two distribution methods the manager determines that the agency method should be continued if annual sales volume continues to be equal to or less than 1 million dollars. If, on the other hand, sales for the following year exceed 1 million dollars, the captive sales force would be preferred.

It is clear that three strategies are open to the marketing manager:

S_1: Continue to use sales agents.
S_2: Switch to captive sales force.
S_3: Delay his decision until the firm has carefully researched the potential demand for the company's products during the forthcoming year.

Two and only two states of nature are possible:

N_1: Sales over $1 million
N_2: Sales equal to or less than $1 million

Presume that the marketing manager and his staff examine the relevant revenues and costs for each strategy/state of nature combination and generate a conditional payoff table as shown in Table 2–6.

TABLE 2–6. Conditional Payoff Matrix—Distribution Problem (annual profit contribution in thousands of dollars)

	Potential Sales Levels	
	N_1: Over $1 million	N_2: Equal to or less than $1 million
	Prior Probabilities	
Strategies	.70	.30
S_1: Sales agents	3	6
S_2: Captive sales force	10	(4)

It may be observed from Table 2–6 that the decision maker has assigned subjective probabilities to the two possible states of nature, N_1 and N_2, of .70 and .30, respectively. These subjective or prior (prior to the solicitation of additional information) probabilities may have been assigned as a result of his own experience or intuition—or following a pooling of the opinions by competent authorities in the firm.

If a final decision were required *now*, he would calculate the expected annual profit contributions for strategies S_1 and S_2:

$$EV(S_1) = 3(.70) + 6(.30) = \$3,900$$

$$EV(S_2) = 10(.70) - 4(.30) = \$5,800$$

Therefore, strategy S_2 (use captive sales force) would be chosen.

However, as previously stated, the final decision may be delayed until new information regarding the probability of occurrence of the two states of nature can be collected and analyzed. In other words, strategy 3 may be used. Hopefully, survey information provided by a consulting firm can be used in such a way that more dependable estimates of the probabilities of the potential sales levels can be obtained.

It is assumed, however, in this example that the decision maker, for reasons best known to himself, decides to undertake the data-collecting procedure *without* first attempting to evaluate the potential posterior results in comparison with the *cost* of the survey by the consulting firm.

Obviously since the consultants are human the survey will surely not yield perfect results. In other words, the decision maker cannot rely 100 per cent upon the information provided by the consulting firm owing to errors in the sample findings. It is evident that the outside survey will provide one of two results: Either sales will exceed \$1 million (Z_1), or sales will be equal to or less than \$1 million (Z_2). Presume that after studying the previous results of the consulting firm under similar problem conditions, it is determined that the information to be purchased will be 90 per cent reliable. Under such circumstances, the relevant conditional probabilities for this example are

(a) $P(Z_1|N_1) = .90$
(b) $P(Z_2|N_2) = .90$
(c) $P(Z_1|N_2) = .10$
(d) $P(Z_2|N_1) = .10$

Statement (a) means that there is a 90 per cent chance that the consulting report will say "sales will exceed \$1 million" and after observing the annual sales, it will be found that sales did, in fact, exceed \$1 million. Similarly, statement (b) means that there is a 90 per cent chance that the survey will predict sales less than \$1 million when this turns out to be the true sales result. Statement (c) indicates that there is a 10 per cent chance that the consulting firm will forecast sales in excess of \$1 million; however, an analysis

TABLE 2–7. Conditional Probabilities of Survey Results Given Each State of Nature

	Actual Results	
Survey Results	N_1: Over \$1 million	N_2: Equal to or less than \$1 million
Z_1: Over \$1 million	.90	.10
Z_2: Under \$1 million	.10	.90
	1.00	1.00

of results will show that sales are less than $1 million. Statement (d) similarly shows an incorrect estimate of sales volume. These conditional probabilities are summarized in Table 2–7.

In accordance with the procedure used in constructing Table 2–5, the joint, marginal, and posterior probabilities may be calculated. The results are shown in Table 2–8 and a detailed explanation will follow.

TABLE 2–8. Calculation of Posterior Probabilities (90 per cent reliable survey)

(1)	(2)	(3)	(4)	(5)	(6)
	Joint Probabilities		Marginal Probabilities	Posterior Probabilities	
Survey Results	$P(N_1) \cdot P(Z_i|N_1)$	$P(N_2) \cdot P(Z_i|N_2)$	$P(Z_i)$	$P(N_1|Z_i)$	$P(N_2|Z_i)$
Z_1	.63	.03	.66	.95	.05
Z_2	.07	.27	.34	.20	.80
Marginal probabilities $P(N_j)$	.70	.30	1.00		

Column 1 lists the two possible survey results, Z_1 and Z_2.

Columns 2 and 3 consist of the joint probabilities which may be obtained by multiplying the marginal (prior) probabilities of the various states of nature by the conditional probabilities of the consultant's survey given by Table 2–7. For example, the row 1 figure of .63 is the product of .70 and .90. The total of column 2 represents the original (prior) probability of N_1. The total of column 3 is $P(N_2)$.

Column 4 indicates the marginal probabilities of the two possible survey results and is obtained by the horizontal addition of the joint probabilities.

Columns 5 and 6 represent the revised or posterior probabilities and are obtained by dividing each value in columns 2 and 3 by the corresponding column 4 value. Again we are using the relationship that conditional probability equals joint probability divided by marginal probability. For example, the .95 value in column 5 means that if the survey result is Z_1, the probabilities of states of nature N_1 and N_2 will be .95 and .05, respectively. Therefore, after the survey has been completed:

1. If the survey predicts sales over $1 million ($Z_1$),

$$EV(S_1) = 3(.95) + 6(.05) = \$3,150$$

$$EV(S_2) = 10(.95) + (-4)(.05) = \$9,300$$

Therefore, the research result would support the original selection of S_2 and the decision maker would in all probability feel reassured.

2. If the survey predicts sales under $1 million (Z_2),

$$EV(S_1) = 3(.20) + 6(.80) = \$5,400$$

$$EV(S_2) = 10(.20) + (-4)(.80) = \$ - 1,200$$

In this case the research findings would contradict the original intuition of the decision maker and S_1 would be the optimal strategy.

2.12   Decision-tree Analysis

The tree diagram of Figure 2–1 serves two major purposes. *First*, it pictorially confirms the calculations of Section 2.11, attesting to the optimal strategy selection in the absence of a survey and following each of the two

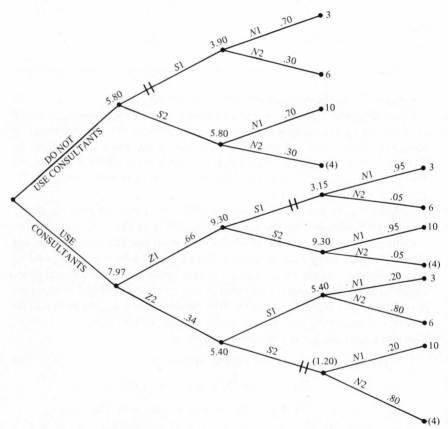

FIGURE 2–1. Decision Tree. Distribution Problem (90 per cent reliable survey; payoffs in thousands of dollars).

possible survey results. *Second*, it demonstrates in easily understood form whether the value of gathering additional data (use of a survey) justifies the cost of the data-gathering procedure.

It is to be strongly emphasized that in the case of posterior analysis the decision maker decides to avail himself of additional information; of more importance he decides to proceed with the information-gathering activities, i.e., trials, surveys, or other research, *without* first investigating the relationship between the *value* of the new information and the *cost* of the information. In other words, he decides not to rely upon prior analysis alone and instructs his research group to gather the required data. The decision-tree diagram in Figure 2–1 schematically integrates the data of Tables 2–6, 2–7, and 2–8 and also provides additional information, which is discussed in the next section. The upper branch of the tree represents the prior analysis of the previous distribution problem. It shows that since the payoff of 5.80 exceeds the payoff of 3.90 (thousands of dollars), strategy S_1 will be blocked off (see parallel slash lines) and strategy S_2 will be employed.

The lower branch represents the posterior analysis section. Beginning at the right-hand side of the lower branch, the terminal values represent the payoffs associated with each $Z_i \ S_j \ N_k$ combination. For example, if the survey had shown a Z_1 result *and* the manager used strategy S_1 and state of nature N_1 occurred $(Z_1 \ S_1 \ N_1)$ the payoff would be 3 (thousands of dollars). For the combination $Z_2 \ S_2 \ N_2$, the payoff would be (4). With a Z_1 survey result the expected value of S_2 exceeds that of S_1; therefore, the S_1 path is blocked off and the value of 9.30 is carried to the fork position to the left. Under Z_2 survey conditions, the larger payoff is 5.40 and so path S_2 is blocked. These are the same results as were given in the previous section. The explanation of the decision tree will continue in the next section.

2.13   Preposterior Analysis

There are a number of situations under which the decision maker has doubts about the reliability of prior analysis and strongly considers the use of additional data-gathering processes; however, he wishes to examine the economics of generating more information *before* authorizing the actual marketing research or trials. In essence, the decision maker is quoted (or estimates) the cost of the research, but *before* he actually allows additional information to be gathered, he decides to perform a series of calculations which will tell him whether the research expense is justified in terms of its returns. This segment of Bayesian decision theory is called *preposterior analysis*.

We may now continue with the explanation of Figure 2–1. In the case of preposterior analysis the entire decision tree is constructed *before* the research is conducted. The decision maker says to himself "If I authorize the consultants to go ahead and Z_1 is their finding, I will select strategy S_2 with a payoff of 9.30. If, however, their finding is Z_2, I will implement strategy S_1 with a payoff of 5.40." He then asks himself: "What is the expected payoff of the use of consultants?" Since the probabilities of each survey estimate, Z_1 or Z_2, are given in column 4 of Table 2–8 as .66 and .34, respectively, the expected payoff of the strategy option "use consultants" is \$7.97, i.e.,

$$9.30(.66) + 5.40(.34)$$

Clearly, then, the use of consultants offers the firm a gain of \$2,170, i.e., \$7,970 − \$5,800 = \$2,170, where \$5,800 is the expected value of the optimal strategy if consultants are *not* employed. Therefore, the expected value of the survey information including optimal terminal action is \$2,170 and the firm could afford to spend up to \$2,170 for such a survey. A survey fee exceeding this amount would not be acceptable since the cost of the additional information would exceed its expected value.

Consequently, the purpose of preposterior analysis is to determine whether the anticipated value of additional information is worth the price of such information. As the name implies, this determination is made *before* posterior analysis is conducted.

2.14   Multistage Data Collection

It is conceivable that even *after* the decision maker has conducted tests and/or surveys, he may continue to feel insecure about the probability distribution associated with the various states of nature. In other words, despite the objective revision of the original prior probabilities, he is still reluctant to make a terminal decision. Assuming that the price is right, he may decide to authorize additional tests or another survey which will further revise the probabilities of occurrence of the various states of nature. The calculated posterior probabilities generated during the first stage of information gathering become the prior probabilities for the second stage and the sequence is repeated.

Essentially, then, the decision maker has an option after each stage to either make a terminal decision or to continue the information-gathering process.

In contrast to "playing it by ear" after each test or survey, the decision maker could decide in advance to initiate a multistage data-gathering procedure where the reliability percentages of each stage could vary. For example, a 70 per cent reliable first-stage survey could be purchased, which in turn could be followed by an 85 per cent reliable second-stage survey. In this case, the second survey could be conducted at less cost than the same survey could be conducted in the absence of a previous stage. This is because of the lack of duplication of certain setup costs. Multistage data collection will be illustrated in Section 2.19.

2.15   Continuous Rather Than Discrete States of Nature

In order to simplify each of the previous examples, only a few discrete states of nature were assumed to be relevant. For example, in Section 2.9 it was assumed that magazine coupon leads would convert into sales at one of five, and only five rates, i.e., .05, .10, .15, .20, and .25. Even if the .05 and .25 values define the relevant conversion-rate range, it is obvious that other intermediate conversion rates could occur such as .06, .07, or even .075. Therefore, the five states of nature could be enlarged to 10, 15, 20, 30, or more states and the computational procedure would be unchanged, although it would be considerably more cumbersome. A more realistic approach would be to consider *all* values between .05 and .25 inclusive. The attendant prior distribution would then be described by a smooth curve. Assuming that the continuous prior distribution could be represented by a normal or other convenient distribution, the resultant posterior distribution may be developed. However, such an example and solution require statistical and mathematical treatments which are appropriately omitted in this simplified text.[15]

2.16   Comparison of Prior, Posterior, and Preposterior Analysis

As illustrated by the previous sections of this chapter, the Bayesian model stresses the relevance of managerial judgment within the marketing-problem-solving framework and the integration of marketing research information with managerial strategy selection.

In the case of prior analysis, a course of action is selected on the basis of current information only. For various reasons the decision maker rejects the opportunity to use marketing research in the form of tests, trials, surveys, and so on, which would serve to modify, revise, and possibly improve his original estimates of the likelihood of occurrence of the relevant states of nature. In other words, he selects the option of gathering *no* additional information. Such a decision may be arbitrary or economic in nature. For example, in many instances, such as the problem of sales-personnel selection, reliable research information may not be available at any cost. Certain firms may not have the funds available to finance the information-gathering process. In other cases, a delay of terminal action may be a critical competitive consideration. Finally, the very process of generating useful research data may release "top-secret" information to the competition. Under such circumstances, a prior-analysis approach may be recommended.

---

[15] Readers who are statistically and mathematically sophisticated are referred to discussions of continuous prior and posterior distribution by Schlaifer, *op. cit.*, pp. 435–456, 670–678; and Alderson and Green, *op. cit.*, pp. 310–317. Also see Richard C. Clelland, *Basic Statistics with Business Applications* (New York: John Wiley & Sons, Inc., 1966), pp. 615–627.

The notion of posterior analysis infers that the decision maker for reasons known to himself prefers to gather supplementary data without first considering the cost of such data collection and/or the potential reliability of the data-accumulation process. He merely gambles that the research program will be accurate enough and/or will be worth the price.

Finally, in the case of preposterior analysis, the decision maker carefully evaluates the wiseness of additional data collection *in advance* of the actual decision to authorize the data collection. If the benefits of the anticipated research do not exceed the cost of the research project, the terminal strategy is selected based on the original, unmodified judgments.

In order to improve the readers' feel for the application of these techniques, several additional illustrative marketing decision cases are offered to supplement those already presented.

2.17   Illustrative Case—New Product Addition, Prior Analysis

A publicly held industrial chemical firm has decided to add a consumer detergent to its product line, and management is faced with the decision as to whether the product should be developed internally or through the acquisition of a firm that is now making and marketing such a product. A third possible strategy is not to add the new product at all. The market for the product is well established; however, management is primarily concerned about the effects that the product addition will have on the market price of the firm's common stock, which is presently selling at $22 per share.

If the acquisition route is followed, less uncertainty will be involved since the sought-after company is already successful, certain required production and marketing resources will be acquired along with an appropriate market access, and the purchase of the acquired firm may be treated as a capital

TABLE 2–9. Conditional Payoff Matrix—New-Product-Introduction Problem (Cell Values Represent Average Market Price of the Firm's Common Stock During the Next 12 Months)

	Potential DJI Values				
	N_1: Under 650	N_2: 650–699	N_3: 700–749	N_4: 750–799	N_5: Over 800
			Prior Probabilities		
Strategies	0	.3	.4	.2	.1
S_1: Internal	10	14	25	33	40
S_2: Merger	16	18	27	32	34
S_3: Do not add product	18	20	22	23	24

investment. If, however, the product is developed internally, there will be high development expenditures which must be treated as current expenses, greater long-run profit potential and a firmer base for long-term growth, a more progressive image for the firm, better utilization of present capacity, and less danger of violating the antitrust laws.

Because of the differences in the two programs and the current unstable general securities market, management is unsure of the optimal strategy to follow. The company feels that the proper decision depends upon the average value of the Dow-Jones Industrial Index (DJI) during the current year. Following minor informal economic analyses and many internal discussions involving the firm's financial and marketing executives, a table of conditional payoffs, as shown in Table 2–9 is prepared. The probabilities assigned to the various states of nature (DJI) represent the "best guess" of the management group.

The expected values of the firm's stock prices are now calculated for each of the three strategies:

Strategy	EV (stock price)
S_1: Add product by internal development	$24.80
S_2: Add product by merger	$26.00
S_3: Do not add product	$21.80

Based upon the criterion of maximizing the expected value of the firm's common stock and predicated upon management's wish to choose a strategy *now*, the firm would elect to acquire the new product by merger. The reader may review Section 2.16 for some of the reasoning to support the use of prior rather than posterior or preposterior analysis. Furthermore, in this example it is possible that an undue delay would result in the acquisition of the available firm by a competitive bidder.

An underlying assumption in this problem is that the average selling price of the firm's stock is a function of general stock-market conditions, i.e., the value of the Dow-Jones Industrial Index.

2.18   Illustrative Case—Sales-force Supervision, Posterior Analysis

A marketing vice president (White) of a land-development company is dissatisfied with the performance of his new salesmen in the Toledo district. White attributes the problem to the fact that the Toledo sales manager (Brown) is not personally field training his salesmen but is instead delegating the field training either to the assistant sales manager (Black) or another salesman (Green). It has been established over time that when Brown does the training, on the average 80 per cent of a new man's presentations will be converted into sales. Analogous percentages for Black's and Green's trainees are 70 per cent and 50 per cent, respectively. When Brown is questioned as to the percentage of newly hired salesmen who are field trained by each trainer, he replies, "I train 50 per cent of all new men myself, Black trains 40 per cent, and only 10 per cent are trained by Green."

Since Brown has been known to "stretch the truth," White arranges to fly to Toledo for the purpose of observing a new salesman's field activity for a day. The new salesman fails to convert his first presentation into a sale. He sells his next two presentations. How much confidence should White have in Brown's statement?

Solution: The same general procedure as before is followed by setting up the table of probabilities shown in Table 2–10.

TABLE 2–10. Calculation of Posterior Probabilities—Salesman-supervision Problem

(1)		(2)	(3) Conditional Probability of the Field Observations, $p(f = 1 \mid N = 3, p)$	(4)	(5)
Salesman's Failure Rate, p		Prior Probability, $p(p)$		Joint Probability, $p(f = 1, p)$	Posterior Probability, $p(p \mid f = 1)$
Brown	.20	.50	.384	.1920	.474
Black	.30	.40	.441	.1764	.434
Green	.50	.10	.375	.0375	.092
		1.0		.4059	1.000

The results tabulated above do nothing to cast doubt upon Brown's statement since there is very little need for revision of the prior probabilities given in column 2.

It will be noted that column 1 lists the sales failure rates rather than the success rates. Either method may be used; however, it is generally recommended that no rates in excess of .50 be shown since binomial probability distribution tables (see Appendix A) normally show p values $\leq .50$.

Column 2 shows the probability of each sales trainer *prior* to the collection of new evidence or information (according to Brown's statement).

It may be noted that the decision maker, White, gathers his data by observing three of a new salesman's presentations which result in two sales and one nonsale. Column 3 gives the conditional probability of one nonsale ($f = 1$) in three presentations ($N = 3$) and each state of nature. For example, the top entry in column 3 is obtained by asking: What is the probability of obtaining one nonsale ($f = 1$) and two sales ($s = 2$) in three presentations ($N = 3$) if Brown was the trainer ($p = .20$)? The first step is to consider the order in which the presentations were observed, i.e., no-sale, sale, sale (f, s, s). Since with Brown as the trainer, $p(f) = .20$ and $p(s) = .8$, $p(f, s, s) = (.20)(.80)(.80) = .128$. However, two sales in three presentations could also have occurred in the orders (s, f, s) or (s, s, f). Therefore, .128 times 3 equals .384. The remaining entries in column 3 are similarly calculated.

The joint probabilities (column 4) reflect the joint occurrence of one nonsale in three presentations and a state of nature (p) and are obtained by the product of the column 2 and column 3 values.

Finally, the entries in column 5 are obtained by dividing each joint probability by the marginal total, .4059. Thus .474 equals .1920 divided by .4059.

Therefore, White's trip to Toledo and his field observation do not markedly revise the initial or prior probabilities assigned by Brown. In fact, based upon the field results, White is inclined to believe that the poor performance of new salesmen is not due to the source of field training.

It is worthwhile to accompany this and other applications of the Bayesian methods with certain of the many criticisms of the technique. First, in the example given in this section, an attempt to close sales may generally not be classified as a Bernoulli process. As indicated in Section 2.8, stability and independence are prerequisites and these are seldom if ever descriptive of behavioral processes. Specifically, a new salesman who is performing under the surveillance of his supervisor, especially the firm's vice president, may be subjected to tensions that might realistically alter his normal ability to convert presentations into sales.

Furthermore, it is argued that the observation of a scant three presentations is hardly a large enough sample to generate conclusive statistical evidence. Despite the soundness of such an argument, in a practical sales-supervision framework, trouble shooting of salesmen and sales methods in most cases takes on the form of a "spotcheck," i.e., the observation of a very small sample of behavior. The practice exercises at the end of this chapter will include an enlargement of the sample size of this specific example.

2.19   Illustrative Case—Sales-force Compensation; Multistage Data Collection, Preposterior Analysis

Mr. I. M. Daring, a young entrepreneur from the Midwest, decides to open the first U.S. automobile distributorship for the "Pango," an exciting new compact from Africa which Daring feels will eventually be competitive with domestic and other imported compact cars. The first Pango has yet to be sold in the United States and in fact, only 2,000 units were sold in Europe during the car's first year of availability.

Daring has a flair for unique innovations, especially in the area of marketing, and is therefore considering the possibility of paying his salesmen on a straight salary basis rather than by use of the conventional straight commission plan used by almost all U.S. automobile agencies. Daring's funds are limited and he has a huge investment to make in fixed facilities such as his building, furniture and fixtures, service department equipment, and inventory. He feels that all variables except "degree of consumer acceptance" can be treated as known. In his own mind, Daring has quantified the two relevant states of nature "good acceptance" and "poor acceptance."

Although he generally prefers to minimize his fixed expenses, his optimistic outlook toward the degree of consumer acceptance leads him to believe that his sales cost per unit will be substantially lower if he pays his salesmen by salary rather than commission. He is sophisticated enough to suspect that the subjective probabilities he has assigned to the two possible states of nature may require revision. He therefore feels that he has three options after constructing a preliminary table of conditional payoffs.

Option 1: Choose compensation plan *now* which will minimize the expected unit sales cost.

Option 2: Delay terminal decision. Purchase an 80 per cent reliable survey. (The research organization, in order to gain a promising new client, has agreed to accept a survey fee of $3.50 for each car sold the first year.) Then choose compensation plan.

Option 3: Delay terminal decision. Purchase the survey mentioned in option 2 along with a second-stage 90 per cent reliable survey at a cost of $4.00 for each car sold the first year. This option will include the privilege to cancel the second stage after Daring has observed the findings of the first stage. Then choose compensation plan.

TABLE 2–11. Conditional Payoff Matrix—Sales-force-compensation Problem (cell values represent dollar sales costs for each automobile that is sold)

	Potential Acceptance of Pango	
	N_1: Good Acceptance	N_2: Poor Acceptance
	Prior Probabilities	
Strategies	.7	.3
S_1: Salary only	40	140
S_2: Commission only	100	100

Daring and his staff, in consideration of the two possible compensation plans, the two states of nature, and relevant recruiting and sales-force turnover costs, develop a matrix of conditional payoffs in terms of unit sales costs which is shown in Table 2–11.

Note that subjective prior probabilities of .7 and .3 have been assigned to states of nature N_1 and N_2, respectively. If the firm decides *not* to gather additional information, a salary-only (S_1) compensation plan will be chosen since the expected value of unit sales cost is \$70 under strategy S_1 and \$100 under strategy S_2.

However, recognizing his optimistic tendencies, Daring decides to investigate the wiseness of collecting more objective data relating to the potential acceptance of the Pango. He recognizes that his selection of strategy S_1 based on prior analysis is predicted on his personal confidence in the product's favorable acceptance. *It must be emphasized* that no survey has yet been purchased or authorized. Daring merely wants to do a little paper work to determine whether the one-stage or two-stage surveys are worth the asking prices of the research firm. Given the degree of reliability of each survey stage, the joint, marginal, and posterior probabilities are calculated for both stages and shown in Tables 2–12 and 2–13.

TABLE 2–12. Joint, Marginal, and Posterior Probabilities—Sales-compensation Problem   First Stage of Survey (80 per cent reliable)

	(1)	(2)	(3)	(4)	(5)
	Joint		Marginal	Posterior	
Survey Result	N_1	N_2		$p(N_1\|Z_i)$	$p(N_2\|Z_i)$
Z_1	.56	.06	.62	.92	.08
Z_2	.14	.24	.38	.37	.63
	.70	.30	1.0		

Table 2–12 follows the exact logic of previously developed Table 2–8. However, a bit of redundancy may help to reinforce the methodology. By definition, an 80 per cent reliable survey means

$$p(Z_1|N_1) = p(Z_2|N_2) = .80$$

$$p(Z_1|N_2) = p(Z_2|N_1) = .20$$

The above conditional probabilities infer that 80 per cent of the time the survey results will correctly predict the correct state of nature.

Since joint probability equals conditional probability times marginal (prior) probability, the joint probability of survey result Z_1 (the prediction that N_1 will occur) and state of nature N_1 may be expressed:

$$p(Z_1, N_1) = p(Z_1|N_1) \times p(N_1)$$

$$p(Z_1, N_1) = \quad .80 \quad \times \quad .70 \ = .56$$

This figure appears in row 1, column 1, in Table 2–12. Similarly,

$$p(Z_2, N_2) = .80 \times .30 = .24$$

$$p(Z_1, N_2) = .20 \times .30 = .06$$

$$p(Z_2, N_1) = .20 \times .70 = .14$$

The column 3 figures are developed by adding the entries in columns 1 and 2, i.e., $.56 + .06 = .62$. Therefore, the probability of survey result Z_1 is .62 and the probability of survey result Z_2 is .38.

The posterior probabilities of columns 4 and 5 are developed as follows:

$$p(N_1|Z_1) = \frac{.56}{.62} = .92 \qquad p(N_1|Z_2) = \frac{.14}{.38} = .37$$

$$p(N_2|Z_1) = \frac{.06}{.62} = .08 \qquad p(N_2|Z_2) = \frac{.24}{.38} = .63$$

Therefore, we may construct the following payoff matrix if the first-stage survey predicts N_1:

	.92 N_1	·08 N_2	EV
S_1	40	140	48
S_2	100	100	100

If, however, the first-stage survey predicts N_2:

	.37 N_1	.63 N_2	EV
S_1	40	140	103
S_2	100	100	100

Seemingly, if the survey's first stage predicts favorable product acceptance, the S_1 strategy is confirmed; a survey prediction of poor acceptance generates evidence in favor of S_2. However, Daring's paperwork is not quite finished; the second stage of the proposed survey must be evaluated before one of the three options is selected.

TABLE 2–13. Joint, Marginal, and Posterior Probabilities—Sales-compensation Problem (two-stage survey)

	(1) Joint N_1	(2) Joint N_2	(3) Marginal	(4) Posterior $p(N_1\|Z_i)$	(5) Posterior $p(N_2\|Z_i)$
(1) $Z_1\|Z_1$	.83	.01	.84	.99	.01
(2) $Z_2\|Z_1$	.09	.07	.16	.56	.44
	.92	.08	1.0		
(3) $Z_1\|Z_2$	.33	.06	.39	.85	.15
(4) $Z_2\|Z_2$	.04	.57	.61	.07	.93
	.37	.63	1.0		

Table 2–13 integrates the results of both stages of the survey. Note that this table follows previous methodology except that the posterior probabilities of the first survey stage become the prior probabilities of the second survey stage. Since the second-stage survey is 90 per cent reliable,

$$p(Z_1|N_1) = p(Z_2|N_2) = .90$$

$$p(Z_1|N_2) = p(Z_2|N_1) = .10$$

Note that four possible two-stage survey results are possible. $Z_1|Z_1$ refers to a second stage Z_1 result given (following) a first stage Z_1 result. $Z_2|Z_1$ refers to a second-stage Z_2 result following a first-stage Z_1 result. Since $J = CM$,

$$p(Z_1|Z_1, N_1) = .92 \times .90 = .828 = .83$$

$$p(Z_1|Z_1, N_2) = .08 \times .10 = .008 = .01$$

$$p(Z_2|Z_1, N_1) = .92 \times .10 = .092 = .09$$

$$p(Z_2|Z_1, N_2) = .08 \times .90 = .072 = .07$$

In calculating the preceding joint probabilities, confusion may be avoided by plugging in the marginal (prior) probabilities of .92 and .08 before any calculations are made.

The joint probabilities of rows 3 and 4 are similarly calculated. Columns 3, 4, and 5 follow the same procedure as used in constructing Table 2–12.

The reader, in observing Table 2–13, will see that four new payoff matrices may be constructed to concur with the four possible combinations of two-stage-survey results. Each matrix will assign a different set of posterior probabilities to the two states of nature N_1 and N_2. However, such a procedure will not be required since the decision tree shown by Figure 2–2 will automatically include such calculations.

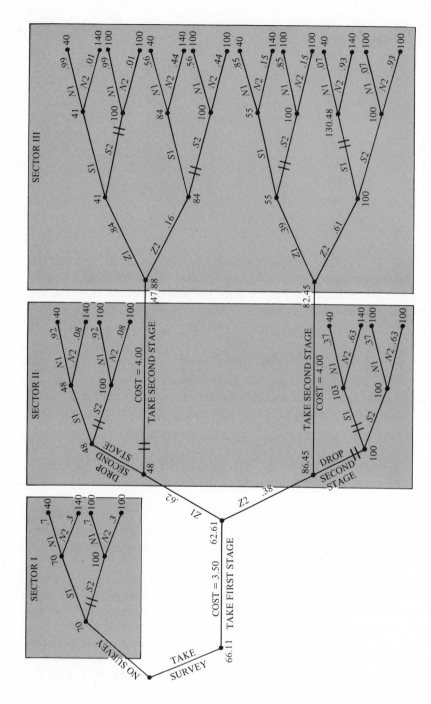

FIGURE 2–2. Decision Tree. Sales-force-compensation Problem. Two-Stage Survey (payoffs in dollars).

62

Sector I of Figure 2–2 summarizes option 1 whereby the terminal decision may be made without conducting either stage of the survey. This sector of the decision tree is merely a representation of Table 2–11 along with a calculation of the expected value of sales cost. Since option 1 involves no survey costs, the net computed expected sales cost of that option is $70.

Sector II of the tree diagram describes the potential results of the first-stage survey. We have already concluded that if a terminal decision is required after the first stage, a Z_1 survey result would dictate strategy S_1 while a Z_2 survey result would suggest strategy S_2. This constitutes option 2, which could be a distinct possibility in the event of the emergence of time, security, or other constraints.

Sector III diagrams the results of the second stage of the survey. When sectors II and III are combined we have a flow chart of option 3, wherein the firm may purchase the two-stage research project, including the right to cancel the second stage. For example, if we assume that both survey stages will be completed, we may refer to the right-hand side of sector III and observe the various payoff values, i.e., 40, 140, 100, and 100. Suppose the first-stage survey yields result Z_1 and the second-stage survey yields result Z_1. The probability of N_1 is therefore .99 and $p(N_2)$ is .01 (see Table 2–13). Therefore, under such circumstances the expected value of strategy S_1 is $40(.99) + 140(.01) = \$41$; the expected value of strategy S_2 is $100(.99) + 100(.01) = \$100$. Since a $41 sales cost is preferred to a $100 cost, the S_2 branch is blocked off. If a Z_2 second-stage survey follows a Z_1 first-stage survey, an expected cost of $84 is computed if strategy S_1 is used.

Therefore, as the left side of sector III of the decision tree indicates, following a Z_1 first-stage result, a Z_1 second-stage result has an expected value of $41, whereas a Z_2 second-stage result has an expected value of $84. Since $p(Z_1|Z_1) = .84$ and $p(Z_2|Z_1) = .16$, the expected value of "taking the second-stage survey" given a Z_1 first-stage result is $41(.84) + 84(.16) = \$47.88$. When the second-stage survey fee of $4.00 is added, the total expected unit sales costs, including second-stage results, total $51.88. Since the sector II results indicate an expected cost of $48 per unit without a second-stage survey, the "take second-stage survey" option is blocked off.

Using the same method of analysis, if the first-stage survey yields a Z_2 result, the expected cost value of the "take second-stage survey" option plus the $4.00 survey is $86.45. If the second stage is dropped, the expected cost is $100; thus the latter option is blocked off. Therefore, we may summarize option 3 as follows:

If the result of the first-stage survey is Z_1, *do not* continue with the second stage.

If the result of the first-stage survey is Z_2, *continue* with the second stage.

Table 2–14 tabulates the results of all calculations comparing the three options open to Mr. Daring. Again, we repeat that all computations and the

construction of Table 2–14 are to be completed before *any* survey contracts
are to be accepted. Since option 3 yields the lowest total sales cost including
the survey fees, this is the recommended strategy.

TABLE 2–14. Comparison of the Three Options—Sales-force-compensation Problem

	Survey Results		Expected Unit Sales Cost Including Survey Fee	Optimal Strategy
Option 1: no survey	None		$70.00	S_1
Option 2: one-stage survey	Z_1		$71.26	S_1
	Z_2			S_2
Option 3:	First stage	Second stage		
Two-stage survey with	Z_1	Cancel		S_1
privilege of cancelling	Z_2	Z_1	$66.11	S_1
second stage	Z_2	Z_2		S_2

The reader will note that the mathematics supporting options 1 and 3
have been explicitly presented in this section. The expected cost of option 2,
$E(O_2) = 48(.62) + 100(.38) + 3.50 = \$71.26$. The construction of a decision
tree for option 2 will be useful in clarifying these results. This exercise will be
included among the exercises at the end of the chapter.

In summary, as shown in Table 2–14, Mr. Daring should contract with the
marketing research firm under the terms of option 3. If the first survey stage
predicts favorable acceptance of the Pango (Z_1), Daring should cancel the
second stage of the survey and install a straight salary plan for his salesmen
(S_1). If, however, the first survey stage predicts poor acceptance of the car,
the second survey stage should be authorized. If the second stage predicts
favorable acceptance (Z_1), the salesmen should be paid on the salary plan;
if the second stage forecasts poor acceptance (Z_2), the sales force should be
compensated by commissions only (S_2).

In this illustration as in the others, certain questionable assumptions are
made for simplicity. These include the willingness of the research firm to be
compensated on a contingency basis and the assumption that the straight-
salary and straight-commission compensation plan constitute a collectively
exhaustive set of sales-force-compensation alternatives. Obviously drawing
accounts, salary plus commission, and bonuses affixed to all plans could be
considered. However, a larger set of strategies and states of nature would do
nothing more than to generate a payoff matrix with larger dimensions,
which would in turn be subjected to the identical procedure that has been
illustrated.

2.20 Bayesian Versus Classical Analysis

Despite the limited number of applications of Bayesian analysis, the method offers many appealing advantages over classical statistical techniques. In the classical method, statistical data are generated and presented to the decision maker for interpretation and a choice between two actions, i.e., *accept* or *reject* the null hypothesis. Size and representativeness of the sample, questionnaire design, and data-gathering procedures are critical factors. The decision-maker's personal judgment is relatively unimportant, at least until the interpretation stage.

The Bayesian approach incorporates managerial opinions, attitudes, beliefs, and experience in the original data. Historical information is not required. It generally reduces research costs by permitting the use of smaller samples. This approach can be used in attacking a wide variety of marketing problems since it can distinguish among the values of many states of nature and allows the choice of the best action to emerge from a many-action situation.

2.21 Some Final Comments About the Bayesian Model

Hopefully this chapter has generated some feeling for the broad array of marketing and other business problems that may be approached by Bayesian techniques. The method combines management science with the manager's experience, which seemingly is the common goal of both the business academician and the practicing business executive. If the marketing decision maker can assign a high reliability to his own judgment and intuition, he may perceive little or no risk in choosing the option of gathering no additional information. If, however, he feels that the gathering of additional objective data will reduce the degree of uncertainty, he may choose to take advantage of the wide range of information-gathering options, available in varying degrees of reliability and cost.

Indeed, the marketing manager may "make or buy" with regard to information. He may choose to "make" information, using his (or his associates') prior experience, or he can "buy" information through marketing research, assuming that the value of such "purchased information" exceeds its cost.[16]

Management science provides the rules; the manager's experience provides the exceptions to the rules.

EXERCISES

1. What is the justification for the use of prior analysis rather than the Wald or Hurwicz criteria?

[16] Ronald E. Frank and Paul E. Green, *Quantitative Methods in Marketing* (Englewood Cliffs, N.J.: Prentice-Hall, Inc., 1967), pp. 22–23.

2. By use of subjective probabilities and the expected value criterion, calculate the following. Support your method of assigning subjective probabilities in each case.
   (a) Your grade in this course.
   (b) Your golf score (or your favorite player's score) during your (his) next round.
   (c) The age of your professor.
   (d) The closing price (to the nearest dollar) of IBM common stock on the second Tuesday of next month.

3. Show how Bayesian analysis combines intuition and science.

4. A study of the performance percentages of the Washington Redskins under varying field conditions showed the following results:

	Dry Field	Muddy Field
Won	.26	.14
Lost	.38	.22

   (a) What are the odds against a victory in the next game?
   (b) Do the Skins prefer a dry or muddy field?
   (c) You expect to see the Redskins play next Sunday. What is the joint probability that the field will be dry and the team will lose?

5. Under what circumstances would *subjective* probabilities be preferred to *objective* probabilities?

6. Wayne McGrath, president of the Canned Tuna Association, is concerned about the government's report that 30 per cent of the cans of tuna on consumers' shelves have an overabundance of mercury content. If this is true, the government could recall all the canned tuna in the distribution channels, thus involving a multimillion dollar loss for the tuna industry. McGrath feels certain that 5 per cent is the correct defective rate and assigns a .90 prior probability to his belief. He assigns an inspector to canvass consumers on a door-to-door basis and 50 cans of tuna are randomly tested; 43 of the cans have an acceptable mercury content. What is the posterior probability distribution of p (the defect rate), assuming that either 30 per cent or 5 per cent is the correct rate?

7. Rework the sales-force-supervision problem of Section 2.18 under the circumstances that White observes 25 field presentations, 15 of which are converted into sales.

8. Refer to the sales-force-compensation problem illustrated in Section 2.19. Construct a decision tree for option 2 which will confirm an expected cost of $71.26.

9. An advertising agency on the West Coast is considering the hiring of five key creative employees at a salary of $40,000 each (employment contract will guarantee employment for 1 full year). The firm would be happy to employ these people if the Dumbarton Chemical Company account could be acquired. The agency managers

feel there is a 50:50 chance of landing the Dumbarton account. However, if the account is acquired and the key employees are not hired, there will be no incremental profits. Based on anticipated billings and the attendant costs, the following conditional payoff matrix is constructed:

CONDITIONAL PAYOFF MATRIX
(Incremental Profit Payoffs in Thousands of Dollars)

	N_1: Account Is Landed	N_2: Account Is Not Landed
S_1: Hire five key employees	740	− 200
S_2: Remain status quo	0	0

A prominent union leader tells the agency that if they will pay him a fee of $20,000, he will use his unique influences to provide explicit information as to whether the agency will acquire the Dumbarton account. The union leader has engaged in such undercover activity before and his information has been correct 80 per cent of the time.

(a) Following the use of preposterior analysis and the construction of a decision tree, what should the agency do?

(b) Is the amount of the fee a critical factor?

10. A large TV retailer contracts to purchase an off-brand television set from the Buckeye Mfg. Co. in lots of 100 sets. If he inspects each TV set (at a cost of $1.35 each) he can be sure the set will not require repairs during the warranty period. If he sells the set without inspecting it, and if the set becomes inoperative during the warranty period, the retailer's average repair cost will be $10 per set. In the absence of inspection, the defect rate can either be 5 per cent, 10 per cent, or 15 per cent. Based upon past experience with off-brand models, the retailer assigns subjective probabilities of .10, .20, and .70, respectively, to the three collectively exhaustive defect rates. The retailer selects three sets at random, inspects them, and finds one defective set.

(a) Should he sell the TV sets with or without inspection? (prior analysis only).

(b) Would his decision be the same using posterior analysis?

(c) Suppose that the decision maker decides to inspect every unit in the first lot of 100 to establish an inspection policy for future shipments. If 11 are defective, what should be his future inspection policy?

(In parts (b) and (c), ignore the costs of the test.)

11. There are 8,000 family units in the wealthy West Pumpkinseed community. An association of these residents is considering the construction of a private golf course which will involve an initial expense of $3,000,000 to cover the downpayment on the land and the construction of the course. Annual costs including maintenance and land amortization are estimated at $160,000 over the first 5 years following construction. Since the land will be paid in full after 5 years and the membership is expected to be substantial at that time, the association is concerned only with the

number of families who would be willing to pay a $3,000 initiation fee and contract for a 5-year membership at $1,000 per year. The association officers estimate the number of potential joining families according to the following discrete prior distribution:

N	$P(N)$
400	.50
800	.40
1,200	.10

(a) Based on a 5 year expected profit criterion, should the golf course be constructed?
(b) If the association used preposterior analysis and decided to question a random sample of five families as to membership intentions, what decision plan should the association adopt?

12. The Los Angeles Dodgers, a professional baseball club, has just completed its 1971 season and is considering certain construction that will modernize its ballpark and increase its seating capacity. However, it has been indicated that attendance is a function of the team's performance. Management must make its construction decision before December 1, 1971, so that any authorized ballpark changes will be completed prior to the 1972 season.

The team did well in 1971; however, two key players require surgery, and competitive clubs appear stronger. After studying the Dodgers' and competitive player resources, LA's general manager is able to generate a conditional profit payoff matrix contingent upon three possible construction strategies and the various performance situations. Prior probabilities for the occurrence of each team performance are developed by face-to-face discussion among club executives.

CONDITIONAL PAYOFF MATRIX
(Profit Payoffs in Millions of Dollars)

	N_1: Winning Season .60	N_2: Ordinary Season .30	N_3: Losing Season .10
S_1: No construction	1.20	0.90	0.50
S_2: Minor construction	1.50	0.50	0.20
S_3: Major construction	2.00	0.60	−0.60

The team's general manager feels that the following choices are available:
(1) Make no changes (S_1)
(2) Authorize minor construction (S_2)
(3) Authorize major construction (S_3)
(4) Delay a decision for 30 days and conduct an informal survey among fans at a cost of $20,000. This study would be 60 per cent reliable; i.e., if the survey

results indicate Z_1 (that the team will have a winning season), there is a 20 per cent chance that this result could have been obtained if the team had an ordinary 1972 season (N_2) and also a 20 per cent chance that this result could have been obtained in advance of a losing season (N_3). Z_2 and Z_3 results are similarly interpreted.

(5) Delay a decision for 60 days and hire a marketing research firm to conduct a two-stage formal survey among baseball reporters, retired ballplayers, gamblers, baseball executives, and knowledgeable fans. The first stage would be 80 per cent reliable and would cost $100,000. The second survey (which is subject to cancellation after observing first-stage results) would be 90 per cent reliable and would cost $70,000.

Using expected profit value as the criterion of choice,

(a) Which of the above five choices should management make?

(b) Construct a decision chart similar to Table 2–14 showing each optimal construction strategy for each option, i.e., no survey, informal survey, two-stage formal survey.

(c) If the team had to choose between no survey and an informal survey, which would be your suggested choice?

13. A direct-selling firm is expanding, and one of its goals is to employ many new field salesmen during the forthcoming 12 months. The sales manager has a choice as to whether he will use an elaborate testing procedure on each of 100 expected applicants, or whether he will hire everyone who applies (without testing). If the test is used on every applicant, only 50 per cent of the applicants will be hired, and the testing cost for each of the 100 applicants will be $240. It is expected that the 50 hired tested salesmen and the 100 hired untested men will produce the same volume of business. However, if the test is used, the failure rate of salesmen will be zero; if the test is not used, the failure rate will be 10 per cent, 20 per cent, or 30 per cent. If a man fails, the firm's out-of-pocket and opportunity costs will be $1,000 per ineffective man. Based upon his past experience the sales manager assigns a probability of .20 that the failure rate will be 10 per cent, a probability of .30 that the failure rate will be 20 per cent, and a probability of .50 that the failure rate will be 30 per cent. To gather more information three new men are hired (without testing) and one fails. Using expected costs as an optimizing criterion, will the posterior analysis support or contradict the sales manager's original (based on prior analysis) strategy?

REFERENCES

ENIS, BEN M., and BROOME, CHARLES L., *Marketing Decisions: A Bayesian Approach* (Scranton, Pa.: Intext Educational Publishers, 1971).

FRANK, RONALD E., and GREEN, PAUL E., *Quantitative Methods in Marketing* (Englewood Cliffs, N.J.: Prentice-Hall, Inc., 1967).

GREEN, PAUL E., and TULL, DONALD S., *Research for Marketing Decisions* (Englewood Cliffs, N.J.: Prentice-Hall, Inc., 1970).

SCHLAIFER, ROBERT, *Probability and Statistics for Business Decisions* (New York: McGraw-Hill Book Company, 1959).

CHAPTER 3

Simulation As a Marketing Tool

Although some readers may disagree, Chapter 2 has demonstrated relatively simple problem situations. This chapter will introduce an additional set of tools which may be used to solve marketing problems under uncertainty. Unlike the Bayesian method, these *simulation* procedures are most useful in situations where the complexity of the decision problem does not allow generalized assumptions concerning the probability distribution governing the situation. In general, simulation is employed to develop solutions for models that are too complex to solve analytically and/or models that may not be easily represented by deterministic relationships. Succinctly put, when all else fails—*simulate*.

3.1 Definition of Simulation

The examples offered in the first two chapters have inferred that the sole prerequisite to making a major marketing decision is a series of computations on a pad of paper. In practice, however, marketing managers prefer to field test the alternative courses of action in the marketplace so as to generate empirical evidence of the operating results of the proposed strategies. However, experimentation with real products, real salesmen, real consumers, and real equipment is costly, time consuming, destructive, and informative to competition. In such cases, it may be more desirable to construct a model of the operational situation and "experiment" with *it* instead of the real-world variables. The manipulation of such models is called *simulation*.[1] In the space program, it is obviously safer, cheaper, and faster to observe scaled models of the lunar module in the manned space laboratories in Houston rather than to experiment during actual flights.

In marketing situations, conceptual rather than physical models are built and manipulated so as to develop data on the results to be obtained when varying input mixes are employed. The marketing analyst views a simulation model as an *imitation* of the process or system under study and attempts to

[1] Paul E. Green and Donald S. Tull, *Research for Marketing Decisions* (Englewood Cliffs, N.J.: Prentice-Hall, Inc., 1966), p. 113.

71

run the system on paper (or by means of a computer) to see "what would happen if" a particular policy were put into operation.[2]

Simulations in marketing may model various systems. In some cases, a firm's entire marketing system may be modeled. Or, a specific aspect of a firm's operations might be depicted. For example, the firm's distribution system might be simulated. Another useful way of looking at simulation is whether the system being modeled is *internal* or *external*. Thus the decision process involved in setting a price for a new product might be simulated (internal), whereas models of competition and consumer behavior would be illustrative of external simulations.

3.2   Types of Simulation

As the reader studies the previous section and then recalls the discussion of models in Chapter 1, he may assume that all *marketing models* are really *simulation models*, since by definition a model is a simulation of the real thing. In this text and others, the term *simulation model* is used to describe models developed for the purpose of exploring the market-response implications of a model by the use of the technique of simulation.[3]

Green and Tull list several major techniques commonly listed under the generic label of *simulation*.[4] These are

1. Tactical simulation
2. Strategic simulation
3. Monte Carlo methods
4. Business gaming
5. Experimental gaming
6. Heuristic programming.

In this text, the last two techniques will be omitted and business gaming will be scarcely touched. This chapter will concentrate on *Monte Carlo methods*, *waiting-line processes* as an example of tactical simulation, and *Markov models* as an example of strategic simulation.

3.3   Procedural Steps in Simulation

Whatever the type of simulation, there are a number of procedural steps involved in developing the model that replicates the system involved:

1. There must be a thorough and detailed analysis of the system to be simulated.

---

[2] *Ibid.*, p. 405.

[3] David B. Montgomery and Glen L. Urban, *Management Science in Marketing* (Englewood Cliffs, N.J.: Prentice-Hall, Inc., 1969), p. 29.

[4] Green and Tull, *op. cit.*, p. 407.

2. A decision must be made as to the relevant independent (causative) variables that significantly explain the dependent (output) variables of the system under analysis.
3. The precise effect of these independent variables on the output variables must be ascertained. In effect, the analyst must determine the direction and intensity of changes in the output variables as the independent variables are varied.
4. The model depicting the relationships between the independent and dependent variables needs to be developed. In most cases, this step embraces the development of mathematical formulas.
5. The simulation needs to be manipulated; i.e., different input values need to be entered into the model to determine the combination that will optimize the desired outputs.
6. These predicted output values need to be compared to actual results so that the validity of the simulation may be ascertained. Usually, the simulation's output values are compared to *past results*; the analyst then has some idea as to how much confidence he can place in the simulation without having to wait for results to compare to the predicted values.

3.4 Business Games

Marketing games range from simple pad-and-pencil exercises to involved games requiring the use of high-speed computers. A number of these have been used in academia and in industry to provide participants with experience in making decisions.[5] Their chief advantage is that mistakes can be made without actually jeopardizing the effectiveness of the firm's operations. Generally, participants are divided into teams which compete with each other for some stipulated objective such as maximum sales, highest profits, lowest cost, etc. In addition to providing the participants with decision-making practice, the marketing game also provides a convenient means for analysis of the behavioral interactions of participants. For example, one of the authors examined a number of behavioral concepts within teams playing a marketing game in a principles-of-marketing course; as a result, some inferences could be made for real-life marketing decision-making groups in industry.[6]

3.5 Waiting-line Theory (Queuing Theory)

The marketing area of the firm is frequently concerned with problems associated with people or physical facilities that need to be serviced. Thus,

[5] An example of the use of business games in industry is Montgomery Ward's computerized retail management workshop called "decision dynamics."

[6] Richard T. Hise, "The Effect of Close Supervision on Productivity of Simulated Managerial Decision-making Groups," *Business Studies* (Fall 1968), pp. 96–104.

a supermarket must check out its customers, a bank must service its depositors, a loading and unloading dock must process trucks that want to load or unload merchandise, and restaurants are required to seat people for Sunday dinner. In these illustrations, as well as in numerous other examples that might have been given, there is the distinct possibility that a line (or queue) may form. *Waiting-line* or *queuing theory* has been developed as a simulation tool to analyze this phenomenon.

It is useful to view any waiting line as being composed of two costs that are *inversely* related; i.e., as one decreases, the other increases. First, there is the cost associated with *not* servicing the waiting queue. These costs arise from the fact that people do not like to wait in line; the longer they do, the more frustration occurs. This frustration, for example, may eventually result in individuals deciding not to purchase the product or service or switching their business entirely to a competitive firm. Quite obviously, there is a cost to the firm—the value of the lost sales. Second, this first cost may be reduced by increasing the number of facilities employed to service the queue involved. In a supermarket, for example, we can add cash registers and clerical help to the extent that no queue would ever form. No one would ever have to wait in line; customers would be immediately processed. Of course the firm pays a price: In reducing the cost of lost sales, there is an increase in the cost of the additional personnel and facilities needed to eliminate waiting time. The general waiting-line problem, in many cases, is to determine that level of facilities and personnel that will minimize total cost, where total cost is the sum of the cost of lost sales and the cost of additional personnel and facilities.

Before proceeding to examine queuing theory in any great detail, it will be necessary for the reader to become familiar with some of the basic concepts involved. *Arrivals* refer to the individual or thing that needs to be serviced. The *service facility* is the facility that is designed to process the arrivals. The *arrival rate* refers to the rate at which arrivals enter the service facility. Usually, this is expressed as, for example, 12 arrivals per hour or one arrival every 5 minutes. The *service rate* consists of the average length of time required to service each arrival, such as 10 minutes per supermarket customer. It should be obvious that the relationship between the arrival rate and the service rate is crucial. Dividing the arrival rate by the service rate yields the *load factor*. Any load factor of less than 1 is of significance because this means that arrivals occur faster than they can be serviced, resulting in a waiting line. If, for example, we had a load factor of .5 (a 5-minute arrival rate divided by a service rate of 10 minutes, for instance), at the end of 1 hour there would be a waiting line of 6 persons. (The reader should verify this figure for himself.)

In the following section, we will illustrate a single queue–single service facility; i.e., a single line of people is to be processed through only one service facility. Other more complicated possibilities include multiple queue–single service facilities, single queue–multiple service facilities, and multiple queue–multiple service facilities. In this example it is assumed that arrivals are handled on a first-come–first-served basis. This makes for a simpler analysis but is not always the case, as, for example, telephone switchboards where incoming calls may be handled randomly. In addition, it will be assumed that a certain number of arrivals occur during each and every time period. This simplifying assumption, in essence, makes this a deterministic model. In the truck-arrival example that appears later, arrivals occur on a probabilistic basis, thereby making that example a stochastic model.

3.6   Single Queue–Single Service Facility (Supermarket)

Let's assume that we have a new branch of the Apex Supermarket Co. opening in a suburban shopping center. The vice president of operations in the home office is trying to decide how much of an investment in cash registers and checkout stations is required for the new store. In working on this problem, he decides to use waiting-line analysis. The objective in his analysis is to assign that number of cash registers and checkout stations that will minimize the total of the following pertinent costs: (1) cash-register acquisition, (2) clerical wages, and (3) the cost of lost sales resulting from impatient customers who switch to competitive stores.

In order to analyze those aspects of the store's operations that are applicable to waiting-line analysis, the vice-president of operations uses data available for similar stores in the chain. In this regard, the following data and assumptions are important:

1. Each cashier is paid $2.50 per hour.
2. The supermarket stays open from 9:00 A.M. to 5:00 P.M. on Monday, Tuesday, and Wednesday and from 9:00 A.M. to 9:00 P.M. on Thursday, Friday, and Saturday.
3. It takes, on the average, 6 minutes for a checker to service each customer.
4. The average gross margin per sale is $15.00.
5. Each customer shops once a week.
6. On Mondays, an average of one customer arrives at the checkout counter every 5 minutes. The arrivals every 5 minutes for Tuesday are 2, for Wednesday 3, for Thursday 5, for Friday 15, and Saturday 15.
7. The above point assumes that the arrival of customers is evenly spread throughout the day and that arrivals occur at the beginning of each 5-minute period.
8. The amortized annual cost of a new cash register and checkout station, including maintenance and floor-space allocation, is $2,000.
9. The probability of any customer leaving the waiting line and switching

permanently to another store is a function of the length of the waiting
line. The relevant data are

Length of Line	Probability
1–2	.00
3–5	.02
6–10	.03
11–15	.05
16–20	.10
21 or greater	.15

10. No more than six cash registers will be employed. Thus, the range of
feasible alternatives is one to six cash registers and checkout counters.

With the aid of the above data, management can now use a simulation
process to help in determining how many cash registers to place in the new
store. Given the number of hours the store will remain open each day and
the arrival rate of customers, an average of 97 customers will approach the
checkout counter on Monday, 194 on Tuesday, 291 on Wednesday, 485 on
Thursday, 1,455 on Friday, and 1,455 on Saturday. As a result, a long-hand
tabulation of the simulation data for a full week for each register alternative
would be quite cumbersome for the reader.

However, Table 3–1 illustrates the single cash-register procedure for the
first 17 customers on Monday. Customer number 1 arrives at 9:00, is serviced
immediately, and is finished at 9:06. Thus there is no waiting time for
customer 1; he is the only one in the store. Therefore, the probability that
he will leave the line and switch his purchase to another store is zero. Column
8 gives the calculations of the expected annual cost of the loss of customer 1's
business. This is obtained by multiplying the average lost margin ($15) by
52 weeks by the probability of the permanent loss of the customer. For the
first customer, this is ($15)(52)(.00) = $0.

The second customer arrives at 9:05 but must wait in line for 1 minute,
until the first customer is checked out at 9:06.

If we skip to customer number 8, we note that he arrives at 9:35. At that
time, customers 6 and 7 would still be ahead of him. Thus the length of the
line would be 3 customers. When customer 7 is finished at 9:42, customer 8
can be checked out after waiting 7 minutes (from 9:35 to 9:42). Thus the
expected annual cost of losing customer 8's business is $15.60 ($15 × 52 ×
.02).

All other customers are simulated in the same way. The reader is en-
couraged to complete the exercise. Note that the final customer of the day
arrives at 5:00. He theoretically must wait until 6:36 to be checked out since

TABLE 3–1. Data for Supermarket Waiting Line (single cash register—Monday)

(1) Customer Number	(2) Time of Arrival	(3) Time Checkout Begins	(4) Time Checkout Is Completed	(5) Waiting Time (Minutes)	(6) Length of Line	(7) Probability That Customer Will Leave the Line	(8) Expected Annual Cost of Lost Customer ($)
1	9:00	9:00	9:06	0	1	.00	00.00
2	9:05	9:06	9:12	1	2	.00	00.00
3	9:10	9:12	9:18	2	2	.00	00.00
4	9:15	9:18	9:24	3	2	.00	00.00
5	9:20	9:24	9:30	4	2	.00	00.00
6	9:25	9:30	9:36	5	2	.00	00.00
7	9:30	9:36	9:42	6	2	.00	00.00
8	9:35	9:42	9:48	7	3	.02	15.60
9	9:40	9:48	9:54	8	3	.02	15.60
10	9:45	9:54	10:00	9	3	.02	15.60
11	9:50	10:00	10:06	10	3	.02	15.60
12	9:55	10:06	10:12	11	3	.02	15.60
13	10:00	10:12	10:18	12	3	.02	15.60
14	10:05	10:18	10:24	13	4	.02	15.60
15	10:10	10:24	10:30	14	4	.02	15.60
16	10:15	10:30	10:36	15	4	.02	15.60
17	10:20	10:36	10:42	16	4	.02	15.60
.							
.							
.							
97	5:00	6:36	6:42	102	17	.10	78.00
							3088.80

the total waiting line consists of 17 customers. The probability that customer 97 will leave the line and shop elsewhere is .10 and the expected cost of losing his business is $78.00 ($15 × 52 × .10).

Management can now determine the total cost of installing one cash register on a Monday. The three costs of significance are cash-register acquisition, clerical wages, and the cost of lost sales. On a per annum basis, these costs for Monday would be

1. Cost of cash-register acquisition—no dollars allocated specifically to Monday since the $2,000 cost is applicable for Monday through Saturday for the alternative of one cash register.

2. Clerical wages—$1,040 (8 hours per day times $2.50 per hour wage times 52 weeks).
3. Cost of lost sales—this is the total of column 8 and is $3,088.80.

Thus the total annual cost of a one-cash-register setup for a Monday's operation would be $1,040 in wages, an expected cost of $3,088.80 in foregone sales, plus a pro-rated portion of the cash register and checkout station cost.

Through the same procedure, the vice president of operations could simulate the total cost of installing one cash register for the year by developing the appropriate data for Tuesday through Saturday. Although space restrictions preclude the detailed coverage that was presented for Monday, the pertinent cost data for these days as well as the figures for Monday indicated above, are given in Table 3–2. The table indicates that a total cost for a year of $456,148.80 would result from the installation of only one cash register. The greatest part of this figure is composed of the cost of lost sales, which become greater during the latter part of the week. This results, of course, from the fact that the waiting line theoretically would grow to tremendously long lengths due to increased numbers of customers desiring service from only one available cash register.

TABLE 3–2. Cost Data for One Year of Operations Assuming Installation of One Cash Register

Day of Week	Cash Register and Checkout Station Costs ($)	Clerical Wages ($)	Cost of Lost Sales ($)	Total Cost per Annum ($)
Monday	—	1,040	3,088.80	4,128.80
Tuesday	—	1,040	19,453.80	20,493.80
Wednesday	—	1,040	31,441.80	32,481.80
Thursday	—	1,560	55,036.80	56,596.80
Friday	—	1,560	168,663.80	170,223.80
Saturday	—	1,560	168,663.80	170,223.80
Total	2,000	7,800	446,348.80	456,148.80

Table 3–3 provides the framework for the delineation of the total per annum cost of two through six cash registers. The procedure is the same as described for one cash register and will be left to the reader to develop. The major task will be the calculation of the cost of lost sales, which then must be added to the cash register and checkout station costs and the costs of clerical wages to obtain the total cost per annum.

The reader will discover that as the number of cash registers and checkout stations is increased, the cost of lost sales decreases. However, this cost reduction is counteracted by increased wage and cash-register-acquisition costs.

TABLE 3–3. Cost Data for One Year of Operations Assuming Different Numbers of Cash Registers

Number of Cash Registers	Cash Register and Checkout Station Costs ($)	Clerical Wages ($)	Cost of Lost Sales ($)	Total Cost per Annum ($)
1	2,000	7,800	446,348.80	456,148.80
2	4,000	15,600		
3	6,000	23,400		
4	8,000	31,200		
5	10,000	39,000		
6	12,000	46,800		

It is evident, also, that when traffic is light, such as during a Monday operation, 6 cash registers, 6 checkout stations, and 6 clerks are not required and those resources which are not being used create a cost of idle facilities. For example, Table 3–4 simulates the checkout of the first several customers under the conditions of a Monday operation and the availability of two checkout stations.

TABLE 3–4. Data for Supermarket Waiting Line (two cash registers—Monday)

Customer Number	Time of Arrival	Time Checkout Begins and Number of Cash Registers in Use	Time Checkout Is Completed	Waiting Time	Length of Line
1	9:00	(1) 9:00	9:06	0	1
2	9:05	(2) 9:05	9:11	0	1
3	9:10	(1) 9:10	9:16	0	1
4	9:15	(2) 9:15	9:21	0	1
5	9:20	(1) 9:20	9:26	0	1
6	9:25	(2) 9:25	9:31	0	1
7	9:30	(1) 9:30	9:36	0	1
8	9:35	(2) 9:35	9:41	0	1

When two cash registers, rather than one, are available on a Monday, waiting time is zero, the waiting line is never longer than one person, and the probability is zero that a customer will leave the line. Therefore, the expected cost of lost sales is zero and the firm has apparently saved $3,088.80 in costs. However, when the store uses the second cash register, two new costs are added:

1. The cost of an additional checkout station—$2,000.
2. The cost of an additional clerk—$1,040.

Thus the increased cost of adding an additional cash register is $3,040, which almost exactly offsets the $3,088.80 of expected lost sales that would be saved if the second register were added. As a result, the store would be almost indifferent as to whether one or two cash registers would be used on a Monday.

3.7   Summary

By increasing one's investment in labor and facilities, one can decrease waiting time and losses in business which result from waiting lines. It is desirable, therefore, to minimize the total of these two costs: costs of investment and operation and costs due to waiting.

We have offered in Section 3.6 a simplified situation of a waiting-line problem. However, in real life, customers do not arrive promptly every 5 minutes. Arrivals may be randomly spaced or may be approximated by a Poisson distribution or some other type of distribution. Similarly, the volume of sales or service time may be of varying amounts or random duration, respectively. An additional checkout station may be opened up during high traffic hours. Although the process may be a bit more complex, these additional considerations may be easily incorporated into the simulation.

Waiting-line models are not limited to checkout counter applications. Other marketing applications include travelers using airline commuter service, customers awaiting appliance repairs, scheduling of dental patients, restaurant service, trucks at a loading platform, raw materials at a processing center, the operation of highway toll booths, and the processing of telephone calls.

3.8   Monte Carlo Method of Simulation

For many kinds of marketing problems, a Monte Carlo method of simulation is the only practical method available. The Monte Carlo method is very helpful in solving marketing problems that have probabilistic outcomes. These outcomes can be predicted through a random sampling process and their results analyzed in terms of the specific decision management must make. The sampling process is very helpful since in many cases the data would be otherwise too difficult to obtain, either because of expense, time, or the fact that the phenomenon being analyzed might have to be destroyed (e.g., actually using new products in order to estimate their length of life).

Unfortunately, Monte Carlo analysis requires as much or even more time and labor than the previously described waiting-line type of problem. As electronic computers became available, these difficulties were removed. An example will help to explain the application of the Monte Carlo technique to a simple new-product planning problem.

3.9   Example of Monte Carlo Method: New-products Planning

Let's assume that the new-product committee of a large manufacturer of consumer products is currently exploring the feasibility of adding new products. Fifty such candidates are being considered. From past experience, management believes that the length of time it takes to get a product ready for full-scale marketing is crucial to its success or failure; products that take excessive amounts of time run the risk of not being successful in the market due to (1) decline of the market's interest for the products, and (2) the development of competitive products. Thus management would like to estimate the total length of time it would take to get each of the 50 potential new products ready for full-scale marketing effort.

There are seven activities that might have to be done on each of the products before it can be sold. These include (1) test market, (2) advertising, (3) marketing research, (4) product design, (5) production, (6) sales promotion, and (7) sales-force training. Because of the varied nature of the products, the company's experience with similar products, and other factors, each of the 50 products does not necessarily require that the same activities be performed. The only activity that is common to all 50 is, of course, the production step. Using the above numbering system for the various activities, let us use Table 3–5 to indicate which activities are required for each product.

Based upon past records, management projects that each activity will take from 1 to 7 weeks to complete. These records are helpful in estimating the probability that each activity will take 1, 2, 3, 4, 5, 6, or 7 weeks to complete. These estimates are included in Table 3–6.

The reader undoubtedly realizes that the row totals add to 1.0, that is, 100 per cent. This is because we have assumed that the activity will take only 1, 2, 3, 4, 5, 6, or 7 weeks; thus these probabilities must add to 1.0 since no possibilities other than 1 to 7 weeks are permitted in the analysis. The individual probabilities in the rows indicate the number of times out of 100 that the specific number of weeks would occur for the specific activity involved. For example, there are 30 chances out of 100 that the advertising campaign would take 6 weeks to complete; there are 10 chances out of 100 that the production phase would take 6 weeks.

We next need to use some procedure for randomly assigning the number of weeks that each activity could take for each product. There are a number of ways that this could be done, including use of a deck of cards, dice, slips of paper in a hat, poker chips or different-colored balls drawn from an urn, and so on. The only criterion necessary is that each number of weeks has the same probability of being drawn for each activity as is indicated in Table 3–6. In most Monte Carlo problems, it is preferable to use either a table of random numbers or a set of random numbers generated by a computer since the other methods indicated are quite unwieldy. For this problem we will use a table of random numbers.

TABLE 3–5. Required Activities for 50 New-product Candidates

Product	Activities Required	Product	Activities Required
1	1–2–3–4–5–6–7	26	2–3–4–5–6
2	1–3–5–6–7	27	1–5–6–7
3	2–4–5–6	28	1–2–3–5–6
4	1–2–3–5	29	1–3–4–5
5	3–4–5–7	30	2–4–5–6–7
6	1–2–5	31	1–5–6
7	3–4–5	32	1–2–3–4–5–6–7
8	5–6–7	33	4–5–6
9	1–2–4–5–6	34	2–4–5–7
10	2–3–5–6	35	2–3–5–6
11	1–2–3–4–5	36	3–4–5–6
12	3–4–5–6–7	37	1–3–5–7
13	4–5–6–7	38	1–3–5–6
14	1–4–5–6–7	39	2–4–5–7
15	2–3–4–5–6	40	2–5–7
16	1–4–5–6	41	3–5–6
17	2–3–4–5	42	1–2–5–6
18	4–5–6	43	1–3–5–6–7
19	3–4–5	44	1–4–5
20	2–5–6–7	45	1–2–3–4–5–6–7
21	1–3–5–7	46	4–5–6–7
22	2–4–5–6–7	47	3–4–5–6
23	3–5–6	48	2–5–7
24	2–4–5–7	49	2–3–4–5–6
25	1–2–4–5–6	50	1–3–5–6

TABLE 3–6. Probability of Completing Each Activity in 1 to 7 Weeks

Activity	Number of Weeks						
	1	2	3	4	5	6	7
Test market (1)	.05	.05	.10	.10	.15	.25	.30
Advertising campaign (2)	.10	.30	.05	.10	.05	.30	.10
Marketing research (3)	.05	.10	.20	.30	.20	.10	.05
Product design (4)	.10	.15	.10	.15	.15	.20	.15
Production (5)	.05	.10	.20	.30	.20	.10	.05
Sales promotion (6)	.10	.25	.05	.20	.05	.25	.10
Sales-force training (7)	.30	.20	.15	.15	.10	.05	.05

Since the probability of 1 through 7 weeks for each activity adds to 1.00 or 100 per cent, we can use the two-digit values in a table of random numbers to represent the distributions involved. Because the two-digit values of 00 through 99 involve exactly 100 items, this task is relatively simple; we need only to be sure that each probability is given the same number of values that exactly coincides to its chances out of 100 of happening. For example, the probability of the marketing research task taking 2 weeks to complete is .10; therefore, of the 100 digits represented by 00 through 99 in a table of random numbers, 10 must be "set aside" or "reserved" for this possibility. To illustrate this procedure in some detail, the reader is referred back to the data for the test market in Table 3–6. There, the probabilities of occurrence for weeks 1 through 7 are, respectively, .05, .05, .10, .10, .15, .25, and .30. In order to reserve the correct block of two-digit numbers from 0 through 99 in the table of random numbers, we could do as follows:

Number of Weeks	Probability of Occurrence	Assigned Two-digit Random-number Values
1	.05	00–04
2	.05	05–09
3	.10	10–19
4	.10	20–29
5	.15	30–44
6	.25	45–69
7	.30	70–99

Thus the probability of occurrence of .05 for 1 week is given 5 of the 100 available numbers (namely, 00–04), the .05 probability for 2 weeks is also given 5 numbers, but a different set (05–09), and so on until all 100 numbers have been assigned.

The same procedure must be done for the other activities. In so doing, we would arrive at the data in Table 3–7.

With the data available in Table 3–7, we can use a table of random numbers (see Appendix B) to determine the number of weeks each new product should require prior to full-scale marketing. We do this by selecting one two-digit number from the table of random numbers for each activity required for each new product candidate, determining the number of weeks involved for that activity, and adding the number of weeks for each activity to secure the total number of weeks required for each product. This is not as involved as it sounds; the concepts can be easily demonstrated by working with product 1.

TABLE 3–7. Assigned Two-digit Random-number Values for Activities 1–7 Given Various Probabilities of Occurrence

Activity	Number of Weeks						
	1	2	3	4	5	6	7
Test market (1)	00–04	05–09	10–19	20–29	30–44	45–69	70–99
Advertising campaign (2)	00–09	10–39	40–44	45–54	55–59	60–89	90–99
Marketing research (3)	00–04	05–14	15–34	35–64	65–84	85–94	95–99
Product design (4)	00–09	10–24	25–34	35–49	50–64	65–84	85–99
Production (5)	00–04	05–14	15–34	35–64	65–84	85–94	95–99
Sales promotion (6)	00–09	10–34	35–39	40–59	60–64	65–89	90–99
Sales-force training (7)	00–29	30–49	50–64	65–79	80–89	90–94	95–99

Product 1 requires that all seven activities be performed (Table 3–5). For each activity, we select a number at random from the table of random numbers, then by referring to Table 3–7, we determine the number of weeks for each activity and add them to get the total number of weeks needed by product 1. In choosing a two-digit number from a table of random numbers, the authors randomly chose 20. Since the number 20 for the test-market activity represents 4 weeks in Table 3–7, we have indicated this figure in Table 3–8 for product 1 for the test-market activity (activity 1). For the advertising campaign (activity 2), we selected randomly 74. In Table 3–7, this simulates 6 weeks. We have placed 6 weeks into the column for activity 2 for product 1 in Table 3–8. For the third activity (marketing research), the number chosen was 96; this means that 7 weeks should be entered in Table 3–8 for the third activity for product 1. For the fourth, fifth, sixth, and seventh activities, the numbers drawn, respectively, were 15, 09, 55, and 91. These correspond, respectively, to 2, 2, 4, and 6 weeks. These values have been entered into their proper places in Table 3–8; the total of the simulated values is 31 weeks.

TABLE 3–8. Monte Carlo Simulation of the Number of Weeks Required Before Full-scale Marketing of 50 New-product Candidates

Product	Activities							Total Weeks
	1	2	3	4	5	6	7	
1	4	6	7	2	2	4	6	31
2	4		4		4	2	1	15
3		6		6	3	3		18
4	6	2	5		4			17
5			5	1	4		5	15
6	6	2			4			12
7			4	3	3			10
8					4	4	6	14

TABLE 3-8. (Continued)

Product	1	2	3	4	5	6	7	Total Weeks
				Activities				
9	4	7		1	5	1		18
10		7	3		5	2		17
11	7	7	4	2	4			24
12			4	1	4	6	4	19
13				2	5	4	3	14
14	6			4	5	2	2	19
15		3	5	6	6	5		25
16	3			6	5	6		20
17		2	3	6	1			12
18				5	5	1		11
19			4	2	5			11
20		2			6	1	5	14
21	7		4		4		3	18
22		6		4	3	6	2	21
23			6		3	2		11
24		2		2	4		4	12
25	7	3		5	6	2		23
26		5	6	6	2	3		22
27	2				4	6	1	13
28	3	2	6		3	4		18
29	4		1	6	3			14
30		6		6	4	2	2	20
31	5				2	6		13
32	6	6	3	7	4	2	4	32
33				7	3	6		16
34		2		3	3		4	12
35		6	2		4	5		17
36			4	1	4	2		11
37	1		4		4		5	14
38	5		5		3	2		15
39		2	2	4		3		11
40		3			4		3	10
41			4		3	4		11
42	3	2			5	1		11
43	3		5		4	2	1	15
44	1			5	3			9
45	7	3	4	4	2	4	1	25
46				5	5	6	1	17
47			4	7	7	5		23
48		6			1		4	11
49		1	6	1	4	2		14
50	3		6		2	2		13

By following exactly the same procedure, the balance of the data in Table 3–8 was obtained for all 50 products involved. The results of this simulation have provided the new-product committee with some valuable information. It can now see how long each product might take to be ready for full-scale marketing. Of special significance would be those that take the longest time periods to complete. This might be a strong factor in whether the decision to market a candidate product would be favorable or unfavorable. The longer a new product takes to be ready for initial introduction, the greater risk it faces. Products 1, 11, 15, 32, and 45 involve the longest times, a factor that should be considered along with competitive and market data in deciding whether to introduce the new product.

3.10   Combining Waiting-line Theory and the Monte Carlo Method

For many kinds of waiting-line problems, it may be very advantageous to employ a Monte Carlo approach. Let us indicate how this might be done by examining a common waiting-line problem: the arrival of trucks to deliver merchandise.

Let's assume that the physical distribution manager of a newly constructed manufacturing plant wants to analyze the arrival of trucks that will make deliveries to the unloading dock. The manager realizes that a problem can occur if the trucks have to wait in line too long since the delivering firms will not appreciate their trucks being delayed. In addition, there are units in his own firm—such as purchasing and production—that need the materials being delivered and do not want to wait an excessive amount of time. On the other hand, the physical distribution manager does not want to add any additional facilities—such as loading docks, personnel, and fork-lift trucks—unless they are absolutely necessary.

In doing some research, the physical distribution manager concludes that a key element in the analysis will be the *arrival pattern* of trucks. The arrival pattern for trucks at many loading docks, he discovers, is very often closely approximated by something called a *Poisson distribution*. He decides, therefore, to assume that a Poisson distribution will explain the arrival of trucks at the manufacturing plant.

Although it is beyond the scope of this book to present an exhaustive explanation of the concepts behind the Poisson distribution, we can provide enough information to permit a basic understanding. The reader needs to be aware that the Poisson distribution will enable the physical distribution manager to calculate the probability that a certain number of trucks will arrive at the unloading dock per unit of time. Once this is done, he can use the Monte Carlo method described earlier to get an idea of what truck arrivals might look like over an entire week, thereby providing himself with the data required to determine if additional facilities might be required.

The formula for the Poisson distribution is

$$P(X) = \frac{\mu X e^{-\mu}}{X!}$$

where $P(X)$ is the probability of X occurring, where $X = 0, 1, 2, 3, 4, \ldots, n$, where μ (the Greek letter "mu") is the mean average of the Poisson distribution, where e is a constant, 2.7 (actually 2.71828, but it is usually rounded to 2.7), and where $X!$ is X "factorial," i.e., the value of X times X minus 1, times X minus 2, times X minus 3, ..., times X minus n, where X minus $n = 1$.

Let us now use the Poisson distribution to determine the probability of different numbers of trucks arriving at the unloading dock each hour. In order to do this, we will assume, as indicated above, that the truck arrivals can indeed be closely approximated by a Poisson distribution and that the mean average (μ) of this particular Poisson distribution per hour is .8. First, let us determine what the probability would be of there being zero trucks arriving in 1 hour:

$$P(X = 0) = \frac{(0.8)^0 2.7^{-0.8}}{0!}$$

In order to work the above formula, the reader needs to know that $(0.8)^0 = 1$ and that $0!$ also equals 1. Appendix C can be used to determine the value for $2.7^{-0.8}$; it is .449. Thus we have

$$P(X = 0) = \frac{(1)(.449)}{1} = .449$$

and this indicates that the probability of there being zero arrivals during a given hour is .449.

Let us next calculate what the probability would be of one truck arriving during 1 hour. The correct expression would be

$$P(X = 1) = \frac{(.8)^1(.449)}{(1)(1)}$$

Since $(0.8)^1$ equals itself, or .8, our answer would be

$$P(X = 1) = \frac{(.8)(.449)}{1} = .360$$

Thus there is a .360 probability that there would be one truck arriving during any hour.

In approximating the probability of there being two arrivals in 1 hour, we would have

$$P(X = 2) = \frac{(.8)^2(.449)}{(2)(1)} \quad \text{or} \quad \frac{(.64)(.449)}{2} = .144$$

The probability of there being two arrivals during any 1 hour is .144. For the probability of there being three arrivals in a given hour, the answer would be .038:

$$P(X = 3) = \frac{(.8)^3(.449)}{(3)(2)(1)} \quad \text{or} \quad \frac{(.512)(.449)}{6} = .038$$

For four arrivals, the probability would be .009:

$$P(X = 4) = \frac{(.8)^4(.449)}{(4)(3)(2)(1)} \quad \text{or} \quad \frac{(.4096)(.449)}{24} = .009$$

Let us next add the probabilities that we have obtained for possibilities zero through four:

Number of Arrivals	Probability
0	.449
1	.360
2	.144
3	.038
4	.009
	1.000

Since the total of 1.000 (or 100 per cent) has been obtained with zero through four arrivals, the limits of the number of arrivals have been indicated. Thus our analysis will be restricted to zero through four possible arrivals.

Let us now use the Monte Carlo method to see how the physical distribution manager would simulate truck arrivals at the unloading dock for a week's time. Based upon the probability distribution just obtained for zero through four arrivals, we can assign *three-digit* random numbers as follows:

Number of Arrivals	Probability	Three-digit Random Numbers
0	.449	000–448
1	.360	449–808
2	.144	809–952
3	.038	953–990
4	.009	991–999

The unloading dock is open 8 hours a day, 6 days a week, for a total of 48 hours per week. Using a table of random numbers, arrivals over the course of a week's operations were generated as shown in Table 3–9.

TABLE 3–9. Monte Carlo Simulation of Truck Arrivals over a Week's Time

	Day of Week					
Time	Monday	Tuesday	Wednesday	Thursday	Friday	Saturday
9:00–9:59	1	1	0	1	1	1
10:00–10:59	2	0	0	3	0	0
11:00–11:59	2	1	1	2	1	1
12:00–12:59	1	1	4	0	1	0
1:00–1:59	0	1	1	1	1	0
2:00–2:59	1	0	0	0	1	1
3:00–3:59	0	0	0	1	0	2
4:00–4:59	1	0	1	1	0	1

The physical distribution manager estimates that it takes, on the average, 1 hour for a crew of three men to unload each truck. Each man is paid $4 per hour. With these data, plus those included in Table 3–9, he is able to estimate the length of the waiting lines, if any, plus the cost of idle time, if any. These figures will be very helpful in determining whether additional facilities are required.

Tables 3–10A and B indicate for each hour of each day the number of trucks arriving at the unloading dock (column 1) and the number that could have been unloaded (column 2). Column 3 represents the net addition or decrease involved (the number of arrivals for the hour minus the number that could be serviced during the hour), while column 4 indicates the size of the waiting line, if any.

A detailed analysis of these tables reveals a number of valuable conclusions. First, waiting lines develop on Monday, Wednesday, Thursday, and Saturday. On Wednesday and Thursday the waiting line becomes three trucks; on Monday, the longest line is two. Saturday's waiting line is only one truck; and this occurs for only 2 hours of the day. Second, no waiting lines occur at all on Tuesday and Friday. Third, slack or idle time occurs on Tuesday, Wednesday, Friday, and Saturday. A slack or idle time occurs when there is no arrival in any hour, provided that there is no waiting line in the previous hour; the slack hours are circled in the tables. The slack periods are most numerous on Tuesday (4) and Friday (3) and Saturday (3), less so on Wednesday (2). Fourth, total slack time is 12 hours (see Table 3–10). When merely considering the cost of lost wages, the idle time cost per week is

TABLE 3–10(A). Monte Carlo Simulation of Delivery Truck Arrivals for
Monday, Tuesday, and Wednesday

	Day of Week							
Time	Monday				Tuesday			
	(1) Number of Arrivals	(2) Number Serviced	(3) (1)–(2)	(4) Waiting Line	(1) Number of Arrivals	(2) Number Serviced	(3) (1)–(2)	(4) Waiting Line
9:00–9:59	1	1	0	0	1	1	0	0
10:00–10:59	2	1	1	1	0	1	−1	0
11:00–11:59	2	1	1	2	1	1	0	0
12:00–12:59	1	1	0	2	1	1	0	0
1:00–1:59	0	1	−1	1	1	1	0	0
2:00–2:59	1	1	0	1	0	1	−1	0
3:00–3:59	0	1	−1	0	0	1	−1	0
4:00–4:59	1	1	0	0	0	1	−1	0

Wednesday			
(1) Number of Arrivals	(2) Number Serviced	(3) (1)–(2)	(4) Waiting Line
0	1	−1	0
0	1	−1	0
1	1	0	0
4	1	3	3
1	1	0	3
0	1	−1	2
0	1	−1	1
1	1	0	1

$144 (12 × $12 per hour wage = $144). This figure would be even greater
if the cost of fork-lift trucks, conveyor equipment, and the dock itself were to
be included. Fifth, the raw data are available to determine the cost of the
waiting lines to the firm. As with the supermarket example, it is likely that
deliverer dissatisfaction will increase as the waiting line grows longer.
Sixth, the isolating of times when waiting lines and slack times appear may
provide some help as to the scheduling of facilities and manpower. For
example, the crew could perhaps be augmented with additional help during
peak periods and might be used for operations inside the warehouse during
slack periods.

3.11   Markov Analysis

Markov analysis is a simulation technique to which marketers have been
giving increasing attention during recent years. Although most usage has

TABLE 3–10(B). Monte Carlo Simulation of Delivery Truck Arrivals for Thursday, Friday, and Saturday

Day of Week

Time	Thursday				Friday			
	(1) Number of Arrivals	(2) Number Serviced	(3) (1)–(2)	(4) Waiting Line	(1) Number of Arrivals	(2) Number Serviced	(3) (1)–(2)	(4) Waiting Line
9:00–9:59	1	1	0	0	1	1	0	0
10:00–10:59	3	1	2	2	0	1	−1	0
11:00–11:59	2	1	1	3	1	1	0	0
12:00–12:59	0	1	−1	2	1	1	0	0
1:00–1:59	1	1	0	2	1	1	0	0
2:00–2:59	0	1	−1	1	1	1	0	0
3:00–3:59	1	1	0	1	0	1	−1	0
4:00–4:59	1	1	0	1	0	1	−1	0

Saturday

(1) Number of Arrivals	(2) Number Serviced	(3) (1)–(2)	(4) Waiting Line
1	1	0	0
0	1	−1	0
1	1	0	0
0	1	−1	0
0	1	−1	0
1	1	0	0
2	1	1	1
1	1	0	1

occurred in the prediction of a firm's future market share, the concept's versatility makes it applicable to a number of other marketing problems. This section will predominantly deal with the use of the Markov process as a method for predicting future market shares, but several other examples will be provided so that the reader can envision the widespread capabilities of the Markov process.

A firm's market share is the proportion of the firm's sales to the total industry sales for a specific product. For example, if total industry sales of product P were 400,000 units and firms F_1, F_2, and F_3 sold 100,000, 120,000, and 180,000 units, respectively, the market share would be 25 per cent for F_1 (100,000/400,000), for F_2 30 per cent (120,000/400,000), and 45 per cent for F_3 (180,000/400,000).

Market share is an extremely flexible concept. Thus it can be calculated for a firm's generic product class (automobiles), for subdivisions of that class (compacts), or for specific brands in the subclass (Falcons). In addition, market shares can be determined for territories, regions, states, and cities. This allows the firm to determine how well its products are doing in specific geographical areas. In many instances, situations will be uncovered where a product is doing very well in some geographical areas and very poorly in others.

Most firms place a heavy emphasis on market share. This is because market share tells a firm how it is doing in comparison to its competition. As a result, it is a better control device than merely examining total sales volume. To illustrate, let us suppose that sales of product P_1 for a firm increase from 50,000 units in 1970 to 60,000 units in 1971. Management might be quite pleased with this state of events. But suppose further analysis revealed that the market share in 1970 was 25 per cent, whereas in 1971 it had fallen to 20 per cent. Thus, despite the increase in sales, in relation to competition, the firm is actually worse off in 1971 than it was in 1970.

Market share is quite often considered to be one of the major goals or objectives of a firm's marketing activities. For example, a firm can attempt to retain a market share of 20 per cent for a given time period or it can strive to increase it to 25 per cent. Market share is such an important objective that one authority in the field has stated that "marketing executives must watch their *market share* just as much as their profits. Present customers can never be taken for granted."[7]

Although the primary interest of most firms is with their own market shares, they also like to know the market shares of competition. Thus they can see which competitors are increasing market shares and which are not.

Business firms, in addition, are of necessity greatly concerned with the *trends* of market shares, both their own and those of competition. It is these trends that will determine a company's market share at some future date. Thus, if a firm finds through analysis that its market share at some future date will be less than it is now, it can engage in competitive action designed to arrest this undesirable trend. On the other hand, if the analysis indicates that the firm's future market share will be greater, the firm knows that its marketing operations are probably fairly effective. This does not, however, insulate the firm from changes in competitive strategy.

It should be obvious to the reader that the various elements of the marketing mix of any firm, especially as they relate to those of competitive firms, will determine its future market share. The marketing mix would include, of course, such factors as price, advertising, personal selling, sales promotion, the product itself and its package, physical distribution, channels of distribution, and so on. In essence, Markov analysis can be used to simulate the *impact or effect* of present policies upon a firm's market share at some

---

[7] Philip Kotler, "The Use of Mathematical Models in Marketing," *Journal of Marketing*, Vol. 27 (October 1963), p. 38.

future time. It cannot, however, indicate precisely *why* the particular market share would be achieved; additional analysis would have to ascertain this.

There are three factors which will interact to determine a firm's market share at some future date. These are

1. The tendency of the firm's present customers to remain loyal to a particular product. This is usually called the *retention rate*.
2. The tendency of the firm's present customers to turn to competitive products. This phenomenon is generally termed the *switching-out rate*.
3. The tendency of the customers of competitive brands to turn to the firm's particular product. This can be considered the *switching-in rate*.

In short, Markov analysis determines these three rates in the present and uses them to predict future share of the market. A major assumption of the Markov process in this regard is that the purchasing behavior in the last time period analyzed will continue in the future. Thus, if a product is usually purchased once a week, the retention, switching-out, and switching-in rates will be based upon the purchasing behavior noticed in the last week under consideration. This assumption is called a *first-order* Markov process. If two or more previous purchases are utilized, a *higher-order* Markov process is operative.

Most applications of the Markov process assume a *discrete state*, i.e., that consumers purchase at regular time intervals. This is a simplifying assumption which will be utilized in the examples presented in this chapter and will make for much easier manipulation. Yet another simplifying assumption is that the size of the market will remain constant over the time period of the analysis.

In summary, the following are assumed in the application of the Markov process that follows:

1. A firm's retention, switching-out, and switching-in rates at a given time depend upon the current state only, not the prior history of the process.
2. The last purchase pattern observed will continue.
3. Consumers purchase at regular intervals.
4. Consumers all purchase equal quantities of the product in a given time period.
5. The same loyalty and switching rates apply to all purchasers.
6. The market size remains constant.
7. No new competitors enter the market.
8. All consumers purchase the product.

Let us now proceed to apply the Markov process to a problem where we would like to predict a firm's future market share.

3.12   Example of Markov Analysis: Predicting Future Market Shares

Let us assume that firm A is competing in a specific market with firm B and firm C. In this market for the month of August, firm A undertakes a study of the purchasers of the product all three firms sell. It finds that out of 1,000 purchasers of this product, 400 bought its product, 400 bought firm B's product, and 200 bought the product sold by firm C. Thus the August 31 market shares for the three firms are as follows:

For firm A 40% (400/1,000)
For firm B 40% (400/1,000)
For firm C 20% (200/1,000)

In doing additional research during the month of September, firm A discovers that all three firms retain some of its August customers, *gain some from* competition, and *lose some to* competition. Let us summarize these findings in Table 3–11.

TABLE 3–11. Customer Gains and Losses for Firms A, B, and C in September

Firm	August 31 Customers	Customers Retained in Sept.	Customers Lost in Sept.	Customers Gained in Sept.	Net Gain or Loss in Sept.	Total Customers Sept. 30	Sept. 30 Market Share
A	400	320	80	40	−40	360	36%
B	400	280	120	100	−20	380	38%
C	200	160	40	100	+60	260	26%
	1,000	760	240	240	00	1,000	100%

In interpreting the results of this table, the director of marketing research for firm A makes the following observations:

1. Firm C was the only firm to show a net increase of customers in September (+60).
2. As a result, the market share of firm C increased to 26 per cent while the market shares of firms A and B, respectively, dropped to 36 and 38 per cent.
3. If the trend noticed in September continues, the market share of firm C will continue to increase while the market shares of firm A and firm B will continue to decrease.

The director of marketing research, as a result, decides that he would like the answers to the following question: What will the final market shares be for each firm once a state of equilibrium occurs, i.e., the point in time beyond which no noticeable changes in brand share will exist for any firms in the industry?

Before addressing himself directly to this problem, the director of marketing research of firm A decides that he needs additional information. Specifically, he wants to know which individual firms are involved in the customer gains and losses for the month of September. Further analysis reveals the break-downs shown in Table 3–12. Thus it can be seen from the table that firm A in picking up 40 new customers, gained 30 from firm B and 10 from firm C; firm B gained 100 customers, 70 from A and 30 from C; firm C also gained 100 customers, 10 from A and 90 from B. Also, firm A lost a total of 80 cus-tomers, 70 to firm B and 10 to firm C. Firm B lost 120 customers, 30 to firm A and 90 to firm C. Firm C lost 40 customers, 10 to firm A and 30 to firm B. The reader should notice that the data in the gained and lost sections are quite similar. This should not really be surprising since, for example, if firm A *gains* 30 customers from firm B, firm B, as a result, *loses* 30 customers to firm A.

TABLE 3–12. Customer Gains and Losses by Specific Firms During September

Firm	Customers Gained from			Total Gained	Customers Lost to			Total Lost
	A	B	C		A	B	C	
A	0	30	10	40	0	70	10	80
B	70	0	30	100	30	0	90	120
C	10	90	0	100	10	30	0	40

From the above gain-and-loss data, the director of marketing research decides to express these data in percentage form (see Table 3–13). In viewing these data, it helps to remember that the vertical *columns* represent retention

TABLE 3–13. Retention, Loss, and Gain of Customers

		Retention and Loss of Customers (columns)		
		A	B	C
Retention and Gain of Customers (rows)	A	$\frac{320}{400} = .800$	$\frac{30}{400} = .075$	$\frac{10}{200} = .050$
	B	$\frac{70}{400} = .175$	$\frac{280}{400} = .700$	$\frac{30}{200} = .150$
	C	$\frac{10}{400} = .025$	$\frac{90}{400} = .225$	$\frac{160}{200} = .800$

and loss of customers, while the horizontal *rows* represent retention and gain of customers. Other texts may express retention and losses in rows and retention and gains in columns. Regardless of the format, the reader should remember that the summation of the retention and losses must equal 100 per cent, while the summation of the retention and gains may be equal to, less than, or greater than 100 per cent.

In order to simplify the above, let us discard the fractions and merely record the resulting decimals in the form of a 3 × 3 matrix of transition probabilities shown in Table 3–14.

TABLE 3–14. Matrix of Transition Probabilities

		Probability of Retention and Loss		
		A	B	C
Probability	A	.800	.075	.050
of Retention	B	.175	.700	.150
and Gain	C	.025	.225	.800

Let us now very explicitly indicate what the matrix of transition probabilities in this problem represents. Starting with the rows, row 1 indicates that firm *A* retains 80 per cent of its own customers and gains 7.5 per cent of *B*'s and 5 per cent of *C*'s; row 2 reveals that firm *B* gains 17.5 per cent of *A*'s customers, retains 70 per cent of its own customers, and gains 15 per cent of *C*'s customers; and row 3 indicates that firm *C* gains 2.5 per cent of *A*'s customers, 22.5 per cent of *B*'s customers, and retains 80 per cent of its own customers. When inspecting the columns, it is apparent that in column 1, firm *A* retains 80 per cent of its customers, loses 17.5 per cent of its customers to *B*, and loses 2.5 per cent of its customers to *C*; in column 2, firm *B* loses 7.5 per cent of its customers to *A*, retains 70 per cent of its own customers, and loses 22.5 per cent of its customers to *C*; and in column 3, firm *C* loses 5 per cent of its customers to *A*, loses 15 per cent of its customers to *B*, and retains 80 per cent of its own customers. It should be understood that the matrix of transition probabilities also represents the likelihood that any randomly selected customer will remain loyal or shift his patronage. If we randomly select one of *A*'s customers, say Sam Jones, column 1 tells us that there is an .80 probability he will remain with *A* during the next period, a .175 probability he will switch to firm *B*, and a .025 probability he will buy from *C*.

The above matrix of transition probabilities and the original market shares are helpful in determining the future market shares for the three firms at equilibrium. In order to illustrate the concepts involved, we need to first multiply this matrix of transition probabilities by a second matrix composed of the original market shares of 40, 40, and 20 per cent for firms *A*, *B*, and *C*, respectively:

$$
\begin{pmatrix} .800 & .075 & .050 \\ .175 & .700 & .150 \\ .025 & .225 & .800 \end{pmatrix} \times \begin{pmatrix} .40 \\ .40 \\ .20 \end{pmatrix}
$$

In order to multiply any two matrices, the number of *columns* in the first (left) matrix *must be equal* to the number of *rows* in the second (right) matrix. Since there are three columns in the first matrix and three rows in the second matrix, we can multiply these two matrices. Another rule of thumb concerns the dimensions of the resultant matrix: It will have the same number of rows as contained in the first matrix and the same number of columns as contained in the second matrix. Thus we can see that the resultant matrix will have three rows and one column, composed of three elements:

$$
\begin{pmatrix} X \\ X \\ X \end{pmatrix}
$$

By designating the position (row and column location) of each of these three elements by numbering the rows and columns, we can facilitate our understanding of how to arrive at the three values in the resultant matrix:

$$
\begin{array}{c}
 & 1 \\
1 & \begin{pmatrix} X \\ X \\ X \end{pmatrix}
\end{array}
$$

1   $\begin{pmatrix} X \\ X \\ X \end{pmatrix}$ row 1, column 1 (1, 1)
2   row 2, column 1 (2, 1)
3   row 3, column 1 (3, 1)

Thus, in order to obtain the value for the (1, 1) element, we would multiply the first row in the first matrix by the first column in the second matrix, being sure to multiply the *first* element in the row by the *first* element in the column, the *second* element in the row by the *second* element in the column, the *third* element in the row by the *third* element in the column, and *adding* the three products. As a result, we would have

$$
(.800 \quad .075 \quad .050) \times \begin{pmatrix} .40 \\ .40 \\ .20 \end{pmatrix} =
\begin{array}{l}
.800 \times .40 = .32 \\
.075 \times .40 = .03 \\
.050 \times .20 = \underline{.01} \\
.36
\end{array}
$$

(row 1 of the first matrix times column 1 of the second matrix)

The rationale for the preceding calculations is as follows:

1. .800 × .40 = .32. The tendency of A to retain its market share (.800) times its original market share (.40).
2. .075 × .40 = .03. The tendency of A to gain customers from B (.075) times B's market share (.40).
3. .05 × .20 = .01. The tendency of A to gain customers from C (.05) times C's market share (.20).

When applying the same procedure to the (2, 1) element, we would obtain

$$(.175 \quad .700 \quad .150) \times \begin{pmatrix} .40 \\ .40 \\ .20 \end{pmatrix} = \begin{matrix} .175 \times .40 = .07 \\ .700 \times .40 = .28 \\ \underline{.150 \times .20 = .03} \\ .38 \end{matrix}$$

(row 2 of the first matrix times column 1 of the second matrix)

The rationale for the above equations is as follows:

1. .175 × .40 = .07. The tendency of B to gain customers from A (.175) times A's market share (.40).
2. .700 × .40 = .28. The tendency of B to retain its market share (.700) times its original market share (.40).
3. .150 × .20 = .03. The tendency of B to gain customers from C (.150) times C's market share (.20).

In a similar fashion for the (3, 1) element, we would have

$$(.025 \quad .225 \quad .800) \times \begin{pmatrix} .40 \\ .40 \\ .20 \end{pmatrix} = \begin{matrix} .025 \times .40 = .01 \\ .225 \times .40 = .09 \\ \underline{.800 \times .20 = .16} \\ .26 \end{matrix}$$

(row 3 of the first matrix times column 1 of the second matrix)

The rationale for the above equations is as follows:

1. .025 × .40 = .01. The tendency of C to gain customers from A (.025) times A's market share (.40).
2. .225 × .40 = .09. The tendency of C to gain customers from B (.225) times B's market share (.40).
3. .800 × .20 = .16. The tendency of C to retain its market share (.800) times C's original market share (.20).

The reader undoubtedly realizes that these three answers (.36, .38, .26) are exactly the September 30 market shares that were found when viewing the brand-switching phenomena in a much less rigorous fashion earlier. Thus we can see that multiplying the matrix of transition probabilities by the market shares existing at the end of a time period will give us the market shares at the end of the next time period.

Let us now proceed to calculate the existing market shares at the end of October. Exactly the same procedure is followed as above with the exception that the original matrix of transition probabilities must now be multiplied by the market shares existing at the *end of September, not the original market shares.* Thus we obtain the following market shares at the end of October:

$$
\begin{pmatrix} .800 & .075 & .050 \\ .175 & .700 & .150 \\ .025 & .225 & .800 \end{pmatrix} \times \begin{pmatrix} .36 \\ .38 \\ .26 \end{pmatrix} = \begin{matrix} .3295 \\ .3680 \\ .3025 \end{matrix}
$$

Thus firm *A*'s market share has dropped further at the end of October to 32.95 per cent. *B*'s has declined to 36.80 per cent, and *C*'s has risen to 30.25 per cent. (The reader should go through the required calculations in order to satisfy himself that the answers given are correct.)

It is apparent that the continued projection of trends embodied in the matrix of transition probabilities will, to a point, result in a continually decreasing market share for firm *A*. We could continue to multiply the original matrix of transition probabilities by each new set of market shares until certain limiting market share values have been obtained. These are referred to as the *equilibrium* shares. For practical purposes, we have reached equilibrium conditions when no further changes in market shares take place with passage of time. Equilibrium can result, however, only if no firm takes action which would alter the values in the matrix of transition probabilities.

The reader undoubtedly realizes that continuing to multiply the original matrix of transition probabilities by new end-of-period market shares could turn out to be a tedious process. Fortunately, we can obtain the market shares at equilibrium by solving a set of simultaneous equations by the method of *substitution*, a procedure with which most readers are probably familiar.

From the original matrix of transition probabilities, we can secure three simultaneous equations. The reader will recall that the original matrix of transition probabilities was as follows:

		Probability of Retention and Loss		
		A	B	C
Probability	A	.800	.075	.050
of Retention	B	.175	.700	.150
and Gain	C	.025	.225	.800

Since A retains 80 per cent of its market share and gains 7.5 per cent of B's and 5 per cent of C's, we can express A's final market share as

$$A = .800A + .075B + .050C$$

Similarly, since B retains 70 per cent of its market share and gains 17.5 per cent of A's and 15 per cent of C's, we can express B's final market share as

$$B = .175A + .700B + .150C$$

And since C retains 80 per cent of its market share and gains 2.5 per cent of A's and 22.5 per cent of B's, we can express C's final market share as

$$C = .025A + .225B + .800C$$

Thus in summary form we have the market shares of firms A, B, and C expressed as

$$A = .800A + .075B + .050C$$

$$B = .175A + .700B + .150C$$

$$C = .025A + .225B + .800C$$

And since the total market is composed of the market shares of firms A, B, and C, we can represent the total market as 1.0 and write a fourth equation:

$$1.0 = A + B + C$$

Thus, we now have four equations:

(1) $A = .800A + .075B + .050C$

(2) $B = .175A + .700B + .150C$

(3) $C = .025A + .225B + .800C$

(4) $1.0 =\quad A +\quad B +\quad C$

Since we have three unknown values (A, B, and C) and have four equations, we can drop one of the three original equations. Let us drop from further consideration equation (2), leaving us with the following three equations:

(1) $A = .800A + .075B + .050C$

(3) $C = .025A + .225B + .800C$

(4) $1.0 =\quad A +\quad B +\quad C$

Let us now subtract A and C from both sides of equations (1) and (3), respectively, leaving us with the following three equations:

(1) $0 = -.200A + .075B + .050C$

(3) $0 =\quad .025A + .225B + .200C$

(4) $1.0 =\quad\quad A +\quad B +\quad C$

Now we are ready to solve for the market shares at equilibrium for firms A, B, and C. Let us do this by the method of substitution, which will involve the following steps.

Step 1: Multiply equation (3) by 8 and add to equation (1), enabling us to eliminate the A values in equations (1) and (3):

$$(1) \quad 0 = -.200A + .075B + .050C$$
$$(3) \quad 0 = \quad .200A + 1.80\ B - 1.60\ C$$
$$\overline{0 = \qquad 0A + 1.875B - 1.55\ C}$$

Step 2: Multiply equation (1) by 5 and add to equation (4) enabling us to eliminate the A values in equations (1) and (4):

$$(4) \quad 1.0 = \quad A + \qquad B + \qquad C$$
$$(1) \quad \ 0 = -A + .375B + .25C$$
$$\overline{1.0 = \qquad 0 + 1.375B + 1.25C}$$

Step 3: Combine the two equations resulting from performing steps 1 and 2, designating them as equations (5) and (6):

$$(5) \qquad 0 = 1.875B - 1.55C$$
$$(6) \quad 1.0 = 1.375B + 1.25C$$

Step 4: Multiply equation (6) by 1.24 and add it to equation (5) in order to eliminate the C term from both equations:

$$(5) \qquad 0 = 1.875B - 1.55C$$
$$(6) \quad 1.24 = 1.705B + 1.55C$$
$$\overline{1.24 = 3.580B + 0}$$

Step 5: Solve for B:

$$1.24 = 3.580B, \qquad B = .3464$$

Step 6: Substituting this value for B into equation (6), solve for C:

$$(6) \quad 1.0 \quad = 1.375B + 1.25C$$
$$(6) \quad 1.0 \quad = 1.375(.3464) + 1.25C$$
$$(6) \quad 1.0 \quad = .4763 + 1.25C$$
$$(6) \quad .5237 = 1.25C$$
$$(6) \qquad C = .4190$$

Step 7: Substituting the values for B and C into equation (4), solve for A:

$$(4) \quad 1.0 = A + .3464 + .4190$$

$$(4) \quad 1.0 = A + .7654$$

$$(4) \quad A = .2346$$

Thus the market shares at equilibrium for firms A, B, and C, respectively, are .2346, .3464, and .4190. The reader is asked to verify that equilibrium market shares have indeed been obtained by checking the following matrix multiplications:

$$\begin{pmatrix} .800 & .075 & .050 \\ .175 & .700 & .150 \\ .025 & .225 & .800 \end{pmatrix} \times \begin{pmatrix} .2346 \\ .3464 \\ .4190 \end{pmatrix} = \begin{matrix} .2346 \\ .3464 \\ .4190 \end{matrix}$$

As indicated earlier, firm A's initial market share was 40 per cent. As the earlier analysis proceeded, it was evident that firm A's 40 per cent market share would gradually be eroded until at equilibrium it would be only 23.46 per cent. Needless to say, the management of firm A should be greatly concerned at such a prediction.

3.13   Implications of Brand-share Analysis and Remedial Strategies

What factors would account for this undesirable trend? Analysis of the original matrix of transition probabilities will be helpful in this regard. This matrix indicates that A retains 80 per cent of its market as compared to 70 per cent for B and 80 per cent for C. Since A's original market share is 40 per cent, it is assured of at least a 32 per cent market share at the end of the first period due to its own retention rate (.40 × .80 = 32 per cent). In this regard, it is better off than firm B and firm C. Firm B's assured market share due to its own retention rate is 28 per cent (its original market share of 40 per cent times its retention rate of 70 per cent) and firm C's is only 16 per cent (its original market share of 20 per cent times its retention rate of 80 per cent). Since A's competitive situation is better than that of the other two firms when retention rates are examined, the reason for A's declining market share must lie somewhere else—namely, its switching-in and switching-out rates in comparison with those of B and C.

Let's first compare firm A to firm B. Since firm A is getting 7.5 per cent of firm B's market share of 40 per cent, it has a gross figure of a *plus* 3 per cent. But its switching-out rate to B is 17.5 per cent of its market share of 40 per cent, or a minus figure of 7 per cent. Netting the two figures indicates that A's market share will drop 4 per cent because of its competitive situation with firm B ($3 - 7 = -4$ per cent). As far as its situation with C is concerned, it can be shown that A is exactly holding its own: It obtains a gain of 1 per cent of market share due to the switching-in rate from C (5.0 per cent of C's market share of 20 per cent equals 1 per cent), but this is entirely offset by the switching-out rate to C (2.5 per cent of A's market share of 40 per cent equals 1 per cent). Thus firm A's market share will drop by 4 per cent to 36 per cent ($40 - 4 = 36$ per cent) and will be caused mainly by its inability to effectively compete with firm B. However, this should not be interpreted to mean that all of firm A's attention should be directed only to firm B. The firm could possibly undertake changes in its marketing programs that would place it in a better competitive position in regard to firm C.

What alternative strategies are available to firm A in arresting this undesirable downward slide of its market share? Two possibilities exist. First, it can attempt to reduce the loss rates to other firms. In essence, the firm is trying to build brand loyalty. This could be done in a number of ways, e.g., lowering its prices, increasing advertising expenditures, changing its package, and so on. Second, firm A could attempt to increase its switching in rates, i.e., draw customers away from firms B and C. The possibilities cited above may be successful in this regard. A detailed indication of what specifically should be done to decrease the switching-out rate and/or increase the switching-in rate is beyond the scope of this text, but some of the following comments are representative of what might be done.

A's product is perhaps of good quality, as indicated by its high retention rate. However, when customers of firms A and C are dissatisfied, they have a tendency to buy from B. No doubt, firm B has a powerful demand stimulation program, perhaps due to heavy promotion and/or lower prices. The lower customer loyalty of firm B (70 per cent) may attest to a lower-quality product. However, three of four customers who leave B prefer C to A. Also, three of four customers who leave C prefer B to A. It therefore becomes evident that firm A is finding it difficult to attract new customers.

One possibility is that A has a high-quality, high-priced product. One strategy might be a lowering of prices. Another might be a promotional appeal to higher-income segments. A number of firms intentionally advertise to the market that is willing to pay a higher price for a better product. Examples are Hallmark greeting cards, Chock-Full-o'-Nuts coffee, and Encyclopaedia Britannica.

3.14   Assumptions of Markov Analysis: Some Additional Comments

At this point it is desirable to discuss the validity of the assumptions under which the preceding analysis operated. It is necessary to keep these in mind when employing Markov analysis.

First, we employed a first-order Markov analysis. That is, we assumed that the purchasing patterns existing at a particular point in time would continue into the future. Thus, we projected that only the last purchase choice affects the current purchases. Quite obviously, this assumption ignores purchasing behavior *leading up to* the point in time under consideration. To illustrate the potential fallibility of this kind of reasoning, let us examine the purchasing patterns of two hypothetical customers, customers C_1 and C_2. Suppose that we are interested in their purchases of toothpaste over the last 6 weeks. Using 1 to represent a purchase of the brand under consideration and 0 to designate the purchase of *any other brand*, suppose that the following consumption patterns were delineated:

	Week					
Customer	1	2	3	4	5	6
C_1	1	1	1	1	1	1
C_2	1	0	0	1	0	1

Under the assumption of a first-order Markov state, C_2 would be just as likely as C_1 to purchase the brand in week 7. And yet, we know that in all likelihood, C_1 would probably be more likely to purchase the brand in week 7 because he has purchased it for 6 consecutive weeks, whereas C_2 has an erratic record of purchase with no consecutive purchases of the brand.

Second, we assumed that the switching-in rates would remain the same until the equilibrium market shares were attained. For example, we presumed that firm *A* would continue to retain 80 per cent of its customers, would gain 7.5 per cent of the customers of *B* and 5.0 per cent of *C*'s, and would lose 17.5 and 2.5 per cent of its own customers to *B* and *C*, respectively. It should be apparent, however, that these rates would change in real life due to variations in marketing strategies of competing firms, including price, advertising expenditures, dealer displays, packaging, and so on.

Third, another assumption of Markov analysis, more implicit than the others, is that the achievement of high market shares is per se a legitimate marketing objective. Several qualifications of this assumption should be noted:

1. Outside forces may affect individual companies differently, thereby invalidating the assumption that outside forces affect all companies equally. If so, the validity of market-share analysis as a control device may be questioned.
2. Market-share analysis is not related to market opportunities. That is, a firm should have greater market shares in markets in which it has more opportunities.

3. New firms may enter a market, thereby driving market shares down. Yet the firm's performance may be as effective or more effective than it previously was.
4. Sometimes a decline in a firm's market share may be indicative of a *more effective* performance. For example, a firm's market share may drop because it is removing unprofitable products, but, as a result, its profit in that market may be enhanced.

The most important qualification of market-share analysis, however, concerns its relationship to profit.

> There is strong disagreement in the business community about the values and uses of market share information. The most obvious problem is that while, say, a rise in market share may indicate more sales than competitors are making, it does not indicate anything about profits.[8]

An even stronger indictment of market-share analysis is provided by Alderson and Green:

> Increasing market position is typically cost incurring. Not infrequently plans which emphasize high market participation are not the most profitable plans. The planner must consider the new financial flows which stem from actions taken to react favorably to the firm's share of the market. There appears to be some support for the assertion that diminishing returns set in as firms try to gain ever larger shares of the market. All of which suggests that the objective of "maximizing market share" is hardly a sound one even though marketing executives may imply that this goal is (or should be) the prime concern of the firm.[9]

Fourth, the reader undoubtedly noticed that we continued to deal with the same-sized market, i.e., 1,000 customers. Although market shares varied over different time periods for the three firms, the total market of 1,000 customers remained constant. In actuality, there would probably be factors operating to increase or decrease the total market size.

Fifth, we assumed that consumers purchased the product at regular intervals. For many products, this may not be the case (e.g., cake mixes may not be purchased every week).

Sixth, the above analysis dealt with the same number of competitors throughout all time periods. In many markets, there may be an influx of competitors.

Seventh, it was assumed that each customer purchased equal quantities, i.e., one unit of the product. For many products, customer needs would necessitate different purchase quantities during buying trips.

[8] John B. Matthews, Jr., *et al.*, *Marketing: An Introductory Analysis* (New York: McGraw-Hill, Inc., 1964), p. 512.

[9] Wroe Alderson and Paul E. Green, *Planning and Problem Solving in Marketing* (Homewood, Ill.: Richard D. Irwin, Inc., 1964), p. 190.

Eighth, the example assumed that the loyalty and switching rates applied to *all* customers. More sophisticated analyses would make provisions for differing rates for various market segments.

There have been a number of attempts to overcome some of the difficulties posed by the above assumptions. Although they undoubtedly make for more realistic usages of the Markov process, they add to the complexity of the mathematics involved and so are beyond the scope of this text. However, a few brief comments are in order.

Through analysis of the market over longer periods of time, more precise estimates of transition probabilities can be obtained. As a result, the transition probabilities are not solely based upon the time period under consideration but involve time periods $n - 1, n - 2, n - 3$, and so on. Generally speaking, it is assumed that the more consecutive purchases made of the brand, the higher the probability that it will be purchased in time period $n + 1, n + 2, n + 3$, and so on. The function in Figure 3–1 is illustrative of the concepts involved.

It can be seen that the probability of purchasing a given brand increases as the number of consecutive purchases increases, but that a 1.0 probability is never achieved.

Some light has been shed on the factors that influence changes in the transition probabilities in subsequent time periods:

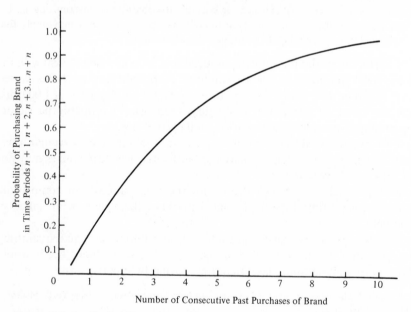

FIGURE 3–1.   Probability of Purchase As a Function of the Number of Consecutive Past Purchases.

Consumers . . . tended to be less loyal towards products with many brands available, where number of purchases and dollar expenditures per buyer are high, where prices are relatively active, and where consumers might be expected to simultaneously use a number of brands of the product. As expected, consumers are brand loyal in markets where brands tend to be widely distributed and where market share is concentrated heavily in the leading brands.[10]

Switches in brands appear to be closely related to two other factors. The first refers to the *net* effect of changes in price, advertising, special promotions, store distribution, or brand quality. That is, if one firm drops its price by a greater amount than a competitive firm, the first would be expected to have a net increase in customers, the latter a net decrease. Similarly, if two companies both increase advertising expenditures for the same product, the firm spending the greater amount would most likely experience a *net* increase in customers and the other a net decrease. Similar results could be projected for the other determinants of brand share. The second is related to the *similarity* between two brands. Obviously, the net effect of different advertising expenditures would be greater for two brands that are similar than two that are dissimilar.[11] "A given difference in advertising may induce little switch between Fords and Cadillacs but a substantial switch between Fords and Chevrolets."[12]

As far as handling the problem of entries to and exits from the market (expanding and contracting market size), this can be partially overcome by allowing customers in experimental settings to switch into and out of "no-purchase" states. This may be done by adding a "none" firm to the switching matrix. Or, the purchase frequency can simply be assigned a "zero" value over a given time period.[13]

Some modifications drop altogether the assumption of regular purchase intervals and instead develop transition probabilities on a purchase-to-purchase basis and represent purchase frequency as a separate variable.[14]

We have spent a great deal of space discussing the utilization of Markov analysis in predicting eventual market-share positions. Since such analysis is the major area of application, the expenditure has been justified. Let us finish this chapter by demonstrating two other ways in which Markov analysis might be applied to marketing operations.

[10] John U. Farley, "Why Does Brand Loyalty Vary Over Products?" *Journal of Marketing Research*, Vol. 1 (November 1964), p. 14.

[11] Purnell H. Benson, "Analysis of Relationships Between Market Conditions and Gain or Loss in Brand Share of the Market," in Wroe Alderson and Stanley J. Shapiro (eds.), *Marketing and the Computer* (Englewood Cliffs, N.J.: Prentice-Hall, Inc., 1963), pp. 390–397.

[12] *Ibid.*, p. 393.

[13] Robert D. Buzzell, *Mathematical Models and Marketing* (Boston: Graduate School of Business Administration, Harvard University, 1964), p. 221.

[14] *Ibid.*, p. 220.

3.15   Using Markov Analysis to Examine the Impact of Population Shifts on Advertising-budget Allocation

One of the tasks that marketing management has to perform is an allocation of the advertising budget to specific geographical territories. For many products with a general appeal (e.g., cereal and soap) advertising allocations can very frequently be established according to a standard criterion such as population. Thus, if a firm were selling such a product in three territories and had $100,000 to apportion, it would probably do it on the basis of the percentage of population found in each of the territories. Thus, if territory T_1 had a population of 5,000,000, territory T_2 had a population of 8,000,000 and territory T_3 had 7,000,000 people, territory T_1 had 25 per cent of the population (5,000,000/20,000,000) and would be appropriated $25,000 of the $100,000 (25 per cent); territory T_2 has 40 per cent of the population (8,000,000/20,000,000) and would probably be appropriated $40,000 of the budget of $100,000 (40 per cent); and territory T_3 has 35 per cent of the population (7,000,000/20,000,000) and would be given an allocation of $35,000 (35 per cent).

Of course, a firm would be interested in any changes in the population of these territories relative to each other since changes of this type would have to be reflected in a reappropriation of the advertising budget. In this regard, Markov analysis might prove to be advantageously employed.

Let us suppose that a firm with nationwide distribution produces and markets a breakfast cereal with general appeal. Let us further assume that it divides the nation into three sales territories: T_1, T_2, and T_3. An analysis of each territory's population reveals that T_1 has 25 per cent of the total population, T_2 also has 25 per cent of the total, and T_3 has 50 per cent of the total. The director of marketing research carefully analyzes the population retention rates of each territory as well as their population loss and gain. This is done through a random sample over a year's time. At the end of the year he is able to develop the following matrix of population retention and gains and losses:

		Retention and Loss		
		T_1	T_2	T_3
Retention	T_1	.700	.050	.050
and	T_2	.200	.800	.050
Gain	T_3	.100	.150	.900

At the end of the following year the percentage shares of total population would be

$$
\begin{pmatrix} .700 & .050 & .050 \\ .200 & .800 & .050 \\ .100 & .150 & .900 \end{pmatrix} \times \begin{pmatrix} .25 \\ .25 \\ .50 \end{pmatrix} = \begin{matrix} .2125 \\ .2750 \\ .5125 \end{matrix}
$$

The reader is asked to verify the results by making the appropriate calculations. The results indicate that T_1 is suffering a decline in share of population, whereas T_2 and T_3 are experiencing increases in their shares.

Naturally, it would be desirable to determine what these shares of population might be at equilibrium. If we had developed the necessary equations and had solved them, we would determine that the final shares at equilibrium would be 14.3 per cent for T_1, 28.6 per cent for T_2, and 57.1 per cent for T_3. Thus there would be significant projected changes in the shares of population for each territory and management would be well advised to keep these in mind when apportioning advertising allocations.

3.16   Another Markov Example: Sales-force Turnover

Let us assume that we are a manufacturer of a highly specialized industrial product of high value. Highly qualified sales personnel are required to sell this product; generally, a degree in engineering is necessary, as well as an intensive year's training with the firm. Such employees are quite scarce.

There are two other firms that compete with the first firm. For all practical purposes, there are no other competitors. The salesmen for the other two firms require the same training and background as do those with the first firm.

Since the industrial customers perceive very few product differences, major competitive activities hinge upon the number of sales people employed by each firm.

Even though our firm (company A) employs 50 per cent of the 400 salesmen in the industry while firms B and C employ 100 each, we are interested in knowing whether our recruiting, training, compensation, and sales-force supervision methods are competitively sound.

Our marketing manager studies the retention, termination, and hiring rates in the industry over a 3-year period and, in comparing 1970 and 1971, discovers the following movement of salesmen:

| | | Retention and Resignations | | |
		A	B	C
Retention	A	180	2	2
and	B	12	90	3
Hiring	C	8	8	95
		200	100	100

The above matrix can be represented by a matrix of transition probabilities as follows:

		Retention and Resignations		
		A	B	C
Retention	A	.90	.02	.02
and	B	.06	.90	.03
Hiring	C	.04	.08	.95

The above matrix indicates that our firm annually retains 90 per cent of its salesmen and gains 2 per cent of the people who work for firms B and C. However, each year 6 per cent of our salesmen go to work for B and 4 per cent switch to C.

In order to learn whether we will be able to maintain a minimum level of 180 salesmen required to service existing customers and secure an acceptable level of new business, our marketing manager decides to calculate the equilibrium conditions. The four appropriate equations are

$$(1) \quad A = .90A + .02B + .02C$$

$$(2) \quad B = .06A + .90B + .03C$$

$$(3) \quad C = .04A + .08B + .95C$$

$$(4) \quad 1 = \quad A + \quad B + \quad C$$

The equilibrium values for A, B, and C, respectively, are 16.7, 27.0, and 56.3 per cent. (The reader is urged to verify these results by using the method of substitution to solve for A, B, and C.)

The analysis, therefore, discloses that company A, in the long run, will be able to retain only 16.7 per cent or approximately 67 salesmen of the 400 in the industry. This is far beneath the required 180 people and an indication of impending disaster.

A quick glance at the first matrix in this section hints that our company is suffering from sales-force problems. Note that each year we lose 20 sales people to our competition and gain only 4. Obviously, our analysis has indicated that our competition, particularly company C, has certain sales administration and management strategies that are superior to our own. Both internal and external sales-force audits are in order. Our problem may be due to sources that range from poor morale in our organization to a higher rate of commission in company C.

3.17   Higher-order Markov Processes

The previous brand-share analysis discussed earlier was based on the assumption that a consumer's probability of purchasing a given brand in any time period is dependent only on his previous purchase. There are, of course, cases where purchasing behavior is more appropriately related to a buyer's entire purchasing history or at least his last two or three purchases. Similarly, in the salesmen's-turnover example, there is evidence that an employee does not base his job-seeking preference on his most recent job and the satisfaction derived from it.

The authors, therefore, believe that an exploration of Markov models would not be complete without at least an elementary look at second-order processes.

Let us assume that two soft-drink firms, company S and company C, are the only producers of bitter-lemon soda in America. Since company S is contemplating a major expansion of its production and marketing resources, market-share data for future years is desired. Despite S company's present 80 per cent share of market, the firm hired a research group to study consumer bitter-lemon buying habits.

The results of the detailed study are shown below, where S denotes a purchase of the product of company S and C indicates a purchase of the product of company C:

Purchase Sequence in Periods 1 and 2	Probability of Purchase in Period 3	
	S	C
SS	.90	.10
CS	.70	.30
SC	.40	.60
CC	.50	.50

The above data may be interpreted as follows:

1. Of those consumers who purchased the SS sequence during periods 1 and 2, 90 per cent will continue to buy S and 10 per cent will switch to C in period 3.
2. Of those consumers who purchased in the sequence CS during periods 1 and 2, in the third period 70 per cent will continue to buy S while 30 per cent will switch to C.
3. The SC and CC sequences are similarly explained.

If the given data matrix is placed in slightly different form, we have the matrix of Table 3–15:

TABLE 3–15. Matrix of Transition Probabilities (Second-order Markov Process)

First- and Second-period Sequence	Second and Third-period Sequence			
	SS	CS	SC	CC
SS	.90	0	.10	0
CS	.70	0	.30	0
SC	0	.40	0	.60
CC	0	.50	0	.50

In interpreting Table 3–15, the letters at the left refer to the sequence in which consumers purchased bitter lemon during the first and second periods. The letters at the top of the exhibit reflect the second- and third-period buying sequence. Therefore, the .90 in the top row means that 90 per cent of the consumers who purchased S brand in both of the first 2 periods will buy S brand again in the third period. In the same row, the .10 means that 10 per cent of the SS buyers in the first two periods will switch to brand C in the third period.

Why is there a zero under the CS and CC columns in the first row? Simply because both entries imply a purchase of brand C in the second period which is, of course, incompatible with the purchase of S in the second period that is indicated by the SS notation at the top of the left column.

For the purposes of calculating equilibrium conditions, SS, CS, SC, and CC can be considered to be individual brands and the array of equations looks like this:

(1) $SS = .90SS + .70CS$

(2) $CS = .40SC + .50CC$

(3) $SC = .10SS + .30CS$

(4) $CC = .60SC + .50CC$

(5) $1 = SS + CS + SC + CC$

The algebraic exercise will be left to the reader. However, the final answers are:

$$SS = .686$$
$$CS = .098$$
$$SC = .098$$
$$CC = .118$$

The final buyers of brand S at equilibrium consist of the sum of SS and CS or $.686 + .098 = .784$. Thus, company S's equilibrium brand share is 78.4 per cent. Since this is not too far from the present 80 per cent share, the company is holding its own.

3.18   Conclusions Concerning Simulation in Marketing

It is safe to say that simulation holds great promise for the analysis of marketing operations. With the additional contributions available from high-speed computers, it is apparent that simulation can provide a rich and viable approach to the determination of optimum tactics and strategies.

If it can be said that simulation holds great promise, it is also necessary to indicate that simulation will probably not be a panacea for analyzing marketing problems for all firms. The reasons for this are many, and it is worthwhile to indicate some of them.

1. Many firms do not possess the requisite personnel for purposes of simulation. The most effective simulation personnel are those who have a solid background in mathematics plus a sophisticated understanding of marketing and, unfortunately, these individuals are comparatively rare.

2. The lack of the proper computer facilities prevents many firms from effectively utilizing marketing simulation; proper computer facilities are a necessary requirement for simulation.

3. Since simulation deals primarily with probabilistic considerations, there is reluctance by many executives to fully endorse the concepts involved; there is a reticence to embrace results based upon data that cannot be defined as precisely as executives would like.

4. The costs of simulation are relatively high, which, when coupled with somewhat uncertain results, may result in a lack of enthusiasm. Gathering the necessary data to develop the simulation is quite costly; computer time is expensive, as is the analyst's.

5. Many simulations are designed to be mainly descriptive or analytical in nature. Simulation in marketing can gain wider acceptance when more examples of simulations actually improving marketing operations are given more widespread dissemination.

This chapter has discussed three kinds of simulation techniques in marketing: waiting-line theory, the Monte Carlo method, and Markov analysis. The reader should not consider these to be exhaustive of simulation in marketing; there are others that could have been included. However, the three methods illustrated will hopefully provide the reader with a basic understanding of simulation concepts that can serve as a foundation for other techniques encountered later in his academic or business pursuits.

EXERCISES

1. Multiply the following two matrices:

$$\begin{pmatrix} 27 & 14 \\ 2 & 3 \\ 8 & 12 \\ 1 & 20 \end{pmatrix} \times \begin{pmatrix} 8 & 12 & 25 \\ 9 & 6 & 2 \end{pmatrix}$$

2. Solve these three simultaneous equations by the method of substitution:

$$2X + 5Y + Z = 35$$
$$3X + 2Y + 4Z = 30$$
$$X + Y + 2Z = 13$$

3. Below is a matrix of retention, loss, and gain probabilities for three firms. Calculate the final market shares at equilibrium.

$$\begin{array}{c c c c} & X & Y & Z \\ X & \begin{pmatrix} .700 & .100 & .300 \\ Y & .200 & .800 & .100 \\ Z & .100 & .100 & .600 \end{pmatrix} \end{array}$$

4. Do we need to know the original market shares in Exercise 3 in order to determine the final market shares at equilibrium? Of what value would it be to know what these initial market shares were?

5. Aside from the examples given in the text, how else might Markov analysis be used in marketing operations?

6. State the basic assumptions of a first-order Markov analysis. What can be done to modify these restrictions?

7. Below is a matrix of retention, loss, and gain probabilities for three firms and their original market shares. Calculate their market shares at the end of period 1.

$$\begin{array}{c c c c} & A & B & C \\ A & \begin{pmatrix} .600 & .100 & .300 \\ B & .300 & .700 & .200 \\ C & .100 & .200 & .500 \end{pmatrix} \times \begin{pmatrix} .50 \\ .30 \\ .20 \end{pmatrix} \end{array}$$

8. Vida Blue is pitching for Oakland against Baltimore in Oakland. Owing to the illness of two of the ticket takers, there is only one booth available to process fans wanting to purchase box seats. The booth opens at 6:00 P.M. for the 8:00 game.

Assume that each customer can be accommodated in 20 seconds and that a fan gets into the queue every 10 seconds. How many fans could be accommodated by 8:00 P.M. in time to see Blue fan Blair, Belanger, and B. Robinson? How long would the waiting line be by 8:00 P.M.?

9. Indicate why the *load factor* is so important to the understanding of waiting-line theory.

10. The Harris Corp. has its customers send in their own purchase orders. In the past the arrival of these purchase orders per day has approximated a *normal* distribution with a mean of 50 and a standard deviation of 6. In terms of the probability of occurrence, the following would be indicated:

Number of Purchase Orders	Probability of Occurrence (%)
26–31.99	.5
32–37.99	2.0
38–43.99	13.5
44–49.99	34.0
50–55.99	34.0
56–61.99	13.5
62–67.99	2.0
68–73.99	.5

Assume that the midpoint of a class represents the class; e.g., the range of 26–31.99 is represented by 29, the range of 32–37.99 is represented by 35, and so on. Using the table of random numbers included in Appendix B, develop a Monte Carlo simulation of the number of purchase orders per day to be expected for the month of June. If the firm can process only 41 orders per day, about how many days in June will the firm be behind schedule? (You should answer this before conducting the Monte Carlo process.) How close to your answer was your actual result?

11. The arrival of customers at a bank can be closely approximated by a Poisson distribution with a mean average of 1.5. What is the probability that there would be two arrivals during any given time period? What is the probability of there being less than two arrivals?

12. You are the general manager of a huge supermarket in a large suburban shopping center. Your September 1 market share in the county is 30 per cent. An elaborate research project discloses that the consumer brand-switching matrix for your store (*G*) and all other regional competitors (*C*) looks like this:

	Next Purchase	
Last Purchase	*G*	*C*
G	.80	.20
C	.30	.70

After calculating your November 1 market share, you decide to doublecheck your calculations by use of a Monte Carlo simulation. Compare your results by each method.

13.

		Retention and Loss			
		A	B	C	Nonbuyer
Retention	A	.7	.1	.0	.1
and	B	.1	.4	.0	.7
Gain	C	.1	.3	.9	.0
	Nonbuyer	.1	.2	.1	.2

Given the above transition probability matrix, check all the following answers which are true. Do not check the false answers.

____Brand *B* represents the easiest entry to the market.

____Brand *C* has the highest brand loyalty.

____Brand *C* will eventually go out of business.

____20 per cent of the population will eventually be nonusers.

If you were the marketing manager of firm *B* and you presently controlled a 40 per cent market share, what would be your strategy?

REFERENCES

DONNELLY, JAMES H., JR., and IVANCEVICH, JOHN M., *Analysis for Marketing Decisions* (Homewood, Ill.: Richard D. Irwin, Inc., 1970).

KOTLER, PHILIP, *Marketing Management* (Englewood Cliffs, N.J.: Prentice-Hall, Inc., 1967).

LEVIN, RICHARD I., and KIRKPATRICK, C. A., *Quantitative Approaches to Management* (New York: McGraw-Hill Book Company, 1965).

SPRINGER, CLIFFORD H., HERLIHY, ROBERT E., NOLL, ROBERT T., and BEGGS, ROBERT I., *Probabilistic Models* (Homewood, Ill.: Richard D. Irwin, Inc., 1968).

WASSON, CHESTER R., *Understanding Quantitative Analysis* (New York: Appleton-Century-Crofts, 1969).

CHAPTER 4

Linear Programming for Marketing Decisions

4.1 Introduction

Most business firms are in existence to achieve a number of basic objectives. Many of these evolve around the profit motive. Thus a firm may be attempting to maximize profits, secure a certain percentage return on investment, reach a stated dollar figure, secure a profit equal to a certain percentage of sales volume, obtain a desired earnings per share, and so on. In addition, other objectives might be stipulated. For example, management could project a certain market-share figure. Or a sales-volume goal could be established. Another objective might involve a particular total cost per unit, while another might be to reduce the numbers of defective products or labor turnover.

Whatever the objectives, the firm finds that it must secure them within fairly well-defined constraints. A manufacturing unit, for example, has a certain capacity production. Only so much money can be allocated for the acquisition of new machinery. There is a limit as to the number of finished products that can be stored in available warehouses.

Another factor to be considered is that the enterprise usually has more than one alternative available in securing its objectives. Thus it usually has a large number of products that it can offer in order to maximize profits, secure a certain sales volume, generate a desired return on investment, and so on. More than one machine can perhaps be utilized in producing the firm's products. Different sources exist for obtaining required financing. Many suppliers could potentially be utilized in acquiring raw materials or semi-finished products. A further consideration is that the choice of alternatives does not necessarily have to be an either/or proposition. In some cases more than one alternative will be utilized and thus the decision becomes one of determining the extent to which the various alternatives will be utilized.

Although the above discussion has essentially focused on the firm as a whole, the same concepts are directly applicable to the marketing area. The marketing department is also required to obtain objectives, work within constraints in so doing, and appraise various alternative methods in achieving these objectives. Some examples of common objectives are obtaining specific sales volumes or market shares for various products, reducing out-of-stock situations, minimizing total distribution costs for the product line, minimizing total spoilage costs of inventory, and, in some cases, maximizing total profit. In attempting to achieve goals, constraints would be encountered, such as a specific advertising budget, a certain number of salesmen, a fixed number of dealer outlets, and the carrying capacity of the firm's fleet of trucks. Various alternatives might be considered in an effort to accomplish indicated objectives. Thus several different advertising media might be evaluated. Or various modes of transportation would have to be considered. Another example would be the several kinds of retail outlets available to sell the firm's products.

In developing the firm's marketing strategies, the marketing manager would certainly appreciate a rigorous methodology that would embrace the above three factors (objectives, constraints, and alternatives) and tell him the best course of action. For many kinds of marketing problems, this can be done by the application of a quantitative technique called *linear programming*.

4.2   Linear Programming: Some General Comments

Linear programming is a precise quantitative tool that indicates to the decision maker the optimum allocation of scarce resources in order to maximize or minimize some stated objective. The major characteristic of this methodology is, as the name implies, the fact that all relationships expressed by the expressed equations are *linear* in nature; i.e., these relationships are represented by a straight line. Although this restriction mitigates against the universal applicability of linear programming to all kinds of business problems, it should be pointed out that a great number of situations can be accurately portrayed by linear relationships, thereby allowing for the application of linear programming.

There are two approaches to linear programming that will be presented in this chapter: graphic and simplex. The graphic method generally involves analysis of a problem in terms of a two- or three-dimensional graph. The simplex method involves a somewhat complicated *algorithm*, or search process. Although the graphic method is easier to understand than the simplex approach, the simplex algorithm can handle much more involved problems. Therefore, it will be the objective of this chapter to explain the simplex method in some detail. However, many of the basic concepts of the simplex method can be more easily understood if the graphic solutions are presented first.

Whichever method is used, there are, as indicated above, three essential aspects: (1) There is an objective to be achieved, i.e., something to be maximized or minimized; (2) there are constraints within which the firm must operate to reach the objective; and (3) there must be more than one alternative approach to attain the objective.

4.3   Linear Programming: Graphic Approach to a Problem of Maximization of an Objective

Let us first utilize the graphic approach to solve a problem where the marketing department is attempting to maximize the contribution to net profit from the sales of a new product.

The Acme Corporation is introducing a new product which sells for $10 per unit. Management estimates the total per unit cost at $8 per unit; therefore, every unit sold contributes $2 to the firm's net profit.

The marketing manager believes that there are two basic strategies available to him in selling the product: personal selling and advertising. He estimates that for every presentation made to retailers, an average of 500 units will be sold, thereby contributing $1,000 to the firm's net profit (500 units times a $2 net profit per unit). An advertisement inserted in trade papers is expected to obtain average sales of 400 units, resulting in an addition to net profit of $800 (400 units times a $2 net profit per unit).

There are two major constraints within which the marketing manager must operate. First, he can use a total of $40,000 in promoting this new offering. In this regard, the cost of one sales presentation is estimated to be $200 and the cost of one trade paper insertion is estimated at $100. Second, he has available a total of 10,000 man-hours which can be devoted to the new product. For each sales presentation, he estimates that a total of 40 hours is required (actual face-to-face selling time, preliminary work, follow-up, clerical help, research, and so on), whereas one advertising insertion uses up 50 hours (copy-writing, research, media liaison, and so on).

Let us now put the above information into a more usable form. The essential data are summarized in Table 4–1.

TABLE 4–1. Data for Maximization Example

	Contribution to Net Profit as a Result of One Sales Presentation or One Advertising Insertion ($)	Cost of One Sales Presentation or One Advertising Insertion ($)	Total Promotional Budget ($)	Number of Hours Used in Making One Sales Presentation or Inserting One Advertisement	Total Man-hours Available
Sales presentation	1,000	200		40	
			40,000		10,000
Newspaper advertisement	800	100		50	

Let us next develop the equations that will be necessary for our analysis. First we will express the equation that represents the objective function, i.e., the firm's desire to maximize contributions to its net profit. Using S to represent a sales presentation, A to represent an advertising insertion, and P to represent net profit, we have

$$P = \$1,000S + \$800A$$

Thus total net profit is represented by $1,000 profit per sales presentation times the number of sales presentations plus $800 profit per advertising insertion times the number of advertising insertions.

Next, we need to indicate in equation form the two constraints which we must recognize in determining the number of sales presentations and advertising insertions that will maximize net profit. We know that total man-hours available are limited to 10,000 and that each sales presentation involves 40 hours and each advertising insertion necessitates 50 hours. Thus the total number of hours assigned to sales presentations plus the total number of hours devoted to advertising cannot be greater than 10,000. Expressing the above in formula format, we arrive at the following:

$$40S + 50A \leq 10,000$$

The reader will recall that the symbol $\leq$ means "less than or equal to." Thus the formula indicates that the number of sales presentations times 40 hours per presentation plus the number of advertising insertions times 50 hours per insertion cannot exceed the constraint of 10,000 man-hours. The total hours used can be 10,000 or can be *less* than 10,000, but they *cannot* be greater than 10,000.

Let us now proceed to express in the same manner the promotional budget constraint. We know that no more than $40,000 can be spent for the two alternatives and that each sales presentation costs $200 and each trade-paper insertion costs $100. As a result, the formula expressing the promotional budget constraint is

$$\$200S + \$100A \leq \$40,000$$

This inequality indicates that the number of sales presentations times $200 (the cost of one sales presentation) plus the number of advertising insertions times $100 (the cost of one trade-paper insertion) must be equal to or less than the promotional budget of $40,000 but *cannot* be greater than this amount.

One other implied constraint must be indicated. Both values for S and P *must be positive*, i.e., equal to or greater than zero. Therefore,

$$S \geq 0$$

$$P \geq 0$$

Let us now summarize what we have done by collecting all the above inequalities. It is common to express the objective function first, followed by the constraint functions. As a result, we have

Maximize:

(1) $P = \$1,000S + \$800A$

Subject to:

(2) $40S + 50A \leq 10,000$

(3) $\$200S + \$100A \leq \$40,000$

(4) $S \geq 0$

(5) $P \geq 0$

The raw data are now available to determine the optimum allocation of sales presentations and advertising insertions that will maximize net profit. In so doing, the following steps must be performed:

Step One: On a two-dimensional graph, draw the functions representing the two constraint equations dealing with total man-hours available and total promotional budget available, assuming that in each equation sales presentations and advertising insertions would each utilize the available resources to the exclusion of the other alternative.

Let us go through this step very carefully. Figure 4–1 is a two-dimensional graph, with number of sales presentations represented by the vertical axis and number of advertising insertions represented by the horizontal axis. If we allocated *all* the 10,000 available man-hours to sales presentations, we would have a total of 250 sales presentations (10,000 total man-hours divided by 40 man-hours per sales presentation). If all the 10,000 man-hours were given to advertising insertions, a total of 200 advertising insertions would result (10,000 man-hours divided by 50 man-hours per advertising insertion). These two points have been joined by a straight line with the corresponding equation indicated. The shaded area to the left of this line is termed the area of feasible solutions. Only combinations of sales presentations and advertising insertions on the line or to its left are potential optimum solutions since any combination to the right of the line will result in the 10,000 man-hour constraint being exceeded. Take, for example, point X, which represents 250 sales presentations and 100 advertising insertions. Total man-hours expended for this combination would be $15,000(250 \times 40 + 100 \times 50 = 10,000 + 5,000 = 15,000)$, well in excess of the upper limit of 10,000.

Next, on a similar graph (Figure 4–2) we repeat the same procedure for the promotional budget constraint of $40,000. If all the available $40,000 were spent for sales presentations, 200 sales presentations would result ($40,000 divided by $200 cost for each sales presentation). If all the available

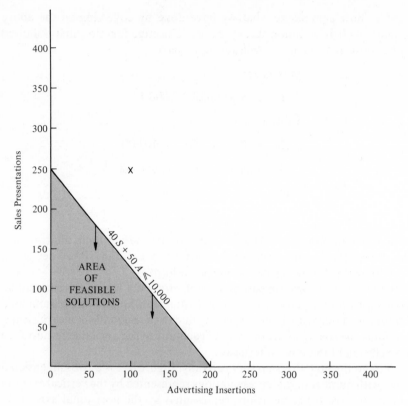

FIGURE 4–1.   Graphing of the Man-Hour Constraint.

promotional funds were allocated to advertising insertions, the firm could schedule 400 advertisements ($40,000 divided by $100 cost for each advertisement). These two resultant points have been connected in Figure 4–2 with the appropriate equation indicated. As with the man-hour constraint, no combination to the right of the line is feasible since the promotional budget of $40,000 would be exceeded.

Let us now place the two inequalities graphed in Figures 4–1 and 4–2 on the same graph (Figure 4–3) and carefully notice the resultant area of feasible solutions. The new shaded area of feasibility is less than in Figure 4–1 or 4–2, i.e., fewer combinations of sales presentations and advertising insertions now exist that will be within the constraints of available man-hours and promotional budget. This, of course, results from the fact that two constraints are now being recognized, together, not individually as was done in Figures 4–1 and 4–2. Thus any combination lying to the right of the area of feasible solutions will not satisfy one or both of the constraints.

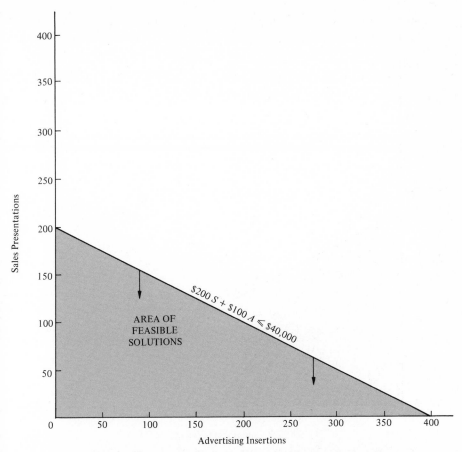

FIGURE 4–2.   Graphing of the Promotional Budget Constraint.

Step Two: The second step is to identify all points of intersection in the area of feasible solutions. Although our task of determining which combination of sales presentations and advertising insertions which will maximize net profit is made easier by there being fewer potential combinations in Figure 4–3 than there were in Figures 4–1 and 4–2, it is apparent that there are still a myriad number of possibilities. However, there is one characteristic of the graphic solution that will reduce the number of potential solutions to a manageable size: *The optimum solution will always be found at one of the points of intersection of the area of feasibility.* Analysis of Figure 4–3 reveals four points of intersection. These are *A* (the intersection of the horizontal and vertical axes), *B* (the intersection of the vertical axis and the equation expressing the advertising-budget constraint), *C* (the intersection of the two equations indicating the advertising-budget constraint and the man-hours

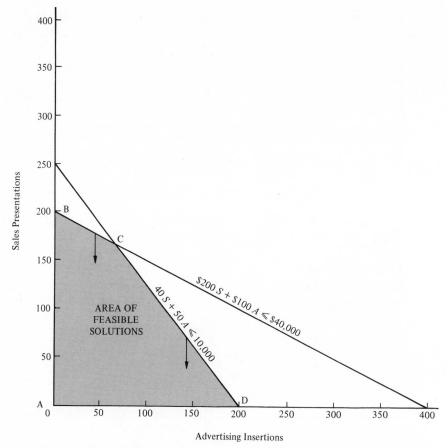

FIGURE 4–3.   Graphing of Man-Hour and Promotional Budget Constraints.

constraint), and *D* (the intersection of the horizontal axis and the equation expressing the man-hours constraint).

Step Three: Determine the quantities of sales promotions and advertising insertions that exist at each of the points of intersection. Except for point *C*, this is a rather simple and straightforward exercise since the values can be quickly and accurately taken from Figure 4–3. For points *A*, *B*, and *D*, the appropriate figures are:

For *A*: zero units of sales presentations and zero units of advertising insertions

For *B*: 200 units of sales presentations and zero units of advertising insertions

For *D*: zero units of sales presentations and 200 units of advertising insertions

Since the graph in Figure 4–3 is accurately drawn, it would be quite simple to determine the precise values for the sales presentations and advertising insertions existing at point C by dropping perpendicular lines to the appropriate axes. However, a better approach is to eliminate the less-than designations from the two equations that intersect at point C, and, by the method of substitution, solve for S and A. The two equations would be

$$(1) \quad 40S + 50A = 10,000$$

$$(2) \quad 200S + 100A = 40,000$$

In order to solve for S and A, let us first multiply equation (1) by 2 and subtract it from equation (2). We would have

$$(2) \quad 200S + 100A = \quad 40,000$$
$$(1) \quad -80S - 100A = -20,000$$
$$\overline{ 120S = \quad 20,000}$$
$$S = 166\tfrac{2}{3}$$

Substituting $S = 166\tfrac{2}{3}$ into equation (1) gives us a value of $66\tfrac{2}{3}$ for A:

$$(1) \quad 40S + 50A = 10,000$$
$$40(166\tfrac{2}{3}) + 50A = 10,000$$
$$6,666\tfrac{2}{3} + 50A = 10,000$$
$$50A = 3,333\tfrac{1}{3}$$
$$A = 66\tfrac{2}{3}$$

Thus point C represents a value of $166\tfrac{2}{3}$ for sales presentations (S) and $66\tfrac{2}{3}$ for advertising insertions (A).

Step Four: Using the values for sales presentations and advertising insertions existing at the four intersections in the area of feasibility, determine the total contribution to net profit by multiplying these values by their appropriate *per unit* contribution to net profit. In this regard, it will be recalled that each sales presentation contributes $1,000 to net profit and each advertising insertion contributes $800.

The values for sales presentations and advertising insertions are, again, at points A, B, C, and D:

Point A: zero S and zero A

Point B: 200S and zero A

Point C: $166\tfrac{2}{3}S$ and $66\tfrac{2}{3}A$

Point D: zero S and 200 A

Inserting the contributions to net profit per unit into these figures provides us with the following total contributions to net profit at the four points:

Point A: 0($1,000) + 0($800) = $0

Point B: 200($1,000) + 0($800) = $200,000

Point C: $166\frac{2}{3}$($1,000) + $66\frac{2}{3}$($800) = $166,667 + $53,333 = $220,000

Point D: 0($1,000) + 200($800) = $160,000

Thus point C, consisting of $166\frac{2}{3}$ sales presentations and $66\frac{2}{3}$ advertising insertions, results in the greatest amount of profit, $220,000. In order to make sure that we have not exceeded our constraint of man-hours, let us multiply the $166\frac{2}{3}$ sales presentations by 40 (number of hours required for one sales presentation) and add it to $66\frac{2}{3}$ advertising insertions multiplied by 50 (number of hours required for one advertising insertion). The total is

$$166\tfrac{2}{3}(40) + 66\tfrac{2}{3}(50) = 6,666\tfrac{2}{3} + 3,333\tfrac{1}{3} = 10,000$$

It can be seen that this combination of sales presentations and advertising insertions uses exactly the 10,000 hours allotted to the new product.

Let us next see how much of the $40,000 promotional budget would be used up by this optimum combination. Remembering that each sales presentation costs $200 and each advertising insertion costs $100, we would have

$$166\tfrac{2}{3}(\$200) + 66\tfrac{2}{3}(\$100) = \$33,333.33 + \$6,666.67 = \$40,000$$

And all the $40,000 promotional budget would be utilized. It should be pointed out, however, that in many problems, total capacities may not be entirely utilized.

It might be worthwhile to discuss in some detail why the combination of $166\frac{2}{3}$ sales presentations and $66\frac{2}{3}$ advertising presentations is indeed the optimum. First, let us examine what happens to total profit as we move from the various points of intersection. In order to facilitate the explanation, Figure 4–4 essentially duplicates Figure 4–3. Suppose that we start at point A. It is obvious that here we have no contribution at all to net profit since there are zero sales presentations and zero advertising insertions. Naturally, it is advantageous to move from point A to point B since we are adding $1,000 in profit for every additional sales presentation. Finally, at point B we secure $200,000 in profit (200 sales presentations times $1,000 net profit per sales presentation equals $200,000 total net profit). It is also advantageous to move from point B to point C. The reader might wonder why this is so, since in so doing we give up units of sales presentations worth $1,000 each in net profit to gain advertising insertions providing $800 profit per unit. The reason is that in moving from B to C we gain *more than one unit* of an advertising insertion for each unit of sales presentation lost, and the profit gained from

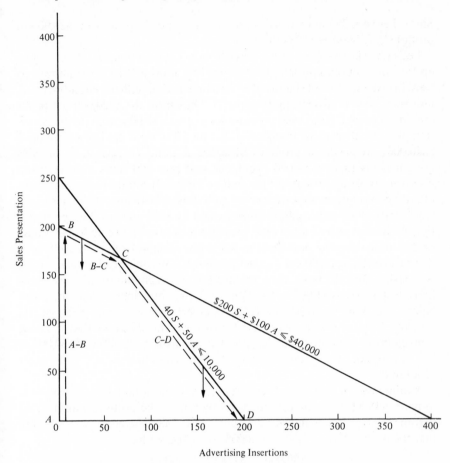

FIGURE 4–4.   Delineation of the Four Points of Intersection.

adding more than one unit of advertising *exceeds* the profit lost from losing one unit of a sales presentation. To illustrate this, in going from *B* to *C* we drop from 200 units of sales presentation to $166\frac{2}{3}$ (a loss of $33\frac{1}{3}$ units, or $33,333.33); but at the same time, we gain $66\frac{2}{3}$ units of advertising insertions worth $800 per unit, or a net profit of $53,333.33. Thus we add $20,000 in net profit ($53,333.33 − $33,333.33 = $20,000). Another way of looking at the same thing is that for every one unit of sales presentations lost we gain 2 units of advertising insertions ($66\frac{2}{3} \div 33\frac{1}{3}$); this results in a deduction of $1,000 per unit of profit for each unit of sales presentations lost, but we gain $1,600 of profit for each unit of sales presentations lost (2 units of advertising insertions times $800 profit per unit). Subtracting a $1,000 loss per unit from a net profit per unit of $1,600 gives us a net contribution per unit of $600.

Since there are $33\frac{1}{3}$ units of sales presentations involved, we gain \$20,000 in profit ($33\frac{1}{3} \times \$600 = \$20,000$).

Let's see what happens as we move from point C to point D. Here we give up $166\frac{2}{3}$ units of sales presentations (from $166\frac{2}{3}$ units of sales presentations to zero) in order to gain $133\frac{1}{3}$ units of advertising insertions (from $66\frac{2}{3}$ advertising insertions to 200 advertising insertions). Thus from the \$220,000 net profit existing at point C ($166\frac{2}{3}$ sales presentations times a \$1,000 profit per presentation plus $66\frac{2}{3}$ advertising insertions times an \$800 profit per insertion equals \$220,000), we secure a profit of \$160,000 at point D (zero units of sales presentations times a \$1,000 profit per unit plus 200 units of advertising insertions times an \$800 profit per unit = \$160,000). Similarly, for every unit of sales presentations that we lose we gain only .8 of an advertising insertion ($133\frac{1}{3}$ units of advertising insertions divided by $166\frac{2}{3}$ units of sales presentations). Thus for every unit of sales presentations lost we give up \$1,000 in net profit, to be offset by only \$640 in net profit secured from each additional unit of advertising (\$800 per unit net profit from one unit of advertising times .8 = \$640). On a net basis, then, we lose \$360 for each unit of sales presentations lost ($\$640 - \$1,000 = \$-360$); and the total loss in moving from point C to point D is \$60,000 ($166\frac{2}{3}$ sales presentation times \$360 equals \$60,000). This, of course, is correct because we already know that in going from point C to point D our net profit drops from \$220,000 to \$160,000, a loss of \$60,000. Clearly, the above analysis indicates that point C is the most profitable.

Another way of demonstrating that point C is the optimum combination is to place a profit function on the graph by setting the profit equation equal to some arbitrary profit figure. Let us choose \$80,000. Therefore, remembering that the profit function is $P = \$1,000S + \$800A$, we have

$$\$80,000 = \$1,000S + \$800A$$

Setting A equal to zero and dividing \$80,000 by $\$1,000S$, we obtain a value of 80 for S. Setting S equal to zero and dividing \$80,000 by $\$800A$, we have a value of 100 for A. Joining the values of 80 for S and 100 for A, we have the line indicated in Figure 4–5. This line represents the fact that any combination of sales presentations and advertising insertions on this line will result in a profit of \$80,000. In addition, it can be seen that this function lies well within the area of feasibility.

Next, let us choose another profit figure that is greater than \$80,000 and moves us more to the right in the area of feasible solutions. A profit of \$160,000 would be expressed as

$$\$160,000 = \$1,000S + \$800A$$

If A is set equal to zero, S equals 160 ($\$160,000 \div \$1,000S$). Similarly, letting S equal zero, A is 200 ($\$160,000 \div \$800A$). This profit function is also drawn on Figure 4–5.

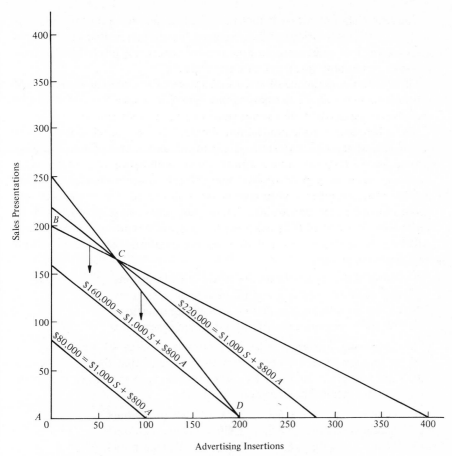

FIGURE 4–5.   Plotting of Three Iso-profit Functions.

By now, the reader has probably grasped a significant concept: *The optimum point of profitability is found when we can draw a profit function as far as possible to the right and still have it touch a point in the area of feasible solutions.* Clearly, in Figure 4–5, this point is point C. Since it is only a point and not an entire straight line like the other two profit functions, there is only one combination of sales presentations and advertising insertions that will maximize net profit: $166\frac{2}{3}$ sales presentations and $66\frac{2}{3}$ advertising insertions. This profit function, which maximizes net profit and is drawn in Figure 4–5, is represented by

$$\$220,000 = \$1,000S + \$800A$$

with S equal to 220 when A is equal to zero ($\$220,000 \div \$1,000$) and A equal to 275 when S is set equal to zero ($\$220,000 \div \$800$).

The reader should not be disturbed by the fact that the optimum combination of sales presentations and advertising insertions resulted in fractional answers, i.e., $166\frac{2}{3}$ sales presentations and $66\frac{2}{3}$ advertising insertions. In many linear-programming solutions, this may occur.

Of course, the existence of fractional answers does present somewhat of a problem. After all, a salesman cannot give $\frac{2}{3}$ of a sales presentation and the advertising department cannot run $\frac{2}{3}$ of an advertisement.

The solution to this dilemma is quite simple : Consider the fractional answer to be represented by the appropriate lower and higher whole numbers bracketing the fraction and determine which combination of sales presentations and advertising insertions will maximize the objective function, as long as the whole-number combinations do not exceed the man-hour and promotional-budget constraints. Thus $166\frac{2}{3}$ sales presentations will be represented by 166 and 167 sales presentations, and $66\frac{2}{3}$ advertising insertions will be represented by 66 and 67 sales presentations. There will be four combinations possible :

1. 166 sales presentations and 66 advertising insertions
2. 166 sales presentations and 67 advertising insertions
3. 167 sales presentations and 66 advertising insertions
4. 167 sales presentations and 67 advertising insertions

Remembering that each sales presentation requires 40 man-hours and each newspaper insertion needs 50 man-hours and that there is a total of 10,000 man-hours available, let's determine which of the above four combinations stay within the man-hour constraint :

1. $166(40) + 66(50) = 6,640 + 3,300 = 9,940$ man-hours
2. $166(40) + 67(50) = 6,640 + 3,350 = 9,990$ man-hours
3. $167(40) + 66(50) = 6,680 + 3,300 = 9,980$ man-hours
4. $167(40) + 67(50) = 6,680 + 3,350 = 10,030$ man-hours

Thus combination 4 (167 sales presentations and 67 advertising insertions) is not feasible because it exceeds the 10,000 man-hours and hence may be excluded from further consideration.

Let us next see if any of the three remaining combinations exceeds the available promotional budget of $40,000. The reader will recall that each sales presentation costs $200 and that each advertising insertion costs $100. Thus the total costs for each of the three combinations still under consideration are

1. $166(\$200) + 66(\$100) = \$33,200 + \$6,600 = \$39,800$ promotional budget
2. $166(\$200) + 67(\$100) = \$33,200 + \$6,700 = \$39,900$ promotional budget
3. $167(\$200) + 66(\$100) = \$33,400 + \$6,600 = \$40,000$ promotional budget

Since the above combinations all utilize a promotional budget of $40,000 or lower and fewer than 10,000 man-hours, they may be examined for their contribution to net profit. Recalling that each sales presentation adds $1,000 to net profit and each advertising insertion contributes $800, we would have

1. 166($1,000) + 66($800) = $166,000 + $52,800 = $218,800 net profit
2. 166($1,000) + 67($800) = $166,000 + $53,600 = $219,600 net profit
3. 167($1,000) + 66($800) = $167,000 + $52,800 = $219,800 net profit

These results indicate that the optimum *feasible* combination of sales presentations and advertising insertions is 167 sales presentations and 66 advertising insertions. This combination generates a net profit of $219,800, which is only $200 less than the net profit ($220,000) generated by the *theoretically* optimum solution of $166\frac{2}{3}$ sales presentations and $66\frac{2}{3}$ advertising insertions.

Although the above example has dealt with a maximization objective, there are many instances in which the marketing department might be desirous of minimizing some objective. The next section will show how the graphic method of linear programming can be employed to analyze this type of objective.

4.4   Linear Programming: Graphic Approach to a Problem of Minimization of an Objective

A small independent Hollywood movie studio plans to produce a minimum of 35 films during the forthcoming three-year period. Based on erotic content, films can be rated G, GP, R, or X. The studio sets its three-year profit goal at $1 million dollars or more and determines that G or GP pictures will generate a profit of $20,000 each, while R or X pictures will generate a profit of $50,000 per film.

Historical evidence indicates that every G or GP film will trigger 50 serious complaints from movie-goers. Each R- or X-rated movie will result in 120 major complaints. Therefore, despite the potential profit benefits, the studio decides that at least 20 of the productions must be G or GP rated.

The company's problem is to find the most appropriate combination of film types which will yield the least number of consumer complaints while satisfying the firm's output, profit, and image requirements.

In order to begin solving the problem, we must first state the problem in mathematical form. The studio expects 50 complaints from each G or GP picture and 120 complaints from each R or X picture. We can let G represent G or GP pictures and use R to represent R or X productions. The objective may then be represented by an equation:

$$T = 50G + 120R$$

where

$$T = \text{total complaints}$$

$$50G = \text{total complaints from G or GP films}$$

$$120R = \text{total complaints from R or X films}$$

There are several constraints which limit the degree to which complaints can be minimized: (1) the minimum-profit requirement, (2) the minimum-output requirement, (3) the minimum number of G or GP pictures required to preserve the firm's image, and (4) the requirement that the firm cannot produce a negative number of R or X pictures. These four constraints may be expressed as inequalities:

Profit constraint (thousands of dollars): $20G + 50R \geq 1,000$

Output constraint: $G + R \geq 35$

Image constraint: $G \geq 20$

Non-negative requirement: $R \geq 0$

Thus the problem may be summarized mathematically.

Minimize:

$$T = 50G + 120R$$

Subject to:

(1) $20G + 50R \geq 1,000$

(2) $G + R \geq 35$

(3) $G \geq 20$

(4) $R \geq 0$

Showing G on the vertical axis and R on the horizontal axis, the first three constraints may be plotted on a graph. The straight line of Figure 4–6(A) was developed by alternatively letting G and R equal zero in constraint inequality (1):

when $G = 0$, $50R \geq 1,000$ and $R \geq 20$

when $R = 0$, $20G \geq 1,000$ and $G \geq 50$

Figure 4–6(B) is similarly constructed. The construction of Figure 4–6(C) is obvious.

It is observed that all combinations of G and R which satisfy the "equal to or greater than" ($\geq$) inequalities of this problem fall above all the lines of Figure 4–6. The upward-directed arrows point to the feasible solution area for each constraint.

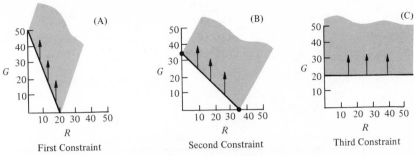

FIGURE 4–6. Plotting of the Individual Constraints for Minimization Problem.

All three constraints are shown in Figure 4–7. Points A, B, and C were obtained by solving simultaneously the equations of the lines that intersect at these points. Point A is obtained by observing that constraint (1) intersects the G axis at $R = 0$, $G = 50$. Point B is obtained by solving $20G + 50R = 1,000$ and $G + R = 35$ simultaneously. Point C is obtained by solving $G + R = 35$ and $G = 20$ simultaneously.

To determine whether point A, B, or C yields the minimum number of complaints, we plug in the R and G values at each point into the objective function ($T = 50G + 120R$) to see which set of values minimizes T:

Point A (0, 50): $T = 50(50) + 120(0) = 2,500$

Point B (10, 25): $T = 50(25) + 120(10) = 2,450$

Point C (15, 20): $T = 50(20) + 120(15) = 2,800$

Since complaints are minimized at point B, this point represents the optimal solution. Therefore, the studio should produce 10 R or X films and 25 G or GP films. We may test the fulfillment of the various constraints by plugging these values into the constraint inequalities:

Profit constraint: $20(25) + 50(10) = 1,000$

Output constraint: $25 + 10 = 35$

Image constraint: $G = 25$

Nonnegative requirement: $R = 10$

Thus it can be seen that all constraints are indeed satisfied. The reader should not be confused by the fact that the values for the first two constraints are exactly equal to 1,000 and 35, respectively. This is perfectly acceptable since the inequality states "*equal to or more than.*"

Although the studio is interested in minimizing total complaints, it might be worthwhile for it to consider the effect on total profits of the combinations

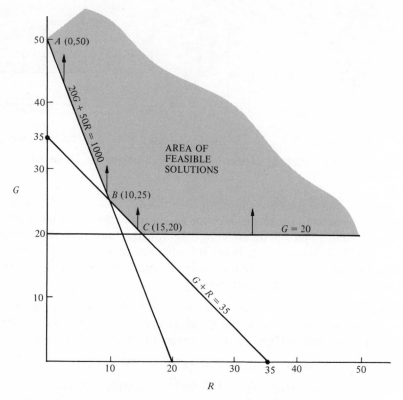

FIGURE 4–7.   Graphing of All Constraints for Minimization Problem.

of G and R at points *A*, *B*, and *C*. The reader will recall that profit was represented by $20G + 50R$. At points *A*, *B*, and *C*, the following profits exist:

$$\text{Point } A: \quad 20(50) + 50(0) \; = 1,000$$

$$\text{Point } B: \quad 20(25) + 50(10) = 1,000$$

$$\text{Point } C: \quad 20(20) + 50(15) = 1,150$$

Thus it can be seen that profit is maximized at point *C*, the combination of G and R that contains the greatest number of complaints (2,800). Since the profit of 1,150 satisfies the profit constraint ($\geq 1,000$), let's see if the other constraints are also satisfied at point *C*:

1. Output constraint ($G + R \geq 35$); at point *C*, $G + R = 20 + 15 = 35$, so this constraint is satisfied.
2. Image constraint ($G \geq 20$); at point *C*, $G = 20$, so the image constraint is also satisfied.

3. Nonnegative requirement $(R \geq 0)$; at point $C, R = 15$, so this constraint
   is fulfilled.

Thus the studio maximizes profit at one combination of G and R (point C)
and minimizes total complaints at another combination (point B).

4.5   Analysis of Trade-offs

Let us examine the trade-offs in moving from these various points—as
we did in the maximization example—in order to conceptually understand
why point B is the least complaint combination. Let us start with point A and
see what happens as we move to point B. At point A, 2,500 complaints are
incurred, based on 50 G films and no R films. In moving to point B, it is
apparent that we are giving up G film units and acquiring R film units. Since
we know that at point B there are 25 G units and 10 R units, this means that
we give up 25 G units and gain 10 R units in moving from point A to B. Since
each G unit generates 50 complaints, there is a decrease of 1,250 complaints
in losing units of G ($25 \times 50 = 1,250$). This decrease of 1,250 complaints is
largely offset by the increase of 1,200 complaints by adding 10 R units
($10 \times 120 = 1,200$). Thus there would be a net decrease of 50 complaints in
moving from point A to point B. In Section 4.4 this difference of 50 complaints
proved to be the rationale for preferring point B to point A.

A similar analysis will show the wisdom of selecting point B over point C.
At point B, there are 25 G units and 10 R units. Thus in moving from C to
B, we gain 5 G units and give up 5 R units. The gained G units cause an increase of 250 complaints ($5 \times 50 = 250$), while the lost R units decrease
complaints by 600 ($5 \times 120 = 600$). The net reduction of complaints in
moving from C to B is 350 ($250 - 600 = -350$). This analysis is also confirmed by observing that point C generates 2,800 complaints while point B
generates only 2,450 complaints.

4.6   Mixed Inequalities

It will be noted that all the inequalities in the minimization problem were
of the equal-to-or-more-than $(\geq)$ variety. Similarly, in the maximization
problem all inequalities (other than the nonnegative constraints) were of the
equal-to-or-less-than type $(\leq)$. In many situations, the set of constraints may
involve both types of inequalities.

We will offer a set of mixed constraint inequalities which are intended
to have no economic significance. In addition, no objective function is
included. The purpose of the graphical exercise is to enable the reader to
determine the area of feasible solutions when the inequalities are mixed.

Assume that a given objective function is subject to the following constraints:

$$(1) \quad 6x + 3y \geq 120$$

$$(2) \quad 6x + 10y \leq 300$$

$$(3) \quad 2x + 5y \geq 100$$

$$(4) \qquad y \geq 10$$

The above three constraints are plotted in Figure 4–8. The arrows pointing upward specify $\geq$ constraints while the downward-pointing arrow designates a $\leq$ constraint.

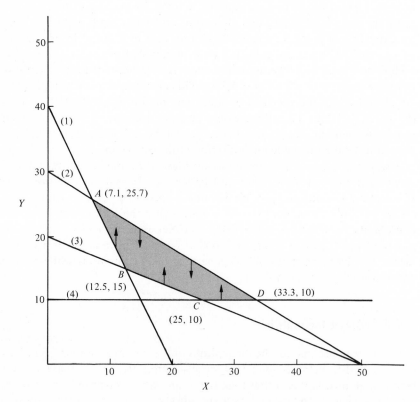

FIGURE 4–8. Graphing of a Set of Mixed Inequalities.

The shaded area in Figure 4–8 indicates the area of feasible solutions. The constraint inequalities used in the determination of points *A*, *B*, *C*, and *D* are

Vertex point	Equations Solved Simultaneously	X	Y
A	(1) and (2)	7.1	25.7
B	(1) and (3)	12.5	15
C	(3) and (4)	25	10
D	(2) and (4)	33.3	10

If an objective function were available, the point of optimal solution could be determined as illustrated by the previous examples.

With this discussion of mixed inequalities, the section on the graphic approach to linear programming is completed. As indicated earlier, although the graphic method is helpful in illustrating some of the basic linear-programming concepts, the simplex algorithm is a much more powerful tool that is capable of solving more complex marketing problems. In order to illustrate the simplex approach, we will present both a maximization and minimization example. Those provided will be those presented in the graphic section so that the reader can concentrate on the methodology involved and not be bogged down with new data.

4.7   Simplex Algorithm: Maximization Problem

In our first discussion of the simplex algorithm, we will provide a maximization example. We will use for an illustration the problem concerning the firm that wanted to determine the optimum combination of sales presentations and advertising insertions that would maximize net profits.

The first step required in the simplex method is to develop the appropriate *slack variables*. Slack variables are required because we are dealing with inequalities. Since the optimum combination of sales presentations and advertising insertions may not use all of the 10,000 man-hours or all of the $40,000 promotional budget available, we need to represent mathematically these unused resources. As a result of expressing these unused resources (slack variables), we will be able to convert the above inequalities to equalities. Let us proceed to do this.

Let us represent any unused man-hours by the symbol U_1. If we add U_1 to the total number of man-hours used by sales presentations and advertising insertions, we will have an expression that accounts for all of the 10,000 man-hours. Since all man-hours are now involved, we can express these relationships by the equation

$$40S + 50A + U_1 = 10,000$$

This equation indicates that the man-hours required for sales presentations plus the hours needed for advertising insertions plus any unused hours are equal to 10,000.

We can also apply the same kind of reasoning to the promotional budget of $40,000. It is quite possible that not all of the $40,000 promotional budget would be utilized at the most profitable combination of sales presentations and advertising insertions. Let us represent any unused promotional dollars as U_2, giving us the following equation:

$$\$200S + \$100A + \$U_2 = \$40,000$$

Thus the promotional dollars utilized by the sales presentations plus those needed by the advertising insertions plus any unused promotional dollars will be equal to $40,000.

In further developing the simplex method, it is necessary to include in each equation any unknown that exists. In terms of the two equations just developed, we must include the slack variable (U_1) found in the equation dealing with the man-hour constraint in the second equation dealing with the promotional budget constraint. Similarly, the slack variable appearing in the promotional-budget-constraint equation (U_2) must also be inserted in the man-hour-constraint equation. Thus we can rewrite these two equations

$$(1) \qquad 40S + 50A + U_1 + \$0U_2 = 10,000$$

$$(2) \quad \$200S + \$100A + 0U_1 + \$U_2 = \$40,000$$

Note that U_2 in equation (1) and U_1 in equation (2) carry coefficients of zero. This is so that the equality relationships in both equations will not be affected.

A final adjustment is required in the profit function before we can begin to work toward the combination of sales presentations and advertising insertions that maximizes total profit. In the original profit function, we need to add terms representing the two slack variables included in the two constraint functions. Since the unused man-hours and promotional dollars have no effect on profit, they will have zero coefficients:

$$P = \$1,000S + \$800A + \$0U_1 + \$0U_2$$

Finally, let us summarize the above in the usual notation for a linear-programming problem before moving to the establishment of an initial solution.

Maximize:

$$P = \$1,000S + \$800A + \$0U_1 + \$0U_2$$

Subject to:

$$40S + 50A + U_1 + \$0U_2 = 10,000$$

$$\$200S + \$100A + 0U_1 + \$U_2 = \$40,000$$

4.8   Developing the Initial Tableau

In order to employ the simplex method, it is necessary to develop an initial tableau. The initial tableau for this example is indicated in Figure 4–9 and is almost entirely developed from the material contained in the problem formulation indicated above. So that the reader will have a fundamental grasp of this initial tableau, we will discuss each segment in some detail.

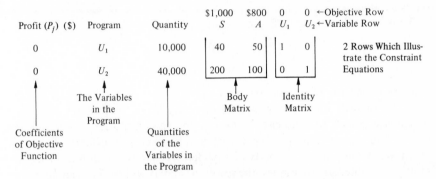

FIGURE 4–9.   Initial Tableau for the Profit-maximization Problem Involving Sales Presentations and Advertising Insertions.

Our first combination of advertising insertions and sales presentations will assume zero quantities of each. The data in the initial tableau reflect this assumption. In the column labeled "profit (P_j)" we list the coefficients of the variables in the first solution. Since the first "solution" involves zero sales presentations and zero advertising insertions, the variables being examined are U_1 and U_2 (the slack variables) and their profit coefficients are zero. The second, or "program" column, lists the letter designation of the variable being examined, in this case the slack variables of U_1 and U_2. The third column ("quantity") indicates the quantity of the variable in the program (10,000 man-hours and \$40,000 promotional budget). Thus the reader should realize that the first three columns are nothing more than an indication of the variables in the program expressed in symbols (U_1, U_2), their per unit contribution to profit $(0, 0)$, and their total quantity available (10,000 and 40,000).

Let us next look at the four rows indicated at the right-hand side of the initial tableau. We will start first with the variable row. This is nothing more than an indication of all the variables that could possibly be utilized in the possible solutions. These, of course, include sales presentations (S), advertising insertions (A), and the slack variables of man-hours (U_1) and promotional budget (U_2). The top row (objective row) indicates the contribution to net profit per unit of the four variables. As we already know, each sales presentation (S) provides \$1,000 to net profit, each advertising insertion (A) \$800, and the slack variables (U_1 and U_2) zero dollars. The 40 and 50 in the third row are the man-hours (U_1) required to utilize one sales presentation and one advertising insertion, respectively. The 200 and 100 in the fourth row refer, of course, to the promotional dollars (U_2) needed for one sales presentation and one advertising insertion, respectively. Collectively, these four coefficients for sales presentations and advertising insertions form a matrix that is called the *body matrix*.

We have said nothing so far concerning the matrix

$$1 \quad 0$$

$$0 \quad 1$$

which is called the *identity matrix* and which is part of the third and fourth rows. An identity matrix is created by inserting 1's in the primary diagonal (northwest corner to southeast corner) of any square matrix (2×2, 3×3, 4×4, and so on) and placing zeros in the other nonprimary diagonal locations. An important property of any identity matrix is that if it is used to multiply another square matrix, the resultant matrix will be the original, non-identity square matrix. The reader can test this property of the identity matrix by multiplying the two matrices below which are, of course, included in the third and fourth rows of our initial tableau:

$$\begin{pmatrix} 40 & 50 \\ 200 & 100 \end{pmatrix} \times \begin{pmatrix} 1 & 0 \\ 0 & 1 \end{pmatrix} = \begin{pmatrix} 40 & 50 \\ 200 & 100 \end{pmatrix}$$

This concept of the identity matrix is a valuable characteristic as far as using the simplex method is concerned. The use of the identity matrix in linear programming will be somewhat clearer in the minimization example to follow.

Before we can proceed to establish an initial solution, two other rows must be added to our initial tableau. These are generally termed the Z_j row and the $P_j - Z_j$ row; they are included in the revised tableau shown in Table 4–2.

TABLE 4–2. Initial Tableau with the Z_j and $P_j - Z_j$ Rows Added

Profit (P_j) (\$)	Program	Quantity	\$1,000 S	\$800 A	0 U_1	0 U_2
0	U_1	10,000	40	50	1	0
0	U_2	40,000	200	100	0	1
	Z_j	\$0	\$0	\$0	\$0	\$0
Net Evaluation Row	$P_j - Z_j$		\$1,000	\$800	\$0	\$0

The Z_j row in the quantity column is used to represent the total profit resulting from the utilization of the particular program. Obviously, in this case the total profit would be zero, since we are employing 10,000 units of U_1 and 40,000 units of U_2. Thus,

$$
\begin{array}{rcccl}
\textit{Quantity} & \times & \textit{Per Unit Profit} & = & \textit{Total Profit} \\
U_1 = 10,000 & \times & 0 & = & 0 \\
U_2 = 40,000 & \times & 0 & = & 0 \\
& & \text{Total profit} & = & \overline{0}
\end{array}
$$

The four values for Z_j that are located in the four variable columns indicate the amounts by which profits would be reduced if one unit of any of the four variables $(S, A, U_1,$ and $U_2)$ were brought into the solution. Thus, if we decided to add one unit of sales presentations (S), the figures in the column under $S \begin{pmatrix} 40 \\ 200 \end{pmatrix}$ indicate that we would have to give up 40 hours of man-hours (U_1) and \$200 of promotional budget (U_2) in order to acquire one sales presentation. In this initial solution where unused man-hours and promotional dollars are considered to be worth nothing, there is no decrease in profit, so

$$U_1 = 40 \text{ man-hours} \times 0 \text{ profit per unit} = 0 \text{ reduction}$$

$$U_2 = 200 \text{ promotional dollars} \times 0 \text{ profit per unit} = 0 \text{ reduction}$$

As we indicated earlier, P_j is the profit added per unit. Since Z_j is the amount by which profit is reduced per unit, it logically follows that $P_j - Z_j$ is the *net addition or subtraction* to net profit if one unit of a variable is added. Thus, the $P_j - Z_j$ row is referred to as the *net evaluation row* in Table 4–2.

Any number in the net evaluation row in a particular column is found by multiplying the elements in the column for the four variables $(U_1, U_2, S,$ and $A)$ by the appropriate values in the P_j column, summing the products, and subtracting this sum (Z_j) from the value indicated at the top of the column. The answer will be $P_j - Z_j$.

Let us illustrate the above concepts by working with the data included in Table 4–2. Let us first calculate the appropriate Z_j's. First, we need to calculate the Z_j value that exists in the quantity column. The reader will recall that this figure represents the total profit resulting from the particular program involved. Since there is a zero profit per unit for U_1 and U_2, total *profit is* also zero:

$$Z_j = \$0(10,000) + \$0(40,000) = \$0$$

Next, let us proceed to determine the Z_j's for the four specific variables (U_1, U_2, S, and A):

$$Z_j \text{ for } U_1 = \$0(1) + \$0(0) = \$0$$

$$Z_j \text{ for } U_2 = \$0(0) + \$0(1) = \$0$$

$$Z_j \text{ for } S = \$0(40) + \$0(200) = \$0$$

$$Z_j \text{ for } A = \$0(50) + \$0(100) = \$0$$

Keeping in mind that Z_j for each variable represents the *profit lost* per unit, let us subtract these Z_j's from each profit per unit in order to determine the figures in the $P_j - Z_j$ row:

Variables	Profit per Unit (P_j)	−	Profit Lost per Unit (Z_j)	=	Net Profit per Unit ($P_j - Z_j$)
U_1	0	−	0	=	0
U_2	0	−	0	=	0
S	1,000	−	0	=	1,000
A	800	−	0	=	800

The reader will recall that these are the figures indicated in the net evaluation row ($P_j - Z_j$ row) in Table 4–2.

The reader will notice that some positive values exist in the net evaluation row (Table 4–2), $1,000 and $800. The signs of the values in the net evaluation row are very crucial in determining whether we can secure a better solution. The rule of thumb for a *maximization problem* is as follows: *As long as there is any positive value in the net evaluation row, a better solution is possible.* Thus, in this example, until all the positive values are eliminated by trying different combinations, a combination of sales presentations and advertising insertions is available that will increase our profit. Since there are positive values in the net evaluation row ($1,000 and $800), we know that there is a better solution. Let us proceed to discover what this is by trying another possibility.

4.9 Developing a Better Solution

The first decision to be made is whether to bring sales presentations (S) or advertising insertions (A) into the solution. The basic rule is to bring in the variable that contributes the greatest profit per unit. This, of course, would be sales presentations since its profit per unit is $1,000, as compared to $800 for advertising insertions and zero for U_1 and U_2.

How many sales presentations can we bring into the solution? This is determined by the constraints. We know that we have 10,000 man-hours and a $40,000 promotional budget. Each sales presentation requires 40 of the available man-hours and $200 of the promotional budget. Dividing 10,000/40 and $40,000/$200 gives us 250 and 200, respectively. Thus the utilization of sales presentations is limited by the availability of promotional budget (U_2). Even though the existence of 10,000 man-hours would allow us to bring in 250 sales presentations (10,000/40 = 250), the fact that there is only enough promotional budget available to accommodate 200 sales presentations ($40,000/$200 = 200) means that we can bring in only 200 sales presentations. To introduce more than 200 sales presentations means that we would violate the $40,000 promotional budget constraint (e.g., 220 × $200 = $44,000).

As a result of this analysis, we can identify a *key column* and a *key row* in the simplex tableau (Table 4–2). The key column is the column in which the greatest contribution per unit of profit occurs; this is the S column since the contribution to profit per unit is $1,000, as opposed to $800 for A and 0 for U_1 and U_2. The key row is the row that yields the lowest value for the variable in the key column; we already know that this is U_2 (promotional budget) since if all the promotional budget were allocated to sales presentations we could utilize 200 units of sales presentations ($40,000/$200 = 200), as opposed to 250 units of sales presentations if all the man-hours were devoted to sales presentations (10,000/40 = 250).

Since the key row and key column will intersect, we can identify a key *intersectional value*. This, of course, will be the value found at the intersection of the key row and the key column and will be valuable in developing an improved solution. The key row, key column, and key intersectional value are indicated in the reproduction of the initial tableau shown in Figure 4–10.

With the delineation of the key row, key column, and key intersectional value, we are now ready to develop a better solution. In so doing, we will be

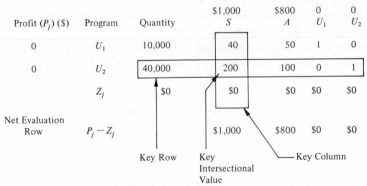

FIGURE 4–10.   Initial Tableau with Key Row, Key Column, and Key Intersectional Value Designated.

replacing U_2 (the key row) with sales presentations (the key column). In other words, we will be replacing the values currently present in the key row with some new values. We determine these new values by dividing each element currently in the key (U_2) row (40,000, 200, 100, 0, 1) by the key intersectional value (200). Thus we would have

$$\frac{40,000}{200} = 200 \qquad \frac{200}{200} = 1 \qquad \frac{100}{200} = \frac{1}{2} \qquad \frac{0}{200} = 0 \qquad \frac{1}{200} = \frac{1}{200}$$

As a result of the above divisions, we can replace the old key-row values with these new values. This has been done below:

Profit P_j ($)	Program	Quantity	$1,000 S	$800 A	0 U_1	0 U_2
0	U_1					
1,000	S	200	1	$\frac{1}{2}$	0	$\frac{1}{200}$

Since we are replacing U_2 (promotional budget) with S (sales presentations), the reader should notice that in the program column we have changed U_2 to S. In addition, we have also indicated in the profit (P_j) column the figure \$1,000 since each unit of sales presentations contributes \$1,000 to net profit. This figure was formerly 0 since U_2, the replaced variable, contributed \$0 to profit per unit.

The reader has undoubtedly noticed that no values in the above partial tableau have been indicated for the U_1 row. Let us now proceed to develop the appropriate values for this row. This will be done in the following manner:

1. Determine the values formerly in the U_1 row. Using Figure 4–10 we can see that these are 10,000, 40, 50, 1, and 0.
2. Determine the value that exists both in the U_1 row and the key column. In Figure 4–10 this, of course, is 40.
3. Multiply the value found in the U_1 row and the key column (40) by the values in the U_2 row which we just determined (200, 1, $\frac{1}{2}$, 0, and $\frac{1}{200}$). This would give us

$$40 \times 200 = 8,000$$

$$40 \times 1 = 40$$

$$40 \times \tfrac{1}{2} = 20$$

$$40 \times 0 = 0$$

$$40 \times \tfrac{1}{200} = \tfrac{1}{5}$$

4. Subtract the values obtained in step 3 (8,000, 40, 20, 0, and $\frac{1}{5}$) from the corresponding values in the U_1 row in Figure 4–10 (10,000, 40, 50, 1 and 0). Thus we have

$$10,000 - 8,000 = 2,000$$

$$40 - 40 = 0$$

$$50 - 20 = 30$$

$$1 - 0 = 1$$

$$0 - \tfrac{1}{5} = -\tfrac{1}{5}$$

5. Place the values obtained in step 4 into the U_1 row. Thus we have

| | | | $1,000 | $800 | 0 | 0 |
Profit P_j ($)	Program	Quantity	S	A	U_1	U_2
0	U_1	2,000	0	30	1	$-\frac{1}{5}$
1,000	S	200	1	$\frac{1}{2}$	0	$\frac{1}{200}$
	Z_j					
Net evaluation row	$P_j - Z_j$					

It is apparent in the above partial tableau that we have not developed any values for the Z_j row and the $P_j - Z_j$ row. Let us now calculate these values.

It will be recalled that the Z_j in the quantity column represents the total profit obtainable from each potential optimum solution. In the second solution developed above, we have brought in 200 units of S (sales presentations) and zero units of A (advertising insertions). Since each sales presentation contributes $1,000 to net profit and each advertising insertion adds $800 to net profit, total profit from this combination is

$$Z_j = \$1,000(200) + \$800(0) = \$200,000$$

The Z_j's for all the variables (S, A, U_1, and U_2) must next be calculated. These are found by multiplying the values (0 and $1,000) found in the profit (P_j) column by the values in the S, A, U_1, and U_2 columns in the partial tableau above. The reader should remember that these resulting figures will indicate the amount of profit lost by introducing one unit of these variables into the solution. Thus we have

$$Z_j \text{ for } S = \$0(0) + \$1,000(1) = \$1,000$$

$$Z_j \text{ for } A = \$0(30) + \$1,000(\tfrac{1}{2}) = \$500$$

$$Z_j \text{ for } U_1 = \$0(1) + \$1,000(0) = \$0$$

$$Z_j \text{ for } U_2 = \$0(-\tfrac{1}{2}) + \$1,000(\tfrac{1}{200}) = \$5$$

Let us place the above Z_j's into our partial tableau:

Profit P_j (\$)	Program	Quantity	$1,000 S	$800 A	0 U_1	0 U_2
0	U_1	2,000	0	30	1	$-\frac{1}{5}$
1,000	S	200	1	$\frac{1}{2}$	0	$\frac{1}{200}$
	Z_j	\$200,000	\$1,000	\$500	\$0	\$5
Net evaluation row	$P_j - Z_j$					

All that now remains is the calculation of the $P_j - Z_j$ row. The reader will recall that this is the difference for each variable of its profit contributed per unit and the amount of profit lost by introducing one unit of the variable into the solution. Thus all we need to do to obtain the $P_j - Z_j$ values for S, A, U_1, and U_2 is to subtract the Z_j values obtained above for S, A, U_1, and U_2 (\$1,000, \$500, \$0, and \$5, respectively) from the net profit per unit contributed by each (\$1,000, \$800, 0, and 0, respectively):

$$\text{For } S, P_j - Z_j = \$1,000 - \$1,000 = \$0$$

$$\text{For } A, P_j - Z_j = \$800 - \$500 = \$300$$

$$\text{For } U_1, P_j - Z_j = \$0 - \$0 = \$0$$

$$\text{For } U_2, P_j - Z_j = \$0 - \$5 = \$-5$$

Thus the $P_j - Z_j$ row values for S, A, U_1, and U_2, respectively, are \$0, \$300, \$0, and \$-5. Let us insert these into the $P_j - Z_j$ row and complete the final tableau dealing with the second potential solution of 200 sales presentations (Table 4–3).

TABLE 4–3. Final Tableau for Second Solution of 200 Sales Presentations

Profit P_j (\$)	Program	Quantity	$1,000 S	$800 A	0 U_1	0 U_2
0	U_1	2,000	0	30	1	$-\frac{1}{5}$
1,000	S	200	1	$\frac{1}{2}$	0	$\frac{1}{200}$
	Z_j	\$200,000	\$1,000	\$500	\$0	\$5
Net evaluation row	$P_j - Z_j$		\$0	\$300	\$0	\$-5

As was indicated earlier, as long as there is a plus value in the $P_j - Z_j$ row, a more optimum solution is possible. Inspection of this row in Table 4–3 indicates that one positive value does remain. This is the \$300 value in the A (advertising-insertion) column. Let us next proceed to develop this improved solution, using the data contained in Table 4–3.

4.10   Developing the Final Solution

In order to develop the improved solution, we use the same procedure that was followed in devising the initial solution of 200 sales presentations. Since a positive value of $300 exists only in the advertising-insertions column, we need to bring advertising insertions into our improved solution. As we did in developing previous solutions, we must first be sure that the number of advertising insertions does not exceed any of the constraints now existing. Table 4–3, the tableau developed from the second solution of 200 sales presentations, indicates that there are now available 2,000 units of U_1 (man-hours) and 200 units of S (the 200 units of sales presentations brought into the second solution). Thus we can see that we will have to give up some of the 200 sales presentations in order to secure some advertising insertions. In the A (advertising-insertion) column, we find a value of 30 in the U_1 row and a value of $\frac{1}{2}$ in the S row. Dividing 2,000 by 30 and 200 by $\frac{1}{2}$ gives us

$$\frac{2,000}{30} = 66\frac{2}{3}$$

$$\frac{200}{\frac{1}{2}} = 400$$

Thus we cannot bring in any more then $66\frac{2}{3}$ advertising insertions because in so doing, the 2,000 units of U_1 (man-hours) would be exceeded. As a result of the U_1 row having the smallest ratio, it now becomes the key row and the A column is, of course, the key column. Both the key row and key column are designated in Figure 4–11, which also includes the key inter-sectional value. The key intersectional value is found, as before, at the intersection of the key row and the key column.

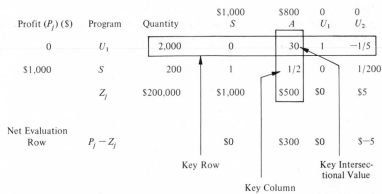

Profit (P_j) ($)	Program	Quantity	$1,000 S	$800 A	0 U_1	0 U_2
0	U_1	2,000	0	30	1	−1/5
$1,000	S	200	1	1/2	0	1/200
	Z_j	$200,000	$1,000	$500	$0	$5
Net Evaluation Row	$P_j - Z_j$		$0	$300	$0	$−5

Key Row   Key Intersectional Value

Key Column

FIGURE 4–11.   Key Row, Key Column, and Key Intersectional Value for the Final Solution.

The reader will recall that in the previous solution we replaced the values in the key row with new values. To do this in Figure 4–11 we divide each element in the key (U_1) row (2,000, 0, 30, 1, and $-\frac{1}{5}$) by the key intersectional value (30). This would give us the following new values:

$$\frac{2,000}{30} = 66\frac{2}{3} \quad \frac{0}{30} = 0 \quad \frac{30}{30} = 1 \quad \frac{1}{30} = \frac{1}{30} \quad \frac{-\frac{1}{5}}{30} = -\frac{1}{150}$$

These values have been inserted into the key row in the partial tableau below. The reader will undoubtedly notice that we have changed the U_1 designation to A because we are in essence replacing U_1 (unused man-hours) with advertising insertions. Also, we need to insert \$800 in the profit (P_j) column since each advertising insertion contributes \$800 to net profit:

Profit P_j (\$)	Program	Quantity	\$1,000 S	\$800 A	0 U_1	0 U_2
800	A	$66\frac{2}{3}$	0	1	$\frac{1}{30}$	$-\frac{1}{150}$
1,000	S					

The S row has no values in it. We need to determine these values by employing the steps indicated earlier for the first improved solution involving 200 sales promotions:

1. Determine the values in the S row that will be replaced. Using Figure 4–11, we can see that these are 200, 1, $\frac{1}{2}$, 0, and $\frac{1}{200}$.
2. Determine the value that exists in the S row and the key column. In Figure 4–11 it can be seen that this value is $\frac{1}{2}$.
3. Multiply the value just indicated as being in the S row and key column ($\frac{1}{2}$) by the values in the A row just determined ($66\frac{2}{3}$, 0, 1, $\frac{1}{30}$, and $-\frac{1}{150}$):

$$\frac{1}{2} \times 66\frac{2}{3} = 33\frac{1}{3}$$

$$\frac{1}{2} \times 0 = 0$$

$$\frac{1}{2} \times 1 = \frac{1}{2}$$

$$\frac{1}{2} \times \frac{1}{30} = \frac{1}{60}$$

$$\frac{1}{2} \times -\frac{1}{150} = -\frac{1}{300}$$

4. Subtract the values obtained in the third step ($33\frac{1}{3}$, 0, $\frac{1}{2}$, $\frac{1}{60}$, and $-\frac{1}{300}$) from the corresponding values currently in the S row in Figure 4–11

(200, 1, $\frac{1}{2}$, 0, and $\frac{1}{200}$). Thus we have

$$200 - 33\tfrac{1}{3} = 166\tfrac{2}{3}$$

$$1 - 0 = 1$$

$$\tfrac{1}{2} - \tfrac{1}{2} = 0$$

$$0 - \tfrac{1}{60} = -\tfrac{1}{60}$$

$$\tfrac{1}{200} - (-\tfrac{1}{300}) = \tfrac{5}{600}$$

5. Insert the values obtained in the fourth step into the S row. Thus we have

Profit P_j ($)	Program	Quantity	$1,000 S	$800 A	0 U_1	0 U_2
800	A	$66\tfrac{2}{3}$	0	1	$\frac{1}{30}$	$-\frac{1}{150}$
1,000	S	$166\tfrac{2}{3}$	1	0	$-\frac{1}{60}$	$\frac{5}{600}$
	Z_j					
Net evaluation row	$P_j - Z_j$					

There are no values in the Z_j and $P_j - Z_j$ rows. These values must next be determined. We want to be particularly aware of the signs in the $P_j - Z_j$ row; if there are no positive signs in this row, we have obtained the optimum combination of sales presentations and advertising insertions. If any of the signs are positive, we must develop another solution that will generate a greater profit.

It will be remembered from the previous example that the Z_j figure in the quantity column refers to the total profit resulting from the potential solution. In the partial tableau above, it can be seen that we are utilizing $66\tfrac{2}{3}$ advertising insertions (A) and $166\tfrac{2}{3}$ sales presentations (S). Since each advertising insertion brings in $800 profit and each sales presentation contributes $1,000 to profit, total profit is

$$Z_j = \$1,000(166\tfrac{2}{3}) + \$800(66\tfrac{2}{3}) = \$166,667 + \$53,333 = \$220,000$$

The Z_j's for all the variables involved in this solution must also be determined. To do this we multiply the values in the profit (P_j) column ($1,000 and $800) by the corresponding values in the S, A, U_1, and U_2 columns

$$Z_j \text{ for } S = \$800(0) + \$1,000(1) = \$1,000$$

$$Z_j \text{ for } A = \$800(1) + \$1,000(0) = \$800$$

$$Z_j \text{ for } U_1 = \$800(\tfrac{1}{30}) + \$1,000(-\tfrac{1}{60}) = \$26\tfrac{2}{3} - \$16\tfrac{2}{3} = \$10$$

$$Z_j \text{ for } U_2 = \$800(-\tfrac{1}{150}) + \$1,000(\tfrac{5}{600}) = -\$5.33 + \$8.33 = \$3$$

Placing the above Z_j values into our tableau gives us

Profit P_j ($)	Program	Quantity	$1,000 S	$800 A	0 U_1	0 U_2
800	A	$66\frac{2}{3}$	0	1	$\frac{1}{30}$	$-\frac{1}{150}$
1000	S	$166\frac{2}{3}$	1	0	$-\frac{1}{60}$	$\frac{5}{600}$
	Z_j	$220,000	$1,000	$800	$10	$3
Net evaluation row	$P_j - Z_j$					

These Z_j's for S, A, U_1, and U_2 indicate the amount of profit that would be lost if one unit of each were introduced into the solution. If these values, respectively ($1,000, $800, $10, and $3.00), are subtracted from the profit per unit contributed respectively by S, A, U_1, and U_2 ($1,000, $800, 0, and 0), we obtain the values for the $P_j - Z_j$ row, which indicates the *net* contribution for each variable:

$$\text{For } S, P_j - Z_j = \$1,000 - \$1,000 = \$0$$

$$\text{For } A, P_j - Z_j = \$800 - \$800 = \$0$$

$$\text{For } U_1, P_j - Z_j = 0 - \$10 = \$-10$$

$$\text{For } U_2, P_j - Z_j = 0 - \$3.00 = \$-3$$

Inserting these $P_j - Z_j$ values, we obtain the completed tableau for the final optimum solution in Table 4–4.

TABLE 4–4. Completed Tableau for the Final Optimum Solution Involving $66\frac{2}{3}$ Advertising Insertions and $166\frac{2}{3}$ Sales Presentations

Profit P_j ($)	Program	Quantity	$1,000 S	$800 A	0 U_1	0 U_2
800	A	$66\frac{2}{3}$	0	1	$\frac{1}{30}$	$-\frac{1}{150}$
1,000	S	$166\frac{2}{3}$	1	0	$-\frac{1}{60}$	$\frac{5}{600}$
	Z_j	$220,000	$1,000	$800	$10	$3
Net evaluation row	$P_j - Z_j$		$0	$0	$-10	$-3

The reader will recall that $66\frac{2}{3}$ advertising insertions and $166\frac{2}{3}$ sales presentations were the optimum combination generated by the graphic method. The fact that this is an optimum combination when the simplex method is employed is indicated by the lack of positive values in the $P_j - Z_j$ row; the values in the $P_j - Z_j$ row for S, A, U_1, and U_2, respectively, are $0, $0, $-10, and $-3.00. There is no better combination; net profit is maximized when we employ $66\frac{2}{3}$ advertising insertions and $166\frac{2}{3}$ sales representations.

Whichever linear-programming approach is used, it is always a good idea to check the supposed optimum combination against the constraints imposed. In this example, we know that we have available 10,000 man-hours and a $40,000 promotional budget, that each of the sales presentations requires 40 man-hours and $200 of promotional budget, and that each of the advertising insertions needs 50 man-hours and $100 of promotional budget. We also know that our optimum combination involves $166\frac{2}{3}$ sales presentations and $66\frac{2}{3}$ advertising insertions. Testing the constraints, we have

$$40S + 50A \leq 10,000$$

$$40(166\tfrac{2}{3}) + 50(66\tfrac{2}{3}) \leq 10,000$$

$$6,666\tfrac{2}{3} + 3,333\tfrac{1}{3} = 10,000$$

$$\$200S + \$100A \leq \$40,000$$

$$\$200(166\tfrac{2}{3}) + \$100(66\tfrac{2}{3}) \leq \$40,000$$

$$\$33,333 + \$6,667 = \$40,000$$

Thus there is no unused capacity. All man-hours and promotional budget dollars are utilized.

4.11   Simplex Method: Minimization Problem

In this section we will introduce the few changes necessary to use the simplex method when minimization of some objective function is involved. Here the concept of the imaginary variables is moderately different. Also the net evaluation row is optimal when no values are negative. Otherwise the two cases are quite similar.

STEP ONE: STATE THE PROBLEM IN ALGEBRAIC FORM.   The reader will recall the movie studio's problem as presented in Section 4.4. The objective function and constraints are repeated: Minimize

$$T = 50G + 120R$$

subject to

(1)   profit constraint: $20G + 50R \geq 1,000$

(2)   output constraint: $G + R \geq 35$

(3)   image constraint: $G \geq 20$

(4)   nonnegative requirement: $R \geq 0$

STEP TWO: INTRODUCE SLACK AND/OR ARTIFICIAL VARIABLES. As in the case of maximization, the constraint inequalities must be stated as equations. Since all the constraints are of the equal-to-or-greater-than ($\geq$) type, a slack variable must be subtracted from the left side inequality. The constraints will then be converted into equations. The first three constraints in equation form are as follows:

$$(1) \quad 20G + 50R - S_1 = 1{,}000$$

$$(2) \quad\quad G + R - S_2 = 35$$

$$(3) \quad\quad\quad G - S_3 = 20$$

The nonnegative requirement may be omitted.

In constraint (1) the purpose of S_1 is to represent the amount of profit in excess of \$1 million. (Remember that the profit constraint is expressed in thousands of dollars.) For example, the graphical solution indicated that at point C, $R = 20$ and $G = 15$. When we plug these values into constraint inequality (1), profits are 1,300 (or \$1,300,000). In this case, slack variables S_1 would assume a value of 300.

Similarly, S_2 represents the number of films produced in excess of 35; S_3 indicates the number of G or GP productions in excess of 20. In essence, each slack variable (S_1, S_2, S_3) takes on whatever value is required to make the equation relationship hold true.

However, at this point a slight complication arises. The reader will recall that in the simplex approach to the maximization problem, the first tableau reflected an assumption of zero advertising and zero sales presentations. The same procedure will be used in attacking the minimization problem. However, when G is zero, the third constraint equation ($G - S_3 = 20$) indicates that $S_3 = -20$. Such a negative solution violates the requirement that the simplex method only considers nonnegative solutions. In fact, the graphical method indicated that all graphing took place in the first quadrant where all variables take on positive values.

Therefore, in order to ensure a nonnegative basic solution at all times, we must insert a second extra variable into the equation. This variable is called an *artificial* variable and will be designated A ($A_1, A_2, \ldots, A_n$). We may think of A_1 as a new hypothetical classification of films which is in addition to the present G and R. However, since A_1 films are imaginary, we would not want such types to appear in the final solution. We therefore assign an abnormally high complaint rate to all A_1 (also $A_2, A_3, \ldots, A_n$ films) pictures, i.e., M (1,000 or more) complaints per film.

It should be clear that the artificial variable has no practical significance. It can be looked at as a technique to get the simplex process started. It will also become apparent that once the slack variables are negative in this problem, an identity matrix cannot be formed without the use of artificial variables.

Since all three constraints are of the $\geq$ variety, an artificial variable must be added to each equation. The final objective function and constraint equations with slack and artificial variables added will appear as follows: Minimize

$$T = 50G + 120R + 0S_1 + 0S_2 + 0S_3 + 1{,}000A_1 + 1{,}000A_2 + 1{,}000A_3$$

subject to

(1) $1{,}000 = 20G + 50R - S_1 + 0S_2 + 0S_3 + 0A_1 + A_2 + 0A_3$

(2) $35 = G + R + 0S_1 - S_2 + 0S_3 + 0A_1 + 0A_2 + A_3$

(3) $20 = G + 0R + 0S_1 + 0S_2 - S_3 + A_1 + 0A_2 + 0A_3$

STEP THREE: CONSTRUCT THE FIRST SIMPLEX TABLEAU. Generally, the simplex tableau used in solving minimization problems is identical to the one used in the maximization case. However, due to the difference in variables, the terminology will be slightly altered. Figure 4–12 provides the framework for the tableau of the movie studio problem.

By setting G, R, S_1, S_2, and S_3 equal to zero and solving for A_1, A_2, and A_3 the initial basic feasible solution to this problem becomes

$$A_1 = 20$$

$$A_2 = 1{,}000$$

$$A_3 = 35$$

The initial tableau (Table 4–5) may now be constructed as in the maximization case. The minor modifications of Figure 4–12 will be included.

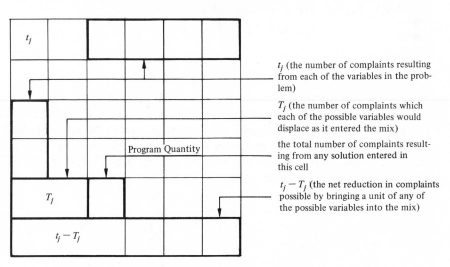

t_j (the number of complaints resulting from each of the variables in the problem)

T_j (the number of complaints which each of the possible variables would displace as it entered the mix)

the total number of complaints resulting from any solution entered in this cell

$t_j - T_j$ (the net reduction in complaints possible by bringing a unit of any of the possible variables into the mix)

Program Quantity

FIGURE 4–12.   Simplex Tableau for the Movie Studio Problem.

TABLE 4–5. Initial Simplex Tableau for Minimization Case

t_j			50	120	0	0	0	M	M	M	
	Program	Q	G	R	S_1	S_2	S_3	A_1	A_2	A_3	
(1) M	A_2	1,000	20	50	−1	0	0	0	1	0	
(2) M	A_3	35	1	1	0	−1	0	0	0	1	
(3) M	A_1	20	1	0	0	0	−1	1	0	0	
	T_j	1,055M	22M	51M	−M	−M	−M	M	M	M	
	$t_j − T_j$		50 − 22M	120 − 51M	M	M	M	0	0	0	

Computations in the T_j row are as follows:

$$1,000M + 35M + 20M = 1,055M$$

$$20M + M + M = 22M$$

$$50M + M + 0M = 51M$$

The remaining columns were similarly calculated, subtracting each value in the T_j row from the corresponding t_j value at the top of the column.

STEP FOUR: IMPROVE THE SOLUTION.   As we observe the $t_j − T_j$ row, we see that the most negative number is $120 − 51M$. Since this number is in the R column, R is the first new variable to be brought into the final solution.

In order to decide which variable is to be replaced, we must divide each number in the quantity column by its corresponding number in the key column (R column). The results are as follows:

row 1: $\frac{1000}{50} = 20$

row 2: $\frac{35}{1} = 35$

row 3: $\frac{20}{0}$ is not defined

Since the lowest quotient is 20, the variable to be replaced is A_2.

At this point we will introduce an alternative procedure for calculating the values in the new tableau. Some students may prefer it to the more popular method demonstrated in the maximization problem. Note that the A_1, A_2, and A_3 columns in combination consists of a 3×3 identity matrix. These columns are conveniently rearranged as

A_2	A_3	A_1
1	0	0
0	1	0
0	0	1

Since R will replace A_2, the R column in the second tableau must be identical to the A_2 column in the first tableau. In other words, the new R column vector must look like this:

R
1
0
0

The rows in all tableaux will be numbered consecutively to facilitate the reader's understanding of this procedure.

In order to generate a *one* at the top of the new R column, the number *50* under R in row 1 must be divided by 50 to yield *one*. Therefore, all numbers in row 1 must be divided by 50. The result of this process will be row 4, which in turn will be the first (R) row of the second simplex tableau. Row 4 will be

	t	Program	Q	G	R	S_1	S_2	S_3	A_1	A_2	A_3
(4)	120	R	20	$\frac{20}{50}$	$\frac{50}{50}$	$-\frac{1}{50}$	$\frac{0}{50}$	$\frac{0}{50}$	$\frac{0}{50}$	$\frac{1}{50}$	$\frac{0}{50}$
					or						
(4)	120	R	20	$\frac{2}{5}$	1	$-\frac{1}{50}$	0	0	0	$\frac{1}{50}$	0

The new A_3 row must supply a zero to the identity matrix. By subtracting the *one* under R in row 4 from the *one* under R in row 2, we get the zero we are looking for. We must then continue to subtract all numbers in row 4 from the corresponding numbers in row 2. The result is now 5:

	t	Program	Q	G	R	S_1	S_2	S_3	A_1	A_2	A_3
(5)	M	A_3	15	$\frac{3}{5}$	0	$\frac{1}{50}$	-1	0	0	$-\frac{1}{50}$	1

Similarly, the new A_1 row must also supply a zero to the identity matrix. If we multiply the *one* under R in row 4 by zero and subtract the result from row 3, we have our required zero. The new row 6 is computed as follows:

	t	Program	Q	G	R	S_1	S_2	S_3	A_1	A_2	A_3
(6)	M	A_1	20	1	0	0	0	-1	1	0	0

When we combine rows 4, 5, and 6 and compute the new T_j and $t_j - T_j$ rows the second tableau is completed as shown in Table 4–6.

TABLE 4-6. Second Simplex Tableau for Minimization Case

t_j	Program	Q	50 G	120 R	0 S_1	0 S_2	0 S_3	M A_1	M A_2	M A_3
(4) 120	R	20	$\frac{2}{5}$	1	$-\frac{1}{50}$	0	0	0	$\frac{1}{50}$	0
(5) M	A_3	15	$\frac{3}{5}$	0	$\frac{1}{50}$	-1	0	0	$-\frac{1}{50}$	1
(6) M	A_1	20	1	0	0	0	-1	1	0	0
	T_j	$2{,}400 + 25M$	$48 + 8/5M$	120	$-\frac{12}{5} + M/50$	$-M$	$-M$	M	$\frac{12}{5} - M/50$	M
	$t_j - T_j$		$2 - 8/5M$	0	$\frac{12}{5} - M/50$	M	M	0	$M - \frac{12}{5} + M/50$	0

156

Computations in the T_j row are as follows:

$$20(120) + 15M + 20M = 2,400 + 35M$$

$$\tfrac{2}{5}(120) + \tfrac{3}{5}M + M = 48 + \tfrac{8}{5}M$$

$$1(120) + 0(M) + 0(M) = 120$$

The reader may confirm the calculations of the balance of the T_j row and the entire $t_j - T_j$ row.

Note that the row vector under R in the second tableau is exactly what we had in mind when we began to construct the second tableau.

The third tableau is constructed by the identical procedure. The most negative value in the $t_j - T_j$ row of the second tableau is $2 - \tfrac{8}{5}M$, so G becomes the new variable. When we divide each value in the *quantity* column by its corresponding value in the G column the results are

$$\text{row 4:} \quad \frac{20}{\tfrac{2}{5}} = 50$$

$$\text{row 5:} \quad \frac{15}{\tfrac{3}{5}} = 25$$

$$\text{row 6:} \quad \frac{20}{1} = 20$$

Therefore, G replaces A_1 and the vector under G in the new tableau must be identical to the vector under A_1 in the second tableau, i.e.,

$$\begin{array}{c} G \\ \hline 0 \\ 0 \\ 1 \end{array}$$

These numbers are "forced" as previously demonstrated and the first three lines of the third tableau along with the computational procedure are given below. Note that row 9 must be developed before rows 7 and 8 can be constructed.

	t	Program	Q	G	R	S_1	S_2	S_3	A_1	A_2	A_3	Method
(7)	120	R	12	0	1	$-\tfrac{1}{50}$	0	$\tfrac{2}{5}$	$-\tfrac{2}{5}$	$\tfrac{1}{50}$	0	row 4 $-\tfrac{2}{5}$ row 9
(8)	M	A_3	3	0	0	$\tfrac{1}{50}$	-1	$\tfrac{3}{5}$	$-\tfrac{3}{5}$	$-\tfrac{1}{50}$	1	row 5 $-\tfrac{3}{5}$ row 9
(9)	50	G	20	1	0	0	0	-1	1	0	0	row 6/1

The completed third tableau is shown in Table 4–7. The reader should verify the calculations of the T_j and $t_j - T_j$ rows.

There are two remaining negative values in the $t_j - T_j$ row. These are $\frac{12}{5} - M/50$ and $2 - \frac{3}{5}M$. The latter is more negative than the former. To doublecheck this, the reader may let $M = 1,000$. Thus S_3 will enter the solution and A_3 will be the replaced variable. The reader should verify this; if any difficulties are encountered, he should review the formation of the previous tableaux.

As indicated by the fourth tableau shown in Table 4–8, the column vector under S_3 is the same as the column vector under A_3. The reader should develop the fourth tableau on his own. However, the methodology is shown in Table 4–8.

Note that the $t_j - T_j$ row contains no negative values. Therefore, the optimal solution has been reached and the fourth tableau is the final tableau. The recommended solution is $R = 10$ and $G = 25$. T_j (total complaints) = 2,450. This concurs exactly with the graphical solution.

4.12   Artificial Variables—Some Final Observations

It is useful to summarize the solutions generated by each of the four tableaux in the minimization problem.

Tableau number	R	G
1	0	0
2	20	0
3	12	20
4	10	25

Observation of Figure 4–7 will reveal that the first three tableaux do not generate feasible solutions. This is unlike the tableaux for the maximization problem, where each iteration (tableau) resulted in a feasible solution. This is due to the presence of artificial variables in the minimization problem. Any time artificial variables are present in the solution, the solution is not feasible (except when the artificial variable has a value of zero). If all artificial variables cannot be removed, no feasible solution can be reached.

4.13   Dual Problem

For a given linear programming problem, the *primal problem*, there exists another, the *dual problem*. The main importance of the relationship between the primal and dual formulation lies in the fact that if one is solved, the solution to the other has been obtained.

The relation between the dual and the primal may be illustrated by writing the coefficients of the film-studio problem in the form shown in Table 4–9.

TABLE 4–7. Third Simplex Tableau for Minimization Case

t_j	Program	Q	50 G	120 R	0 S_1	0 S_2	0 S_3	M A_1	M A_2	M A_3
(7) 120	R	12	0	1	$-\frac{1}{50}$	0	$\frac{2}{5}$	$-\frac{2}{5}$	$\frac{1}{50}$	0
(8) M	A_3	3	0	0	$\frac{1}{50}$	-1	$\frac{3}{5}$	$-\frac{3}{5}$	$-\frac{1}{50}$	1
(9) 50	G	20	1	0	0	0	-1	1	0	0
	T_j	$2{,}440 + 3M$	50	120	$M/50 - \frac{12}{5}$	$-M$	$\frac{3}{5}M - 2$	$2 - \frac{3}{5}M$	$\frac{12}{5} - M/20$	M
	$t_j - T_j$		0	0	$\frac{12}{5} - M/50$	M	$2 - 3/5M$	$8/5M - 2$	$M + M/50 - \frac{12}{5}$	0

TABLE 4–8. Fourth Simplex Tableau for Minimization Case

t_j	Program	Q	50 G	120 R	0 S_1	0 S_2	0 S_3	M A_1	M A_2	M A_3	Method
(10) 120	R	10	0	1	$-\frac{1}{30}$	$\frac{2}{3}$	0	0	$\frac{1}{30}$	$-\frac{2}{3}$	row $7 - \frac{2}{5}$ row 11
(11) 0	S_3	5	0	0	$\frac{1}{30}$	$-\frac{5}{3}$	1	-1	$-\frac{1}{30}$	$\frac{5}{3}$	row $8\frac{3}{5}$
(12) 50	G	25	1	0	$\frac{1}{30}$	$-\frac{5}{3}$	0	0	$-\frac{1}{30}$	$\frac{5}{3}$	row $9 +$ row 11
	T_j	2,450	50	120	$-\frac{7}{3}$	$-\frac{10}{3}$	0	0	$\frac{7}{3}$	$\frac{10}{3}$	
	$t_j - T_j$		0	0	$\frac{7}{3}$	$\frac{10}{3}$	0	M	$M - \frac{7}{3}$	$M - \frac{10}{3}$	

TABLE 4–9. Relationship Between the Primal and the Dual

		G	R	≥	Max
E_1		20	50		1,000
E_2		1	1		35
E_3		1	0		20
	≤				
	min	50	120		

The primal problem is repeated.

Minimize:

$$50G + 120R$$

Subject to:

$$20G + 50R \geq 1,000$$
$$G + R \geq 35$$
$$G \geq 20$$

Table 4–9 allows us to write the objective function of the dual problem and its constraints.

Minimize:

$$1,000E_1 + 35E_2 + 20E_3$$

Subject to:

$$20E_1 + E_2 + E_3 \leq 50$$
$$50E_1 + E_2 \leq 120$$

We shall not attempt to explain the practical significance of the variables E_1, E_2, and E_3 except to say that they represent the measure of the effectiveness of the profit, output, and product mix efforts upon the complaint level. The reader may refer to the final tableau of Table 4–8 and observe that in the $t_j - T_j$ row, $S_1 = \frac{7}{3}$, $S_2 = \frac{10}{3}$, and $S_3 = 0$. S_1, S_2, and S_3 are equivalent to E_1, E_2, and E_3. Similarly, if the dual problem had been solved rather than the primal, the $t_j - T_j$ row would have shown $R = 10$ and $G = 25$.

The point is that the LP problem may be easier to solve through the use of the dual rather than the primal. This is true when in the primal problem, the number of real products is much less than the number of slack variables. One example would be the same film-studio problem involving G and R pictures which are subject to 10 constraints. In such a case, the problem could be best solved by the use of the dual since the first simplex tableau would contain 2 rows rather than 10. The desired solution would appear in the $t_j - T_j$ row rather than in the t_j column.

4.14   Treating the Various Constraint Types

Working with the simplex method is almost an automatic process once the several constraints have been converted from inequalities to equations. We have already worked with inequalities of the $\geq$ and $\leq$ types. A constraint that is already in equation form is another possibility.

For example, suppose one of the constraints to be included in a marketing problem requires that a gasoline distributor handling three types of gasoline must ship exactly 10,000 gallons to a retail outlet. This requirement may be expressed as

$$G_1 + G_2 + G_3 = 10,000$$

where G_1, G_2, and G_3 represent quantities of each gasoline type in gallons. If we follow our previous procedure of letting all real variables equal zero in the initial simplex solution, $G_1 = G_2 = G_3 = 0$, we have an untrue statement, i.e., $0 + 0 + 0 = 10,000$. Therefore, in order to develop a row in the first tableau corresponding to this constraint, we add an artificial variable, A_1. Then when $G_1 = G_2 = G_3 = 0$, $A_1 = 10,000$ and we may proceed with the first tableau. Table 4–10 offers the methodology for handling all types of constraints.

TABLE 4.10. Methodology for Preparing Various Types of Constraints for the Initial Simplex Tableau

Constraint Type	Methodology
$\geq$	Subtract a slack variable and add an artificial variable
$\leq$	Add a slack variable
$=$	Add an artificial variable

For example, assume the following set of mixed constraints:

$$(1) \quad 24x + 10y = 240$$

$$(2) \quad x + y \leq 20$$

$$(3) \quad 7x + 12y \geq 168$$

When the appropriate slack and artificial variables are inserted, these constraints become

$$(1) \quad 24x + 10y + A_1 + 0S_1 + 0S_2 + 0A_2 = 240$$

$$(2) \quad x + y + 0A_1 + S_1 + 0S_2 + 0A_2 = 20$$

$$(3) \quad 7x + 12y + 0A_1 + 0S_2 - S_2 + A_2 = 168$$

The initial simplex tableau may now be constructed.

4.15   Conclusions

This presentation of linear programming as applied to marketing operations has been simplified to facilitate understanding of the basic concepts. And yet sufficient depth was presented so that the value of linear programming in solving marketing problems would be apparent.

In such a brief description it was not possible to describe all the uses of linear programming in marketing. Other books and articles can be consulted by the reader interested in furthering his knowledge of this subject. However, it might be worthwhile to mention two fairly ubiquitous applications of linear programming to marketing. The first of these is in the *transportation problem*. The general format of this type of problem is that we have a number of factories that ship a product to a number of warehouses. Each factory can ship the product to any or all of the warehouses. A specific cost exists in shipping a unit for each combination of factory and warehouse involved. Each factory has a specific amount of the product to ship; each warehouse has a certain capacity that determines a specific number of the product that can be received. The objective is to determine the combination of shipments that will minimize the total transportation charge. The simplex approach to linear programming can be employed to achieve this objective. The second application is the utilization of linear programming, especially the simplex method, in *media mix problems*. Here there might be a number of different advertising media in which an advertisement could be inserted. Each medium would cost the advertiser so much per insertion. Each medium would generate so many exposures per insertion among a readership, including various percentages of demographic characteristics considered important, such as 20 per cent with incomes over $20,000 per year, 15 per cent professional, 10 per cent blacks, and so on. A certain total promotional budget would exist that could not be exceeded. In many cases, management might decide that at least a certain figure should be spent in each medium. The objective is normally to maximize total exposures, within the constraints imposed, the assumption being that there is a positive relationship between exposures and sales.

It should be indicated, however, that linear programming cannot be applied to all marketing problems. One of the basic assumptions of linear programming is, of course, that there is a linear relationship among variables. In the examples presented in this chapter, we assumed constant (linear) prices and costs in generating a profit estimate. The reader undoubtedly realizes that the values of such factors vary with the number produced and are, as a result, curvilinear in nature. The assumption of linear costs and prices required us to employ a constant dollar profit per unit of output. This may, in reality, vary over different ranges of output. Another linearity assumption involved the relationship of units sold to advertising insertions and sales presentations. It was taken for granted that each advertising insertion and sales presentation would result in a constant number of units sold. Such an assumption does not allow for salesmen becoming more adept in making presentations or for advertising insertions becoming less productive due to saturation of the market, and so on. In relaxing the assumption of linearity, however, the analyst is forced to use more powerful techniques.

Perhaps one of the most significant obstacles to utilizing linear programming in marketing is the task of obtaining the data necessary. In our sales presentation–advertising insertion example, we made a number of estimates concerning the profit contributed per unit of sales presentation and advertising insertion, the number of promotional dollars required by each sales presentation and advertising insertion, the number of man-hours needed by each, and the total number of man-hours and promotional dollars available. In practice, the determination of such values may be quite difficult.

Despite the above reservations, linear-programming analysis has, in the past, made valuable contributions to the analysis and solution of marketing problems and will, undoubtedly, continue to do so in the future.

EXERCISES

1. Use the graphic method to solve the following problem.

Maximize:

$$\$10A + \$5B$$

Subject to:

$$5A + 4B \le 60$$
$$2A + 3B \le 30$$
$$4A + 16B \le 80$$

2. Use the graphic method to solve the following problem.

Minimize:

$$\$8X + \$10Y$$

Subject to:

$$3X + 6Y \ge 36$$
$$9X + 3Y \ge 45$$

3. The Optimo Duplicating Equipment Company is considering a direct-mail campaign. Two direct-mail pieces are under consideration. Direct mailer A is a simple triple-fold, three-color mailer which has historically generated 4 per cent returns (4 returns for every 100 pieces mailed). Five per cent of the returns have in the past been converted into sales. This piece will cost the company $20 per thousand and promotes the company's smaller machine. Each order contributes $1,000 to the

company's net profit. Direct mailer *B* is more elaborate and will cost $50 per thousand. It has historically generated 1.5 per cent returns, and 10 per cent of the returns will be converted into sales. Since this mailer features a larger, more expensive product each order will contribute $2,000 to company profits. Since the mailers will be mailed with other mailings to prospective customers, postage costs may be omitted. However, the total cost for this direct-mail campaign must be limited to $500 or less. Owing to the limited number of prospects for each product, no more than 12,000 type-*A* mailers and 6,000 type-*B* mailers are to be mailed. If the firm's objective is to maximize total contribution to net profit, how many mailers of each type should be sent out? Solve by both the graphical and simplex methods.

4. Use the simplex method to solve the following problem.

Maximize:

$$\$2X + \$4Y$$

Subject to:

$$4X + 6Y \leq 24$$
$$3X + 10Y \leq 30$$

5. Use the simplex method to solve the following problem.

Minimize:

$$\$8A + \$6B$$

Subject to:

$$6A + 4B \geq 48$$
$$9A + 3B \geq 45$$
$$3A + 9B \geq 36$$

6. Indicate two examples of marketing decisions that could make use of linear-programming analysis. Do not use any examples given in the chapter.

7. Explain why use of the simplex method enables an optimum solution to be achieved.

8. The following set of constraints is given:

(1)	$X_1 \geq 60$
(2)	$8 \geq X_2 \geq 0$
(3)	$16X_1 + 240X_2 \leq 3,840$
(4)	$4X_1 + 180X_2 \geq 720$
(5)	$X_1 + 4X_2 = 80$

(a) Using the graphical method, determine the feasible solution points.
(b) Prepare the constraints for the initial simplex tableau by inserting the appropriate slack or artificial variables.
(c) Would the dual approach be preferred to the primal?

9. A specialty Christmas gift distributor has the problem of determining the optimal mixture in a cheese basket consisting of two kinds of cheese, Gruyère (G) and imported Swiss (S). Each package of Gruyère cheese costs the distributor 16 cents and each package of Swiss cheese costs him 36 cents. He wishes to minimize the cost of the cheese basket. However, he wants the weight of the total basket (not including wrappings and the basket itself) to be at least 126 ounces and the total volume of the cheeses not more than 780 cubic inches. Furthermore, consumer requirements dictate that the basket include at least six packages of Gruyère. Available data and package requirements are as follows:

	G	S	Entire basket
Weight/package (oz)	6	9	126
Size/package (in.)	60	30	780
Cheese-mix requirements (packages)	6	No requirement	No requirement
Cost/package (cents)	16	36	Minimize

How many packages of each type of cheese should be included in the basket? Work by use of both the graphical and simplex methods. Which tableaux generate feasible solutions to the problem?

10. In Exercise 9, suppose that the distributor requires that the basket must consist of at least 18 or more packages of cheese. What would then be the optimal assortment of cheeses and what would be the effect on costs?

11. A manufacturer of cookies is contemplating a new offering to the market: a combination of vanilla-fudge cookies and lemon creme cookies. Each kind of cookie weighs 2 ounces; each takes up 1 cubic inch. The manufacturer believes that the package must weigh 32 ounces (2 pounds) or more. However, because of a desire to secure maximum shelf facings with retailers, the package cannot contain any more than 48 cubic inches. To secure a balance of offerings, there must be at least six units of each kind in the package. If it costs 2 cents to produce one vanilla-fudge cookie and 1 cent to produce one lemon creme, how many units of vanilla-fudge and lemon creme cookies will enable the manufacturer to minimize total cost? Solve graphically.

REFERENCES

BIERMAN, HAROLD, JR., BONINI, CHARLES P., and HAUSMAN, WARREN H., *Quantitative Analysis for Business Decisions* (Homewood, Ill.: Richard D. Irwin, Inc., 1969).

GASS, SAUL I., *Linear Programming: Methods and Applications* (New York: McGraw-Hill Book Company, 1964).

KING, WILLIAM R., *Quantitative Analysis for Marketing Management* (New York: McGraw-Hill Book Company, 1969).

LEVIN, RICHARD I., and LAMONE, RUDOLPH P., *Linear Programming for Management Decisions* (Homewood, Ill.: Richard D. Irwin, Inc., 1969).

FERRERO DI ROCAFERRERA, GIUSEPPE M., *Introduction to Linear Programming Processes* (Cincinnati: South-Western Publishing Company, 1967).

CHAPTER 5

Optimization and Differential Calculus

5.1 "Why" of Calculus

The numbers studied in algebra may be constants or they may vary (variables), but in any particular problem the numbers remain constant *while a calculation is being made*, i.e., throughout consideration of that particular problem.

There are, however, certain kinds of problems in business and economics in which the quantities involved, or the numbers expressing these quantities, are continually changing.

Many such examples will be cited in this chapter; in fact, such problems form the greater part of those arising in natural phenomena and in business. To perform the calculations involved in such problems and to study the relations of the various factors entering into them, methods other than those of arithmetic or algebra have been developed. The branch of mathematics that treats these methods is called the *calculus*.

But calculus does more than develop methods and rules for solving problems involving changing quantities. It investigates the inner nature of such a quantity, its origin, the parts of which it consists, the greatest and least values that it may have under stated considerations, its relations to other numbers, and sums of very great numbers of very small quantities. In short, calculus deals not only with the use of numbers as does arithmetic and with the symbolism and methodology of writing numbers as does algebra but also and more particularly with the nature and the *variation* of numbers.

This chapter deals with only one segment of calculus—differential calculus. Most applications of differential calculus to marketing arise in *optimization* problems, those in which the decision maker wishes to find the best way of performing a certain operation. For example, among other things, the marketing manager can use differential calculus to determine which combination of inputs will maximize or minimize some company result or objective.

5.2 Nonlinear Functions

We have previously used the mathematical method of linear programming to achieve a desired marketing objective when both the objective function and the constraining functions could be expressed in the form of linear equations and/or inequalities. In previous courses the student has undoubtedly been exposed to the notion of "breakeven analysis," whereby the total revenue (TR) and total cost (TC) have also been expressed by linear graphs and equations. For example, Figure 5–1 is the breakeven chart for the situation where total revenue is defined by the function $TR = f(Q) = \$10Q$ and total cost is defined by the function $TC = 16 + 6Q$, where Q is the quantity of product units produced and sold. The intersection of the two straight-line (linear) graphs is the breakeven point; i.e., $TC = TR$ and profits (π) are exactly zero. The profit function is therefore $\pi = TR - TC = 10Q - (16 + 6Q) = 4Q - 16$. At the breakeven point $\pi = 0$ and $4Q - 16 = 0$. Therefore, $Q = 4$ units at the breakeven point.

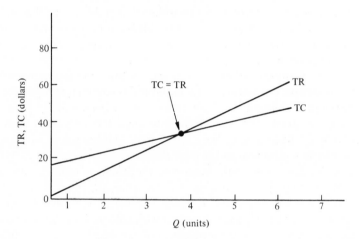

FIGURE 5–1. Breakeven Chart.

There are occasions in the business enterprise when the cost, total revenue, and profit functions are all linear functions of output (Q); however, if the price of a product changes with different levels of output, the revenue and profit functions will not be linear but will instead be curved. Such functions are called *nonlinear* or *curvilinear*. In fact, total costs may also be expressed as a nonlinear function. Figure 5–2 pictures TR, TC, and π as nonlinear functions of Q. Under such circumstances the analysis becomes much more complicated.

5.3 Business Is a Study of Changes

The salient feature of the nonlinear function (in comparison to the linear function) is that the rate at which one of the variables changes relative to the

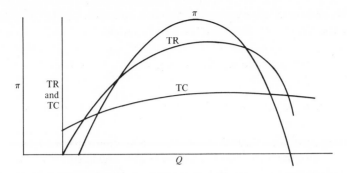

FIGURE 5–2.   TR, TC, and π as Nonlinear Functions of Q.

other variable is not constant. For example, in Figure 5–2, total revenue is a nonlinear function of units produced and sold, i.e., $TR = f(Q)$, where TR is the dependent variable and Q is the independent variable. Normally, the dependent variable will be shown on the vertical axis and the independent variable on the horizontal axis. Note that as the value of Q increases by a constant amount, the value of TR increases up to a maximum and then begins to decrease. The important point is that the differences between successive values of TR diminish in value. For example, suppose that the specific relationship of TR and Q in Figure 5–2 is $TR = 100Q - 10Q^2$. We can now examine some of the points on the total revenue curve and write them in tabular form in Table 5–1.

TABLE 5–1. Tabulation of the Equation
$TR = 100Q - 10Q^2$

Q	TR	ΔQ	ΔTR
0	0		
		1	90
1	90		
		1	70
2	160		
		1	50
3	210		
		1	30
4	240		
		1	10
5	250		
		1	−10
6	240		

By studying Table 5–1, we see that as Q increases by a constant amount (i.e., one unit), TR at first increases by $90, then $70, then $50, then $30, then $10, then decreases by $10, and so on. This is quite a different phenomenon from the behavior of the linear functions of Figure 5–1, where $TR = 10Q$. In the latter case, when $Q = 1$, $TR = 10$; when $Q = 2$, $TR = 20$; when $Q = 3$,

TR = 30, and so on. In other words, for each unit increase in Q, TR increases at a constant rate (i.e., 10 units). We can say then

$$\text{when the relationship is linear, } \frac{\Delta \text{TR}}{\Delta Q} \text{ is constant;}$$

$$\text{when the relationship is nonlinear, } \frac{\Delta \text{TR}}{\Delta Q} \text{ is not constant.}$$

Referring again to Figure 5–1 we see that the linear total cost function is TC = 16 + 6Q. Such an expression assumes the algebraic form $y = b + mx$, where this constant rate of change is given by the slope, m. The given total cost is increasing at the rate of $6 per unit. This is because the firm has fixed costs of $16 and a variable cost of $6 for each unit produced and sold. If, however, the total cost function is nonlinear, say TC = $16 + 6Q^2 + Q/2$, we encounter considerably more difficulty in attempting to measure the rate of change of TC with respect to constant changes in Q. This is because the concept of the *slope* of a curve which is not a straight line is not defined.

As one studies the firm, he continuously studies *changes*: *changes* in sales over time, *changes* in the price of the firm's common stock, *changes* in the firm's cost of capital or the firm's internal rate of return. The observer is concerned with potential *changes* in demand for the firm's product as prices are *changed* or *changes* in dollar sales as advertising expenditures are increased. The marketing manager is always interested in knowing whether a *change* or manipulation of one or more of the variables in the marketing mix will enable his organization to achieve its objectives more easily. The strategy of a firm should be considered only in the light of *how well the implementation of that strategy will affect the rate of change of goal attainment.*

5.4   Tangent to a Curve

Since the changes in a firm are normally related to the variables producing those changes in a nonlinear fashion, it is useful to investigate a method for examining the rate of change of a nonlinear function.

The slope of a straight line is determined by the value of the tangent of the angle that the line makes with the horizontal; as discussed in Section 5.2, the slope (m) measures the constant rate of change of the straight line. The instantaneous rate of change of a nonlinear curve is determined by the introduction of the concept of a *tangent* to a curve. Consider the curve $y = 100x - 10x^2$ (Figure 5–3). Suppose that we were interested in constructing a straight line which touches the curve only at one point P which has the coordinates (x, y). We would connect point P with any other point on the curve, Q, which has the coordinates $(x + h, y + k)$, with a straight line AB. If we then slide point Q along the curve toward point P, line AB will approach

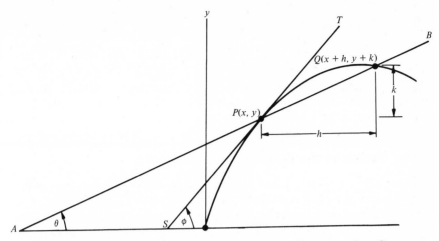

FIGURE   5–3.   Construction   of   the   Tangent   Line   to   the   Curve
$y = 100x - 10x^2$.

position ST. We define the *tangent line* at P to be the position ST which AB
approaches as Q slides toward P. We wish to find $\tan \phi$, i.e., the slope of the
tangent line at P. As AB swings toward ST, angle θ approaches angle ϕ
and h approaches zero. Therefore, $\tan \phi$ can be found by setting up an expression for $\tan \theta$ in terms of h and obtaining the limit of this expression as h
approaches zero.

We proceed as follows: Since Q lies on the given curve, $y = 100x - 10x^2$,
we have

$$y + k = 100(x + h) - 10(x + h)^2$$

$$k = 100(x + h) - 10(x + h)^2 - y$$

$$= 100(x + h) - 10(x + h)^2 - (100x - 10x^2)$$

$$= 100x + 100h - 10(x^2 + 2xh + h^2) - 100x + 10x^2$$

$$= 100x + 100h - 10x^2 - 20xh - 10h^2 - 100x + 10x^2$$

$$= 100h - 20xh - 10h^2$$

$$\frac{k}{h} = 100 - 20x - 10h$$

But $\tan \theta = k/h$. Therefore, $\tan \theta = 100 - 20x - 10h$ and $\tan \phi$ is the limit
which $100 - 20x - 10h$ approaches as h approaches zero. In symbols,[1]

[1] The fraction k/h may present something new in the student's experience as both the nu-
merator and denominator approach zero and yet the fraction approaches a definite limit *not*
zero.

$$\tan \phi = \lim_{h \to 0} \tan \theta = \frac{k}{h}$$

$$= \lim_{h \to 0} (100 - 20x - 10h) = 100 - 20x$$

Therefore, the slope of the tangent line ST to the curve $y = 100x - 10x^2$ at any point is $100 - 20x$. For example at the *particular* point $(4, 240)$, the slope is $100 - 20(4) = 20$.

5.5   Derivative of a Function

The result of the operation of Section 5.4 is called the first *derivative* of the function, and the process of finding the derivative is called *differentiation*. When we have found the derivative of y with respect to x we have found the instantaneous rate of change of the function for any value of x, since that rate of change is measured by the value of the slope of the tangent line to the curve. If the values of a function are given by $y = f(x)$, the corresponding values of the derivative can be written dy/dx. This symbol is indicative of the operation of differentiation in the same way that a plus sign indicates the operation of addition and a minus sign indicates the operation of subtraction.

dy/dx means the derivative of y with respect to x; it is a symbol and does *not* mean dy divided by dx. However, if and when the reader broadens his knowledge of the calculus, he will indeed find that dy means the differential of y and dx means the differential of x, where the differential of a variable may be considered to be an incremental change in the value of a variable. For present purposes dy may then be considered to be an approximation to Δy, and dx may be considered to be an approximation to Δx. Therefore, without subjecting the reader to higher mathematics and at the risk of introducing minor confusion, the derivative may be thought of as a quotient of two differentials.

There are a number of notations to indicate the derivative of y with respect to x. These include y' and $f'(x)$ and of course dy/dx.

For example, in Section 5.5 we determined that the slope of the tangent line to the $y = 100x - 10x^2$ is $100 - 20x$. We may also say that if

$$y = f(x) = 100x - 10x^2$$

then

$$\frac{dy}{dx} = y' = f'(x) = 100 - 20x$$

5.6   Finding Derivatives of Specific Functions

Obviously the method of Section 5.4 would be quite cumbersome and time consuming if it were required every time we wished to find the derivative

of the dependent variable with respect to the independent variable. Therefore, despite the wish of the authors to minimize the memorization of formulas, one differentiation formula will be offered in this section and it should
be memorized. The formula was developed by the use of the procedure of
Section 5.4; however, the derivation of the formula will be omitted.

FORMULA FOR THE DERIVATIVE OF A POWER FUNCTION. If
$y = f(x) = kx^n$, where k is any constant, then

$$\frac{d}{dx}kx^n = nkx^{n-1}$$

Examples

1. $y = 100x; \dfrac{dy}{dx} = 100$

   In terms of the above formula, $k = 100$ and $n = 1$. Therefore,
   $(1)(100)x^{1-1} = 100x^0$. Since any number or variable raised to the zero
   power equals 1, $100x^0 = 100$.

2. $y = -x^2; \dfrac{dy}{dx} = -2x$

   In this case, $k = -1$, $n = 2$. Therefore, $2(-1)x^{2-1} = -2x^1 = -2x$.

3. $y = 13x^3; \dfrac{dy}{dx} = 39x^2$

   In this case, $k = 13$, $n = 3$. Therefore, $3(13)x^{3-1} = 39x^2$.

4. $y = 4x^{-3}; \dfrac{dy}{dx} = -12x^{-4}$

5. $y = \frac{1}{2}x^{-5}; \dfrac{dy}{dx} = -\frac{5}{2}x^{-6}$

6. $y = \dfrac{x}{\sqrt{2}}; \dfrac{dy}{dx} = \dfrac{1}{\sqrt{2}} = \dfrac{\sqrt{2}}{2}$

7. $y = x; \dfrac{dy}{dx} = 1$

   In this case, $k = 1$, $n = 1$. Therefore, $(1)x^{1-1} = x^0 = 1$.

8. $y = 16; \dfrac{dy}{dx} = 0$

   In this case, $k = 16$; $n = 0$. For example, $y = 16$ is the same as $y = 16x^0$.

Therefore, $(0)(16)x^{0-1}$ = zero. The answer is intuitive since by definition of a constant, it does not change. Therefore, the rate of change of any constant with respect to x is zero.

9. $y = \dfrac{16}{\sqrt{x}}; \dfrac{dy}{dx} = \dfrac{-8}{x^{3/2}}$

By algebraic manipulation $16/\sqrt{x}$ is the same as $16/x^{1/2}$ or $16x^{-1/2}$. Therefore, $k = 16$ and $n = -\frac{1}{2}$; $-\frac{1}{2}(16)x^{-1/2-1} = -8x^{-3/2} = -8/x^{3/2}$.

The assortment of examples given indicates the need for converting the algebraic expressions used in problems in this text to the form $y = kx^n$. However, many other differentiation formulas are available for expressions that take other forms. These are available in textbooks covering basic calculus or in books containing mathematical tables.[2]

The derivative of a polynomial function in x is the sum of the derivatives of the terms of the polynomial with respect to x. For example, the function previously discussed in Section 5.4 is a polynomial function, i.e., $y = 100x - 10x^2$. Therefore,

$$\frac{d}{dx}(100x - 10x^2) = \frac{d}{dx}(100x) + \frac{d}{dx}(-10x^2)$$

The solution is $100 - 20x$, as previously discovered when the value of the slope of the tangent line was calculated in Section 5.4.

Examples

1. $y = 32x^2 - x^3; \dfrac{dy}{dx} = 64x - 3x^2$

2. $y = \dfrac{x}{3} + \dfrac{3}{x}; y' = \dfrac{1}{3} - \dfrac{3}{x^2}$

3. $f(x) = \dfrac{24}{\sqrt{x}} - 30 + x; f'(x) = \dfrac{-12}{x^{3/2}} + 1$

5.7   Exercises in Differentiation

For each of the following functions, find the derivative of the dependent variable with respect to the independent variable:

1. $y = 3x^2$
2. $Q = P/4$
3. $R = 16Q^2 - 3Q$

[2] For example, see Samuel M. Selby (ed.), *Standard Mathematical Tables* (Cleveland: Chemical Rubber Company, 1965), pp. 303–306.

4. $y = 90x^{3/2} - 40 + x/\sqrt{x}$

5. $f(x) = x(x + 2)$

6. $y = x + 2/x$

7. $A = \pi r^2$

8. $V = 10$

9. $TC = DS/Q + QpI/2$, where D, S, p, and I are constants

5.8   Business Interpretations of a Derivative

We have previously pointed out that the *derivative* is a general name given to all instantaneous rates. Hence if one wishes the instantaneous rate of change of a function, he finds its derivative. The interpretation given to such a derivative depends upon the kind of quantity represented by the function.

In business and economics it is frequently necessary to make use of the rate of change of one variable with respect to another. For instance, the marginal revenue (MR) is defined as the rate of change of total revenue (TR) with respect to the number of units (Q) sold. Thus if Q is the number of units sold and TR is the total sales dollars generated from selling these Q units, the marginal revenue indicates the rate of increase or decrease of TR with respect to the increase in units sold, Q. Obviously, TR will only decrease with increases in Q if a price decrease preceded the increase in Q. Since when TR $= f(Q)$, the derivative of TR with respect to Q provides a measure of the change of total revenue with respect to sales units, the derivative of TR with respect to Q is equal to the marginal revenue.

This may be expressed

$$MR = \frac{d\text{TR}}{dQ}$$

For example, if we again refer to Table 5–1, we see that TR $= f(Q) = 100Q - 10Q^2$. If we wish to find the marginal revenue when the firm sells three units,

$$MR = \frac{d\text{TR}}{dQ} = 100 - 20Q$$

Substituting $Q = 3$,

$$MR = 100 - 20(3) = \$40$$

However, we see from Table 5–1 that when $Q = 3$, TR $= \$210$ and when Q increases to four units, TR rises to $\$240$. Since marginal revenue traditionally refers to the additional revenue received by selling one unit, and since selling four rather than three units increases total revenue from $\$210$ to $\$240$, it would appear that the marginal revenue is $\$30$, not $\$40$. The confusion arises because dy/dx is only an approximation to $\Delta y/\Delta x$, as discussed in Section 5.5. The fact that the relationship between TR and Q has been expressed as a continuous rather than a discrete function implies that Q is increased by much less than a single unit, say 1/1,000 of a unit. Even though we can hardly sell 1/1,000 of a refrigerator, the marginal revenue at a point implies an instantaneous rate of change that is triggered by an infinitely small change in the independent variable (Q).

Both methods are accepted as being correct. However, since this chapter deals with instantaneous changes and infinitesimal changes we will use the MR $= d$TR$/dQ$ approximation. From a practical point of view, the smallest acceptable change in Q would appropriately be one unit, i.e., one refrigerator, one candy bar, or one grapefruit.

Similarly, marginal cost (MC), mathematically speaking, is the derivative of the total cost function with respect to quantity produced and sold, i.e.,

$$MC = \frac{d\text{TC}}{dQ}$$

Using the same reasoning as before, despite the fact that the smallest change in Q would be one unit, we will consider that dTC$/dQ$ is a sufficiently accurate estimate of ΔTC$/\Delta Q$.

We may now construct the nonlinear revenue and cost curves shown in Figure 5–4. Since profit is the positive difference between total revenue and total cost ($\pi = $ TR $-$ TC, where TR $>$ TC), we may construct vertical TR $-$ TC lines between the two breakeven points A and B. The longest vertical line (the darkest line) represents the maximum profit available and the dashed-line extension of the maximum profit line indicates the quantity of product in units that must be produced and sold (Q_0) to yield maximum profits. If a demand function is available where output is a function of price, $Q = f(p)$, we may quickly calculate the optimal pricing policy to maximize profits.

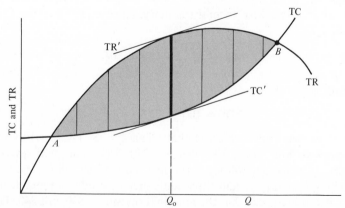

FIGURE 5–4. Total Cost and Total Revenue Functions.

If we observe the construction of tangent lines to the TR and TC curves at the Q_0 output, we see that the tangent lines are parallel; i.e., they have the same slope, thus TR′ = TC′. Since TR′ = MR and TC′ = MC, MR = MC. Therefore, we confirm the traditional economic theory that profit is maximized at the point where marginal revenue equals marginal cost. As we move to the right and left of Q_0 the heights of vertical profit lines decrease and the slopes of tangent lines to the two curves could not be equal. At point Q_0, total revenue has not been maximized nor has total cost been minimized. Both TR and TC have been optimized and π has been maximized.[3]

5.9 Maxima and Minima

A fundamental use of differential calculus in business and economics is as an optimization technique—that of setting the variables of the marketing mix to achieve maximum effectiveness. Maximizing effectiveness could mean maximizing profits, maximizing total revenue, minimizing total costs, or achieving any other predetermined corporate or department goal. For example, suppose that an advertising manager has determined that advertising expenditures, A, and the firm's total profit, π, are related such that

$$\pi = f(A) = 40\sqrt{A} - 2A$$

The advertising manager wants to know the proper level of advertising expenditures required to achieve a maximum level of profit. He could set up a chart as shown in Table 5–2, whereby he could select various arbitrary values of A and calculate corresponding values of π. Next, using the data of Table 5–2, he could construct a smooth continuous curve as shown in Figure 5–5. Since he did not calculate π for every value of A, he has reason to wonder whether a value of A between 81 and 100 or between 100 and 121 would generate a total profit value in excess of 200. Obviously, these additional calculations would be time consuming since the square roots of these additional A values would yield fractional numbers. In fact, the entire procedure of developing Table 5–2 and/or Figure 5–5 makes little sense if the advertising manager understands the use of the derivative. Furthermore, the reader should realize that if the function to be analyzed is considerably longer and more complex than $\pi = 40\sqrt{A} - 2A$, the previous methodology

---

[3] Two important exceptions are the problems of nondifferentiability and limited variable range.

    1. In the presence of kinks or discontinuities, the derivative is not defined.

    2. Although a function may be continuous from the mathematical point of view, it may be discontinuous in the sense that it can assume only discrete values. The concept of continuity refers to the mathematical domain of a function, while real-world discontinuity is a problem of empirical interpretation of the results.

See Walter B. Wentz and Gerald I. Eyrich, *Marketing Theory and Applications* (New York: Harcourt, Brace Jovanovich, Inc., 1970), pp. 66–70 for a parallel treatment of this area.

TABLE 5–2. Finding the Amount of Advertising to
Maximize Total Profit—Trial-and-Error Method

π (Thousands of Dollars)	A (Thousands of Dollars)
0	0
38	1
72	4
128	16
150	25
168	36
182	49
192	64
198	81
200	100
198	121
192	144

could be quite vexing. For example, suppose that $\pi = 18A^2 - 2\sqrt{A} + 3A + A^3/160$. In such a case, the charting and graphing could leave our advertising manager with a king-size headache.

If, however, we refer again to Figure 5–5, we note that if we construct a tangent line to the curve at its maximum point (the point at which π reaches its peak value), the slope of such a tangent line is parallel to the horizontal axis; i.e., the slope of the tangent line is zero. This is analogous to saying that

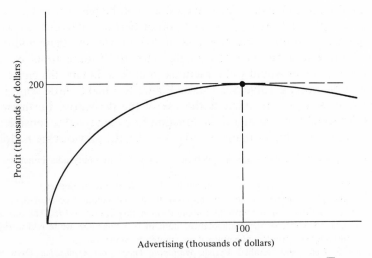

FIGURE 5–5.   Graphic Representation of the Function $\pi = 40\sqrt{A} - 2A$.

at the point where π is maximum, the first derivative is zero. Therefore, our problem seemingly may be solved in less than 2 minutes by use of three simple steps:

1. Find the first derivative of π with respect to A.
2. Set the answer equal to zero.
3. Solve the resultant equation for A.

We proceed accordingly:

Step 1: Find $d\pi/dA$.

$$\pi = 40\sqrt{A} - 2A$$

$$= 40A^{1/2} - 2A$$

$$\frac{d\pi}{dA} = \tfrac{1}{2}(40)(A)^{-1/2} - 2$$

$$= \frac{20}{A^{1/2}} - 2 = \frac{20}{\sqrt{A}} - 2$$

Step 2: Set the derivative equal to zero.

$$\frac{20}{\sqrt{A}} - 2 = 0$$

Step 3: Solve for A.

$$\frac{20}{\sqrt{A}} - 2 = 0$$

$$\frac{20}{\sqrt{A}} = 2$$

$$20 = 2\sqrt{A}$$

$$400 = 4A$$

$$A = 100$$

We may now plug the optimal value of A ($A = 100$) into the original function to determine the maximum value of π:

$$\pi = 40\sqrt{A} - 2A$$

$$= 40\sqrt{100} - 2(100)$$

$$= 400 - 200$$

$$= 200$$

However, inasmuch as our shortened method, using the first derivative, did not require a chart of values or a plotted graph, we may not intuitively determine the shape of the curve and we may not know immediately whether $A = 100$ *maximizes* or *minimizes* π. If we imagine a curve shaped like a coffee cup, the slope of the tangent line constructed at the lowest point of the curve would also be equal to zero. In our present experiment, all we know is that the point $A = 100$, $\pi = 200$, is an extreme point, either a maximum or a minimum.[4] We are not sure which.

We could answer our question with a brief experiment. *If we have located a maximum point*, the slope of the tangent line just preceding the extreme point should be positive while the slope of the tangent line just after the extreme point should be negative. *If we have located a minimum point*, the reverse should be true. (See Figure 5–6).

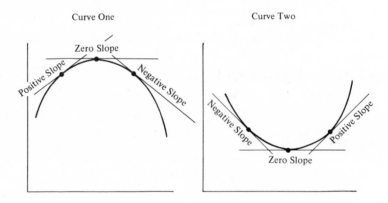

FIGURE 5–6.   Slopes at and Near the Extreme Point.

We have already determined that $d\pi/dA = \dfrac{20}{\sqrt{A}} - 2$. We know that when $A = 100$ the derivative is zero. If we move to a point just preceding the extreme point; i.e., $A = 99$, $dTR/dA = \dfrac{20}{\sqrt{99}} - 2 =$ a positive value. If we now move to a point just following the extreme point, i.e., $A = 101$, $d\pi/dA = \dfrac{20}{\sqrt{101}} - 2 =$ a negative value. Therefore, the derivative assumes a positive value, then a zero value, then a negative value exactly corresponding to curve one in Figure 5–6. Thus we have verified the fact that the extreme point is a maximum point.

---

[4] An inflection point is another possibility.

5.10   Application of the Second Derivative

A simpler approach is by use of the second derivative. Since the first derivative measures the rate of change of y with respect to a change in x—the slope of the tangent line to the curve, the second derivative measures the rate of change of the slope of the tangent line with respect to a change in x. If, then, in the vicinity of the extreme point the slope is becoming more negative (or less positive), the second derivative will be negative and we have a *maximum*. If in the vicinity of the extreme point the second derivative is positive, we have a *minimum*. The commonly used symbols for the second derivative are d^2y/dx^2, $f''(y)$, and y''.

The steps to be used in determining whether the extreme point is a maximum or a minimum are

1. Find the second derivative by differentiating the first derivative with respect to x.
2. Plug the optimizing value of x into the resulting equation.
3. If y'' is positive, we have a *minimum*. If y'' is negative, we have a *maximum*.

To illustrate the method we refer to our advertising example of Section 5.9. We were given the relationship between π and A, i.e.,

$$\pi = 40\sqrt{A} - 2A$$

We found the first derivative of π with respect to A such that

$$\pi' = \frac{20}{\sqrt{A}} - 2$$

We set the first derivative equal to zero and solved for A such that

$$A = 100$$

We may now differentiate the first derivative or find $d(\pi')/dA$, which will in turn yield the second derivative, π'':

$$\pi'' = -10A^{-3/2} = \frac{-10}{A^{3/2}} = \frac{-10}{100^{3/2}}$$

Since, in this example, the second derivative is always a negative value, this means that the slope of the tangent line to the curve in the vicinity of $A = 100$ is becoming more negative, indicating that the extreme point ($A = 100$, $\pi = 200$) is a maximum point (see Figure 5–6, curve one). The reader will note that π'' takes on a negative value for any nonnegative value of A. This may not always be the case.

For example, let's analyze the function of Figure 5–7, whose equation is $y = 3x^2 - x^3$. Differentiating twice with respect to x, we get

$$y' = 6x - 3x^2$$

$$y'' = 6 - 6x$$

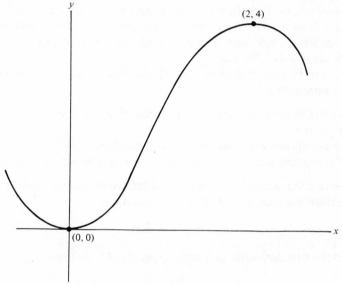

FIGURE 5–7.   Graphic Representation of the Function $y = 3x^2 - x^3$.

Setting the first derivative equal to zero,

$$6x - 3x^2 = 0$$
$$3x(2 - x) = 0$$

$3x = 0$	$2 - x = 0$
$x = 0$	$x = 2$
$y = 0$	$y = 4$

We therefore have two extreme points, i.e., $(0, 0)$ and $(2, 4)$. If we had not drawn Figure 5–7, we could not be sure whether a relative maximum exists at each of the two points, whether a relative minimum exists at each of the two points, or whether a minimum exists at one point and a maximum at the other. (See Figure 5–8 for an example of a graph that has two relative maxima and two relative minima.[5]) However, it would be helpful to analyze

---

[5] By relative maximum or minimum, we mean that the value of the function at a point is greater than or less than the value of the function at any point in the immediate neighborhood of the point where the relative maximum or minimum occurs.

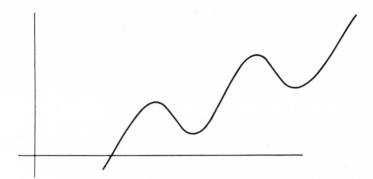

FIGURE 5–8.   Relative Maxima and Minima.

the second derivative, which has been given as $y'' = 6 - 6x$. Considering the first extreme point $(0, 0)$ and plugging $x = 0$ into the expression for y'', we find $y'' = 6 - 6(0) = 6$. Since y'' is positive, point $(0, 0)$ is a *minimum* point. Considering the second extreme point $(2, 4)$, and plugging $x = 2$ into the expression for y'', we find $y'' = 6 - 6(2) = -6$. Since y'' is now negative, point $(2, 4)$ is a *maximum*.

5.11   Points of Inflection

We have investigated the possibilities of both negative and positive values of the second derivative; however, we have failed to consider the case where the second derivative is equal to zero. In such a case the tangent line is not turning in a negative direction or in a positive direction; seemingly, it has stopped turning. For example, the curve $y = x^3$ (Figure 5–9, curve one) has $dy/dx = 3x^2$ and $d^2y/dx^2 = 6x$. If dy/dx is set equal to zero, a critical point is found to exist at $(0, 0)$. Plugging $x = 0$ into $d^2y/dx^2 = 6x$, the second derivative is equal to zero, indicating that the tangent line to the curve at $(0, 0)$ has stopped turning. It will also be noted that at a point immediately to the left of the critical point, say $x = -1$, the tangent line is turning in a negative direction; at a point immediately to the right of the critical point, say $x = 1$, the tangent line is turning in a positive direction. Therefore, $(0, 0)$ is a *point of inflection, inflection point,* or simply an *inflection*. The proof is as follows:

$$\text{when } x = -1, \; y'' = 6x = 6(-1) = -6$$

$$\text{when } x = 1, \; y'' = 6x = 6(1) = 6$$

We may generalize by saying that an inflection point exists when the second derivative changes sign, since the tangent line stops turning one way and

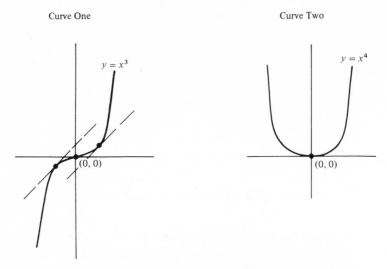

FIGURE 5–9.   Investigation of Inflection Points.

begins to turn the other way. Obviously, then, if the critical point is an inflection point, the second derivative at the point must be equal to zero, *and* the second derivative on either side of the critical point must have opposing signs.

We may now refer back to Figure 5–7, which graphs the function $y = 3x^2 - x^3$. We have already determined that point $x = 0$ is a minimum and point $x = 2$ is a maximum. Let's examine the function for an inflection point. Since one of the necessary conditions for a point of inflection is that y'' is zero, we may set $y'' = 6 - 6x = 0$. Solving for x, we find that y'' is zero when $x = 1$. Thus we *suspect* that the point $x = 1, y = 2$, is an inflection point. In order to test the signs of y'' on each side of $(1, 2)$,

$$\text{when } x = \tfrac{1}{2}, y'' = 6 - 6(\tfrac{1}{2}) = 3$$

$$\text{when } x = \tfrac{3}{2}, y'' = 6 - 6(\tfrac{3}{2}) = -3$$

Therefore, the point $(1, 2)$ is an inflection point.

It is worthwhile to repeat that a second derivative equal to zero is not sufficient to assure the existence of an inflection point. For example, if we differentiate the function $y = x^4$ (see curve two, Figure 5–9),

$$y' = 4x^3 \qquad \text{and} \qquad y'' = 12x^2$$

If y' is set equal to zero, a critical point is found to exist at $(0, 0)$. Plugging $x = 0$ into $y'' = 12x^2$, the second derivative is equal to zero. However, when $x = -1, y'' = 12$; when $x = 1, y'' = 12$. Therefore, since the sign of the second derivative does not change, an inflection point is not present.

Since when $x = -1$, $y' = -4$ and when $x = 1$, $y' = 4$, the extreme point $(0, 0)$ is a minimum. This is true since the tangent line is first negative, then zero, then positive as illustrated by curve two, Figure 5–6.

5.12 Exercises in Maxima, Minima, and Inflection Points

Analyze the following functions for maxima, minima, and inflection points.

1. $y = 2x^2 - 4x + 5$
2. $y = 10x - x^2$
3. $y = 5 - 3x^2 + x^3$
4. $f(x) = 2x - \frac{3}{2}x^2 + \frac{1}{3}x^3$

5.13 Applied Problems in Maxima and Minima

The theory of maximum and minimum values discussed in the preceding sections is of great use in the solution of problems in business and economics that require the determination of maximum or minimum values of a quantity when the quantity is expressible as a function of a single independent variable defined over some interval. The symbols dy/dx and y' (and d^2y/dx^2 and y'') will be used at random; however, the student should remember that y' and y'' indicate differentiation with respect to the independent variable.

Example 1: A wholesale-meat-processing plant has in cold storage 10,000 pounds of beef, which the firm can sell now at 16 cents/pound. It is anticipated that the potential selling price will increase steadily at the rate of 1 cent/week/pound while the beef will lose 100 pounds/week in weight. The fixed overhead storage charges are 60 dollars/week. How long should the beef be held before selling for the greatest profit?

Solution: The variable that we wish to maximize (dependent variable) is profit, π. The variable that is subject to control by the decision maker (independent variable) is time in weeks, n.

With 100 lb/week shrinkage, the total weight in n weeks will be $10,000 - 100n$. The current price is 16 cents and with a 1 cent increase/lb/week, the price per pound in n weeks will be $(16 + n)$ cents/pound. The total revenue (TR) to be received in n weeks will be the total weight times the price per pound, or $(10,000 - 100n)(16 + n)$ cents. The total overhead costs at the end of n weeks will be $60n$ dollars or $6,000n$ cents.

The profit at the end of n weeks will be

$$\pi = \text{TR} - \text{TC}$$

$$= (10,000 - 100n)(16 + n) - 6,000n$$

Multiplying and simplifying,

$$\pi = 160,000 + 2,400n - 100n^2$$

The value of n is to be found which makes π a maximum.
Differentiating,

$$\frac{d\pi}{dn} = 2,400 - 200n$$

and for π to be a maximum $d\pi/dn = 0$,

$$2,400 - 200n = 0$$

$$n = 12$$

is the condition for a maximum value of π. That is, the meat should be held 12 weeks in order to maximize profits.

In order to verify the fact that $n = 12$ yields a *maximum* rather than a minimum value of π, we may find the second derivative:

$$\frac{d^2\pi}{dn^2} = -200$$

Since a negative second derivative is indicative of maximization, the result is confirmed.

Example 2: A burglar-alarm company specializing in high-rise apartment building alarm systems agrees to install a central-station alarm system in a large building for 100 tenants or less at a uniform charge of $20 per apartment. To encourage a large number of tenants to apply, the company agrees to deduct 10 cents from this uniform charge for each tenant for every installation in excess of 100; for example, if they were to install systems in 110 apartments, each system would be priced at $19. For what number of installations would the company generate the highest dollar sales?

Solution: Here the variable to be maximized is dollar sales or total revenue, TR. If exactly 100 installations were made, TR will be $20 \times 100 = \$2,000$. If 101 installations were made, TR will be $\$19.90 \times 101 = \$2,009$. Therefore, it is evident that TR will be maximized at some level in excess of 100 installations, i.e., $(100 + e)$ installations, where e represents the number of installations in excess of 100. Since the installation price decreases by 10 cents per installation in excess of 100, the unit price will be 2,000 cents ($20) minus 10 cents per excess installation, i.e., $p = 2,000 - 10e$.

Since TR will be the product of the unit price and the number of installations,

$$TR = (2,000 - 10e)(100 + e)$$

Multiplying and simplifying,

$$TR = 200,000 + 1,000e - 10e^2$$

The value of e is to be found which makes TR a maximum. Differentiating,

$$TR' = 1,000 - 20e$$

Setting the derivative equal to zero,

$$e = \frac{1,000}{20} = 50$$

Therefore, since e represents the number of installations in excess of 100, the optimal number of installations would be 150.

Since $TR'' = -20$, the existence of a maximum is verified.

Example 3: A brewery is required to construct a rectangular tank with a square base and open at the top with a capacity of 500 cubic feet. What must be its dimensions in order to require the least material?

Solution: In Figure 5–10, let the base of the tank measure a by a square feet; let the height measure b feet. The area of the tank may be expressed as

$$S = a^2 + 4ab$$

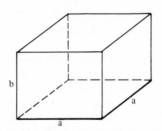

FIGURE 5–10.

However, since S is expressed as a function of both a and b, it would be well to eliminate one variable, either a or b. Since the volume of the tank is to be 500 cubic feet, $V = a^2b = 500$. Therefore, $b = 500/a^2$.

$$S = a^2 + 4a\frac{500}{a^2}$$

$$= a^2 + \frac{2,000}{a}$$

Differentiating and setting the result equal to zero,

$$S' = 2a - \frac{2,000}{a^2} = 0$$

$$2a^3 = 2,000$$

$$a^3 = 1,000$$

$$a = 10$$

Therefore,

$$b = \frac{500}{(10)^2} = 5$$

The optimal dimensions call for a base of 10 ft square and a height of 5 ft. Taking the second derivative,

$$S'' = 2 + \frac{4,000}{a^3}$$

when $a = 10$, $S'' = 2 + 4,000/1,000 = 6$. Since the second derivative is positive, the existence of a minimum is verified.

5.14   Exercises—Applied Problems in Maxima and Minima

1. The Apex Manufacturing Co. was faced with a packaging problem. Postal regulations specify that for a package to be sent by parcel post the sum of its length and girth must not exceed 120 inches. Find the volume of the largest rectangular package with square ends that would come within the above regulations.

2. A large retailer anticipates that he will sell D units of a particular product in 1973. He does not know whether to order his entire annual needs at the beginning of the year or whether he should place n equal orders of Q units each, spaced linearly over the year. Each unit costs him p dollars and there is no quantity discount. It will cost him S dollars to place each order and his inventory carrying cost will be I per cent of his average dollar inventory. He also feels that he will have customer requests for the D units at a linear rate, i.e., $\frac{1}{52}$ of the units will be demanded each week. How many units should he request on each order so as to minimize the total of his inventory ordering costs and carrying costs?

3. During the current football year, season tickets for the home schedule of the Baltimore Colts sell for $42 for the 7 games to be played in Baltimore. All 60,000 seats at Memorial Stadium are sold out. However, owing to rising player salaries, a price increase may be required. A preliminary investigation of fan attitudes indicates that if the price is increased $1 per game next season (a season ticket will then cost $49), the team will lose 4,000 season ticket holders. If club officials may assume that price and attendance are related on a similar linear basis, what price should be charged for season tickets so as to bring in the greatest dollar ticket sales?

4. An intercom-system franchisee is attempting to anticipate his cash requirements prior to signing an agreement with the franchisor. The franchisee will be required to pay a franchise fee of 10 per cent of all cash received. In addition, he will be subjected to the following out-of-pocket cash expenses:

Cost per unit of equipment:	$200
Cost of installation supplies/unit:	$3
Cost of installation labor/unit:	$30
Sales commissions/unit:	$70
Fixed expenses/month:	$200

On each sale, the franchise will take in a $50 cash installation fee and he will receive an $18 monthly rental payment for a 5-year period. The rental payments begin the month following installation of the equipment. Assuming that the franchisee anticipates a constant sales rate of 30 units/month with immediate installation of each unit and no delinquent accounts,

(a) What will be the franchisee's maximum ultimate cash investment and during which month will his investment be maximized?

(b) After how many months will his entire investment be recovered?

(*Hint*: The cumulative cash inflow at the end of t months is the sum of the first t terms of an arithmetic progression.)

5. An aggressive chain retailing Scandinavian furniture in the State of Maryland presently has a 10 per cent share of the market in the state and presently does no advertising. The firm is convinced that its market share will increase 2 per cent for every 1,000 dollars of weekly advertising expenditures. In other words, if the firm spent $10,000 a week in advertising, the firm would acquire 30 per cent of the market for its product line. However, the primary objective of the firm is to maximize weekly profits, and since advertising represents a current cost, profits and advertising costs are related such that $\pi = 600A - 10A^2 - 16$, where π = weekly profit (dollars) and A = advertising expenditures (thousands of dollars). What will be the firm's share of market when profits are maximized? If the firm increases advertising outlays until 100 per cent of the market is achieved, what will be the amount of the firm's profit at that time?

5.15   Optimizing the Price Variable

Of all the controllable variables in the marketing mix, the determination of the optimal product price has received the most attention from economists and governmental policy makers. However, it is to be emphasized that the *price variable* is only one of a number of internal and external stimulators that affect the demand for a firm's product. When we say that the number of product units to be sold by a firm is a function of the product's price $[Q = f(p)]$, we omit the fact that demand is also a function of the price of substitute products, consumer tastes and income, governmental influences, and the several other internal controllable variables such as product quality, channel design, advertising expenditures, the personal selling program, and so on.

In economic theory, profit maximization is normally thought to be the goal of the company's price setter. Although such an assumption is an over-simplification of industry practice, the resultant model affords the student an opportunity to apply the differential calculus to develop an elegant solution for optimum price. In this model, we assume a profit-maximizing firm which knows the demand and cost functions of the product for which it seeks to determine a price. The demand function implies that the expected number of units (Q) which will be purchased by consumers in a given time period is a function of the various prices (p) which may be charged for the product. In a subsequent section of this chapter, additional independent variables which influence demand will be employed. However, for the moment we may assume that

$$Q = f(p)$$

To illustrate, presume that the objective is to set a price that will maximize profits of the Todd Adams Company, a producer of electronic coffee-makers for industry. First, consider that all the production and marketing costs can be accurately obtained by the cost-accounting department such that

Fixed costs (FC) = \$10,000

Variable costs/unit (v) = \$40

Next, infer that following an evaluation of all external and internal uncontrollables and based upon a fixed setting of the nonprice variables in the marketing mix, the demand schedule relating price and units sold is shown by columns (1) and (2) of Table 5–3. It may be noted that in this simple example, linearity of the demand (Q) and total cost (TC) functions is proposed. The total cost function will have the form

$$TC = 10,000 + 40Q$$

TABLE 5–3. Demand–Price Relationships—Todd Adams Company

(1) p	(2) Q	(3) TR	(4) TC	(5) π
30	5,000	150,000	210,000	− 60,000
40	4,500	180,000	190,000	− 10,000
50	4,000	200,000	170,000	30,000
60	3,500	210,000	150,000	60,000
70	3,000	210,000	130,000	80,000
80	2,500	200,000	110,000	90,000
90	2,000	180,000	90,000	90,000
100	1,500	150,000	70,000	80,000

The demand equation may be derived as follows:

1. Select any two values of p and the corresponding values of Q, i.e.,

$$p_1 = 50 \qquad Q_1 = 4{,}000$$
$$p_2 = 70 \qquad Q_2 = 3{,}000$$

2. Find the slope (m) of the demand curve

$$m = \frac{p_1 - p_2}{Q_1 - Q_2} = \frac{50 - 70}{4{,}000 - 3{,}000} = -\frac{1}{50}$$

3. Using the m value found in step 2, any point (Q, p) may be substituted for point (Q_2, p_2) such that

$$-\frac{1}{50} = \frac{50 - p}{4{,}000 - Q}$$

4. The above equation may be solved for Q:

$$-4{,}000 + Q = 2{,}500 - 50p$$
$$Q = 6{,}500 - 50P$$

5. Transforming the above equation and solving for p,

$$p = 130 - \frac{Q}{50}$$

Since $TR = PQ$,

$$TR = \left(130 - \frac{Q}{50}\right)Q$$

$$= 130Q - \frac{Q^2}{50}$$

Since $\pi = TR - TC$,

$$\pi = 130Q - \frac{Q^2}{50} - 10{,}000 - 40Q$$

$$= 90Q - \frac{Q^2}{50} - 10{,}000$$

Differentiating π with respect to Q,

$$\pi' = 90 - \frac{Q}{25}$$

Setting $\pi' = 0$ and solving for Q,

$$90 - \frac{Q}{25} = 0$$

$$Q = 2{,}250$$

Therefore,

$$p = 130 - \frac{2{,}250}{50} = \$85$$

Since $\pi'' = -\frac{1}{25}$ we are assured that the price of \$85 maximizes profits.

It was indicated in Section 5.7 that the profit of the firm is maximized when marginal revenue equals marginal cost. This method of marginal analysis is precisely equivalent to the previous procedure. To illustrate, let us solve the problem of the Todd Adams Company by a second method.

$$TR = 130Q - \frac{Q^2}{50}$$

$$MR = \frac{dTC}{dQ} = 130 - \frac{Q}{25}$$

$$TC = 10{,}000 + 40Q$$

$$MC = \frac{dTC}{dQ} = 40$$

$$MR = MC$$

$$130 - \frac{Q}{25} = 40$$

$$Q = 2{,}250$$

$$p = \$85$$

Suppose we were interested in determining the appropriate price for maximizing TR:

$$TR = 130Q - \frac{Q^2}{50}$$

$$\frac{dTR}{dQ} = 130 - \frac{Q}{25} = 0$$

$$Q = 3{,}250$$

$$p = 130 - \frac{3{,}250}{50} = \$65$$

Since TR'' is negative, the price of \$65 will *maximize* total revenue.

We may now clarify the behavior of the profit function by investigating the breakeven point(s), i.e., the zero profit point(s). Setting profit equal to zero,

$$\pi = 90Q - \frac{Q^2}{50} - 10,000 = 0$$

$$4,500Q - Q^2 - 500,000 = 0$$

$$Q^2 - 4,500Q + 500,000 = 0$$

The roots of the above general quadratic equation[6] are

$$Q = 4,386 \text{ and } 114$$

The existence of these two breakeven points means that there is a profit range that surrounds the point of maximum profit.

Figure 5–11 explicitly shows the graphical relationships between quantity produced and sold (Q) and the values of profit (π), total revenue (TR), and total cost (TC). Implicitly, π, TR, and TC are shown as functions of the product price. The student should study Figure 5–11 quite carefully to reinforce the results that have been developed by the use of the calculus and other mathematical procedures.

The center curve indicates that the maximum total TR of $211,250 will be developed at a sales output of 3,250 units (when price is $65 per unit). This result is obtained when the maximizing value of $Q = 3,250$ is plugged into the TR equation:

$$\text{TR} = 130Q - \frac{Q^2}{50}$$

Since line AB in the center diagram of Figure 5–11 is the longest vertical line that can be constructed between the TR curve and the TC curve, the value of Q that corresponds to this point ($Q = 2,250$) and its associated price ($p = \$85$) defines the profit-maximizing strategy.

This is confirmed by the bottom curve, which shows the maximum profit of $111,250 at the point where $Q = 2,250$. This value of profit is obtained when $Q = 2,250$ is plugged into the π equation:

$$\pi = 90Q - \frac{Q^2}{50} - 10,000$$

---

[6] The quickest method of solving $Q^2 - 4,500Q + 500,000 = 0$ is by use of the quadratic formula. In this case,

$$Q = \frac{-b \pm \sqrt{b^2 - 4ac}}{2a}$$

where $a = 1, b = -4,500, c = 500,000$.

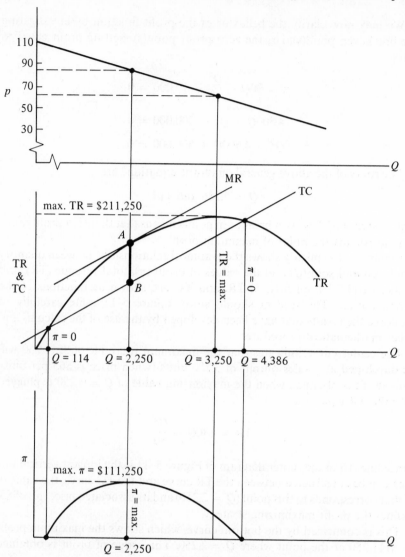

FIGURE 5–11.   Graphical Relationships Among π, TR, TC, and Q.

Finally, the two breakeven points, $Q = 114$ and $Q = 4,386$, are visually indicated by the center and lower curves. The reader will also note that the tangent line constructed to the center curve at point A is parallel to the slope of the TC curve, thereby verifying that profit is maximized when $dTR/dQ = dTC/dQ$ (MR = MC).

5.16   Exercises—Applied Problems in Pricing Strategy

1. The total production and marketing cost functions of several products have been computed. Determine the marginal cost function in each case and explain why the given total cost function would be typical of each product.
   (a) Product A, TC $= 7,000$
   (b) Product B, TC $= .03Q$
   (c) Product C, TC $= 10,000 + \dfrac{Q}{200}$
   (d) Product D, TC $= 7,000 + 6Q + .0008Q^2$
   (e) Product E, TC $= 800,000 + 8,000Q + 2Q^2 + .002Q^3$

2. Determining the equation of a linear function:
   (a) Find the equation of the straight line joining the points $(x = 7, y = 5)$ and $(x = 9, y = 7)$. Is the slope upward or downward? Is the slope negative or positive?
   (b) A firm invests $10 million in a new facility that has a net return of $500,000 per year. An investment of $20 million would yield a net income of $2 million per year. What is the linear relationship between investment and annual income? What would be the annual return on an investment of $15 million?
   (c) Two salesmen, Ted Brown and Art White, observe that their individual annual earnings increase at linear rates. In 1966, Brown earned $7,000 and White earned $9,000. In 1970, Brown earned $11,400 and White earned $12,600. Assuming that the earnings of both men continue to increase at the same rates, during what year will their annual earnings be equal?

3. A firm determines that its cost function is TC $= 2Q^2 + 1,200$. Its product has been selling for $500 per thousand units. How many units must it sell to maximize profits and what is the maximum profit obtainable? (*Note:* Q is given in thousands of units.)

4. The firm mentioned in Exercise 3 assumes that it faces a linear demand curve and raises the price of its product to $550 per thousand units. The firm now sells 100,000 units. Its marketing manager subsequently states that the firm could increase its profits by an additional increase in price. Is he correct?

5. The Robert Nance Corp., after conducting test marketing in several representative areas, determines that its *dollar* sales volume is related to the pricing of its product in accordance with the following relationship:

$$S = 5,000p - 10p^2$$

where

$$S = \text{total sales in } \textit{dollars}$$
$$p = \text{price in dollars}$$

The firm predicts that it will incur fixed costs of $40,000 and variable costs of $100 per unit. Assuming that the optimizing criterion is to be profit maximization, determine the appropriate product price.

6. The Write-Right Ball Point Pen Co., following considerable research, determines that its cost per unit (c) is related to output Q in accordance with the relationship

$$c = \frac{\$1,200}{Q} + \$.10$$

The demand schedule at various volumes is

p (\$)	Q
.30	5,000
.40	4,000
.50	3,000
.60	2,000
.70	1,000

What is the maximum profit available to the firm?

7. A Japanese exporter of high-quality cameras sells 12,000 cameras in the United States, where the duty charged is \$120 per camera. When the duty is increased to \$130 per unit, the exporter sells only 8,000 cameras. What duty rate should the U.S. government charge to realize maximum duty revenue on this item?

5.17   Elasticity and the Demand Function

It was indicated in Section 5.15 that the pricing model previously discussed is based on several highly restrictive assumptions that limit the model's applicability to actual pricing problems, including the following[7] :

1. The firm's objective in setting price is to maximize short-run profits on the particular product. In practice, a company may prefer market penetration or market-skimming objectives. Other commonly used pricing objectives include pricing to achieve a predetermined rate of return on investment or a specific dollar profit value, pricing to achieve a specific market share, pricing to conform with channel margin requirements, pricing to meet or prevent competition, pricing to effect an early recovery of cash outlays, and loss-leader pricing.

2. The only party to consider in price setting is the firm's immediate customer. In the business world, the firm must consider all channel members, the final consumer, competitors, suppliers, government, executives in nonmarketing functional areas, and others.

[7] Much of the material relating to the assumptions of the profit-maximizing pricing model was taken from Philip Kotler, *Marketing Management* (Englewood Cliffs, N.J.: Prentice-Hall, Inc., 1967), pp. 356–369.

3. Demand is a function only of the price variable in the marketing mix but the firm must also consider such controllable variables as channel strategy, branding policy, product policy, and advertising and personal selling decisions.
4. The fixed and variable costs can be estimated with accuracy. Even though cost curves are not easily determined, modern methods of econometrics and cost accounting are somewhat effective for developing cost functions from available data.
5. The demand schedule and the attendant equation equating demand and price can be estimated with accuracy. This is a truly vexing problem and will be discussed later.

The responsiveness of demand to changes in product price is measured by an index called *price elasticity*. For most products, price elasticity of demand is a negative value, since as price is reduced, the number of product units demanded will increase; the reverse is true for price increases. The demand for a product is said to be "price elastic" when its index of elasticity is more negative than -1 (say -2) and "price inelastic" when it is between -1 and zero. Inherent in the definition of price elasticity is the highly theoretical notion that *all external* and *internal controllable* and *incontrollable* variables remain unchanged as the price variable is manipulated.

Mathematically, *price elasticity* is the ratio of the percentage change in product units demanded induced by a percentage change in price. For example, suppose that when an airline raises its fare from $90 to $96 for a Baltimore-to-Chicago Monday morning flight, the number of monthly passengers on that flight drops from 540 to 460.

the mean average number of passengers, Q, is $\dfrac{540 + 460}{2} = 500$

the change in demand, ΔQ is -80

the mean average price, p, is $\dfrac{90 + 96}{2} = \$93$

the change in price, Δp, is $\$6$

Therefore, the percentage change in Q is

$$\frac{\Delta Q}{Q} = \frac{-80}{500}$$

the percentage change in p is $\dfrac{\Delta p}{p} = \dfrac{6}{93}$

Therefore, the price elasticity of demand, e, equals[8]

$$\frac{\%\ \text{change in}\ Q}{\%\ \text{change in}\ p} = \frac{\Delta Q/Q}{\Delta p/p} = -\frac{80/500}{6/93} = -2.5$$

Since -2.5 is more negative than -1, the demand is elastic. We can also view price elasticity in terms of the effect of price manipulation on the firm's total revenue. Continuing with the same example,

$$\text{before the price change:}\quad TR = p_1 Q_1 = \$90 \times 540 = \$48,600$$

$$\text{after the price change:}\quad TR = p_2 Q_2 = \$96 \times 460 = \$44,160$$

Since total revenue dropped with a price increase we have verified an *elastic* (highly sensitive to price change) demand. In chart form,

	and Total Revenue	
When Price Is	Increases	Decreases
Increased	Inelastic	Elastic
Decreased	Elastic	Inelastic

Airline executives, in observing an elastic demand and a resulting decreasing revenue, may conclude that the price increase was an undesirable strategy. On the other hand, a condition of *inelastic* demand suggests that a price increase would generate increased revenue.

In the airline example we computed the elasticity between two separate points on the demand curve. Such a computation is an interval estimate, and the resultant elasticity coefficient is an *arc elasticity*. We have already indicated by use of footnote 8 that the computed value of e depends upon the values of Q and p used. Obviously, then, the coefficient of arc elasticity is an approximation. The farther apart the points between which arc elasticity is calculated, the less meaningful will be the result. If the two points between which arc elasticity is measured are moved closer and closer together, they merge into a single point. *Point elasticity* is simply arc elasticity when the distance between the two points approaches zero. When we are operating at a single point, there is no doubt as to which p and Q to use. We are now dealing with instantaneous changes in Q and p at a point on the demand curve. Therefore, we may use the notion of the differential introduced in Section 5–5, where dp means an instantaneous change in price and dQ means

---

[8] The values of p and Q used in the elasticity formula can be the quantity and price before a change, the quantity and price after a change, or the mean average of the two. The latter is the recommended method.

an instantaneous change in Q. Therefore, in terms of point elasticity,

$$e = \frac{dQ}{Q} \Big/ \frac{dp}{p} = \frac{dQ}{dp} \cdot \frac{p}{Q}$$

Suppose, then, the airline problem is restated in terms of computing the point elasticity of demand when a ticket is priced at $100. We must first derive the demand curve, which is possible since we know two points on a demand curve that is assumed to be linear.

The slope of the demand curve

$$m = \frac{p_1 - p_2}{Q_1 - Q_2} = \frac{90 - 96}{540 - 460} = -\frac{6}{80}$$

Therefore,

$$-\frac{6}{80} = \frac{p_1 - p}{Q_1 - Q} = \frac{90 - p}{540 - Q}$$

$$Q = 1,740 - \frac{80}{6} p$$

Differentiating,

$$\frac{dQ}{dp} = -\frac{80}{6}$$

When $p = \$100$,

$$Q = 1,740 - \frac{80 \times 100}{6} = 406$$

Therefore,

$$e = \frac{dQ}{dp} \cdot \frac{p}{Q} = -\frac{80}{6} \cdot \frac{100}{406} = -3.28$$

When the price is $96,

$$e = \frac{dQ}{dp} \cdot \frac{p}{Q} = -\frac{80}{6} \cdot \frac{96}{460} = -2.78$$

When the price is $90,

$$e = \frac{dQ}{dp} \cdot \frac{p}{Q} = -\frac{80}{6} \cdot \frac{90}{540} = -2.22$$

It may be seen, therefore, as the price decreases from $100 to $96 to $90, the point elasticity moves from -3.28 to -2.78 to -2.22; i.e., demand is becoming less elastic.

In Section 5.15, the Todd Adams Co., after observing its demand schedule and cost equation, found that in order to maximize profits, the firm should price its product at \$85, in which case 2,250 coffeemakers would be sold. In order to maximize total revenue, the firm should set a \$65 price leading to the sale of 3,250 units. The company's cost equation is $TC = 10,000 + 40Q$; the demand function is $Q = 6,500 - 50p$ or $p = 130 - Q/50$. It will be useful to revise Table 5–3 so as to include values for elasticity of demand, marginal revenue, and marginal cost at all points on the demand curve (see Table 5–4). Columns 1, 2, 3, 6, and 8 are extracted from Table 5–3. Column 7 is marginal cost, which is TC' and is \$40 at all levels.

TABLE 5–4. Demand–Price–Revenue–Cost–Elasticity Relationships

(1) p	(2) Q	(3) TR	(4) e	(5) MR	(6) TC	(7) MC	(8) π
30	5,000	150,000	−0.30	−70	210,000	40	−60,000
40	4,500	180,000	−0.45	−50	190,000	40	−10,000
50	4,000	200,000	−0.63	−30	170,000	40	30,000
60	3,500	210,000	−0.85	−10	150,000	40	60,000
70	3,000	210,000	−1.12	10	130,000	40	80,000
80	2,500	200,000	−1.60	30	110,000	40	90,000
90	2,000	180,000	−2.25	50	90,000	40	90,000
100	1,500	150,000	−3.33	70	70,000	40	80,000

Column 4 lists the point elasticity values along the demand curve. As previously discussed, $e = (dQ/dp) \cdot (p/Q)$. In this example, $dQ/dp = -50$. Therefore, when $p = 30$ and $Q = 5,000$, $e = (-50)(30/5,000) = -0.30$. When $p = 40$ and $Q = 4,500$, $e = (-50)(40/4,500) = -0.45$. The remaining values in column 4 are similarly calculated.

The marginal revenue values of column 5 may be calculated by plugging various values of Q into the marginal revenue equation, $MR = 130 - Q/25$. There is also a precise relationship between the elasticity of demand and marginal revenue which serves as a useful tool:[9]

$$TR = pQ$$

$$\frac{dTR}{dQ} = MR = p + Q\frac{dp}{dQ}$$

[9] This follows from the rule for the derivative of a product:

$$\frac{d(uv)}{dx} = u\frac{dv}{dx} + v\frac{du}{dx}$$

where u and v are any differentiable functions of x.

Since

$$e = \frac{dQ}{dp} \cdot \frac{p}{Q}, \qquad \frac{dp}{dQ} = \frac{p}{Qe}$$

By substituting this in the formula for marginal revenue, we get

$$MR = p + \frac{p}{e} = p\left(1 + \frac{1}{e}\right)$$

This is to say that marginal revenue is equal to price times 1 plus the reciprocal of elasticity. We now have a second method for filling in column 5. For example, at a price of \$30, MR = 30[1 + (1/−0.3)] = −70. The remaining values of column 5 are similarly calculated.

By extrapolation, it may be determined that when $p = \$65$, TR is maximized, MR is zero, and $e = -1$. When elasticity equals -1, we have a condition of unitary elasticity.

The foregoing results can be summarized on the linear demand curve of Figure 5–12. As we move down the demand curve (decrease price and increase quantity sold) elasticity of demand is decreasing. Thus TR will be increasing. As we pass point P, elasticity continues to decrease and is on the zero side of -1. After passing point P, TR begins to decrease. It follows that at point P, where elasticity is unitary, TR is maximum.

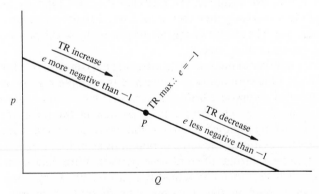

FIGURE 5–12.   Total Revenue and Elasticity of Demand.

5.18   Estimating the Demand Curve

Most elementary texts, including this one, allow the reader to assume that the pricing decision maker is handed a neat demand schedule or linear equation relating demand and price. Unfortunately, the process is not quite that simple. First, the estimation of the demand schedule may be quite complex; second, even after the demand schedule has been estimated, the resultant demand curve is seldom linear.

Hawkins's study in 1957 indicates that at that time, there were few instances of large firms performing demand studies for pricing purposes.[10] Ten years later, another study disclosed that about half of the responding firms performed studies of prices and their effect on sales volume.[11] In both studies, pricing decision makers depended heavily on educated guesses, industry norms for markups, "ballpark" pricing, and various other subjective estimates of demand/price relationships.

The demand for a new or modified product may be estimated by considering the prices of competing substitutes. For example, the price of a labor-saving device could be set in such a way as to make the new product competitive with the total costs (including labor) of the old method of performing the job. The growth of sophisticated industrial cost-accounting systems has permitted this to be done increasingly in practice; however, differences in evaluating the precise value of various substitutes can often cause difficulty in deriving a generalized demand curve for a particular product.[12]

A frequently used but imprecise means of determining price elasticity of demand is through the use of questionnaires and surveys directed to present or potential customers or to sales-force members and other personnel in the firm. One method might be to ask salesmen how many units of a given product they could sell at various prices.[13] Inquiries involving customers take many forms. For example, the Eastman Kodak Company once asked camera-club members whether they would pay $10 for an automatic timer for darkroom use. The answers were not encouraging, so the product was not put on the market at that time.[14]

There are a number of methods of statistical analysis available for deriving demand curves. One commonly used method is a simple regression of price and quantity sold. Suppose a historical series of data such as that shown in Table 5–5 is available. The data can be plotted in the form of a scatter diagram as shown by Figure 5–13. These data may have come from different company territories during the same period of time, or they might have come from the same area during different time periods. With data from different time periods, it is customary to adjust the various prices by some index of the inflationary trend in the economy. The quantity data must also be adjusted to record any increase over time of the buying population. A demand

[10] E. R. Hawkins, "Methods of Estimating Demand," *Journal of Marketing* (April 1957), p. 37.

[11] P. E. Green and D. S. Tull, *Research for Marketing Decisions* (Englewood Cliffs, N.J.: Prentice-Hall, Inc., 1967), pp. 18–19.

[12] Frederick D. Sturdivant *et al.*, *Managerial Analysis in Marketing* (Glenview, Ill.: Scott, Foresman and Company, 1970), pp. 503–504.

[13] *Ibid.*

[14] Hawkins, *op. cit.* pp. 504–505.

TABLE 5–5. Historical Sales Data

Period	Price (constant dollars)	Number of Units Sold (thousands) (adjusted for population changes)
1	21	190
2	33	120
3	26	120
4	13	270
5	18	260
6	17	310
7	21	230
8	27	180
9	38	90
10	32	100

curve might be obtained from the adjusted historical data in Figure 5–13 by sketching a continuous curve to fit the points in the scatter diagram. One objective approach is known as the least-squares regression technique, chosen because it fits a straight line to the points of the scatter diagram so as to minimize the sum of the squared vertical deviations between the points

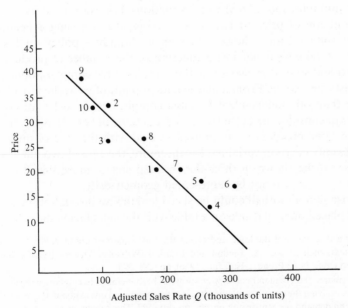

FIGURE 5–13.   Scatter Diagram of Price and Sales Data.

and the fitted line.[15] Some decision makers may prefer a nonlinear curve as an approximation of the demand function. On the other hand, because variables other than price influence unit sales, there are those who prefer multiple regression analysis or experimental approaches to the simple linear regression previously described.[16]

5.19   Exercises in Demand Curves and Elasticity

1. Given the demand curve, $Q = (25 - p)/5$, find
   (a) TR
   (b) e
   (c) marginal revenue

2. In Exercise 1, what is the elasticity of demand when the product is priced at $15?

3. Given the demand function $p = 1,000 - 2Q - 3Q^2$, what is the elasticity of demand when the product is priced at $200?

5.20   Partial Differentiation

In our previous examples of differential calculus, we have assumed that the dependent variable is always a function of *only one* independent variable, that is, $y = f(x)$ or $Q = f(p)$ or $TC = f(Q)$. Such assumptions are unrealistic simplifications of real-world situations. For example, demand is not just a function of price. It is also a function of advertising expenditures, personal selling effort, choice of channels, branding policy, and so on. Similarly, total cost is not just a function of the number of product units produced and sold. It is also a function of sales-force compensation, advertising costs, and so on. From a mathematical point of view, the introduction of more than one independent variable complicates the calculations. This section will consider the optimization of functions of two-decision variables since the same procedure can be used to deal with the case of three, four, five, or twenty decision variables. Furthermore, the case of two independent variables can be shown in three-dimensional space; more than two independent variables cannot be represented geometrically.

Suppose that a football could be sliced lengthwise through its center and one half placed on its flat side on a table with the laces facing the ceiling. Let

---

[15] For a discussion of the logic underlying the least-squares technique, see any standard statistics text, such as John E. Freund and Frank J. Williams, *Modern Business Statistics*, Englewood Cliffs, N.J.: Prentice-Hall Inc., 1966), pp. 288–293.

[16] This material on demand-curve estimation has been included to emphasize the difficulties involved in deriving the equation relating Q and p. For a detailed discussion of the methods used in estimating demand see Sturdivant, *op. cit.*, pp. 498–547. This section was substantially based on this material.

the table be an xy plane with the x dimension running left to right and the y dimension running from the back to front of the table. To determine the rate at which the height of the football (Z) above the table changes with respect to changes in both the length (x) and the width (y) of the football, we can differentiate Z with respect to both x and y. The height of the laces above the xy plane may be represented by $Z = f(x, y)$.

In order to observe the change in Z as a result of changes in x alone, it is necessary to hold y constant. This is accomplished by passing a plane through the football parallel to the xz axis any distance y_1 from the xz plane. The front view of this plane is shown in Figure 5–14. With y fixed at y_1, any change in Z is a result of changes in x only and the slope of the tangent line constructed to the curve of the football slice is

$$\frac{dZ}{dx}.$$

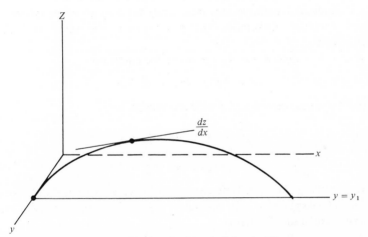

FIGURE 5–14.   Cutting the Football by the Plane $y = y_1$.

The observer may now move to the left side of the table and a plane may now be passed through the football parallel to the yZ axis any distance x_1 from the yZ axis. The variable x is now being held constant and any change in Z will be attributed to a change in y only. As shown in Figure 5–15, we are now observing the football from the left side of the table and dz/dy may be determined.

The process of finding the derivative of Z with respect to x while holding y constant is called *partial differentiation*. The partial derivative of Z with respect to x may be written as $\partial Z/\partial x$ (where ∂ is the lowercase Greek letter *delta*). Similarly, $\partial Z/\partial y$ refers to the partial derivative of Z with respect to

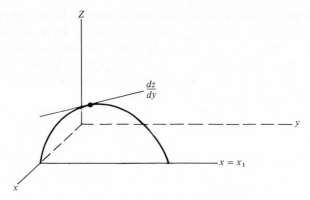

FIGURE 5-15.   Cutting the Football by the Plane $x = x_1$.

y, and in performing this operation, x is automatically held constant. To summarize the process of partial differentiation, we differentiate with respect to one independent variable at a time while holding all other independent variables constant. Otherwise, the procedure is the same as ordinary differentiation.

To illustrate, suppose that we are given the equation

$$Z = 3x^3 - 4xy - y^2 + x$$

To find $\partial Z/\partial x$, y is treated as if it were a constant, i.e.,

$$\frac{\partial Z}{\partial x} = 9x^2 - 4y + 0 + 1$$

$$= 9x^2 - 4y + 1$$

Note that when $-4xy$ was differentiated with respect to x, $4y$ is constant. Therefore, $\partial(-4xy)/\partial x = -4y$. Similarly, $\partial(-y^2)/\partial x = 0$. To find $\partial Z/\partial y$, x is treated as a constant. Therefore,

$$\frac{\partial Z}{\partial y} = 0 - 4x - 2y + 0$$

$$= -4x - 2y$$

The second partial derivatives are obtained as follows. Differentiating $\partial Z/\partial x$ with respect to x (y is constant),

$$\frac{\partial^2 Z}{\partial x^2} = 18x$$

Differentiating $\partial Z/\partial x$ with respect to y (x is constant),

$$\frac{\partial^2 Z}{\partial y\,\partial x} = -4$$

Differentiating $\partial Z / \partial y$ with respect to y (x is constant),

$$\frac{\partial^2 Z}{\partial y^2} = -2$$

Differentiating $\partial z / \partial y$ with respect to x (y is constant),

$$\frac{\partial^2 Z}{\partial x \, \partial y} = -4$$

5.21   Maxima and Minima, Two or More Independent Variables

Suppose that we wish to find the highest point on the half-football described in Section 5.20, i.e., the center point of the laces? By finding the partial derivative of Z with respect to x, holding y constant at y_1 as shown in Figure 5–14 and setting the result equal to zero it is possible to find a maximum for the curve in this direction. Similarly, as shown in Figure 5–15, it is possible to find a maximum for the curve in a perpendicular plane by holding x constant at x_1. Since the planes intersecting the half-football in each direction were arbitrarily selected as $y = y_1$ and $x = x_1$, these planes do not necessarily lead to the extreme point for the entire figure, i.e., the highest point on the football. We are seeking simultaneously the highest point in the x direction and the highest point in the y direction. To find the highest point on the half-football, it must be cut with planes in the x and y directions in such a way that an extreme point in each direction occurs at the same point. Therefore, it seems logical that this point will be at the point of tangency of the football with a plane parallel to the table, i.e., the xy plane.[17]

In general, then, if $Z = f(x, y)$ and if the problem is such that it is evident that a maximum (or a minimum) exists, the conditions $\partial z / \partial x = 0$, $\partial Z / \partial y = 0$ are sufficient to determine the extreme points.[18] The steps to be followed are as follows:

1. $\partial Z / \partial x$. Find the partial derivative of Z with respect to x by differentiating as though y is constant.
2. $\partial Z / \partial y$. Find the partial derivative of Z with respect to y by differentiating as though x is constant.
3. $\partial Z / \partial x = 0$; $\partial Z / \partial y = 0$. Set each partial derivative equal to zero and solve the two resultant equations simultaneously for the values of x and y.

[17] A portion of this geometric explanation was borrowed from A. K. McAdams, *Mathematical Analysis for Management Decisions* (New York: The Macmillan Company, 1970), pp. 116–125.

[18] In general, the conditions $\partial Z / \partial x = 0$ and $\partial Z / \partial y = 0$ are neither necessary nor sufficient to ensure a maximum (or minimum). These conditions are sufficient only in problems in which it is evident that a maximum (or minimum) exists.

4. Perform the second derivative tests as follows using the values of x and y found in step 3.
   (a) $\partial^2 Z/\partial x^2$. Find the second partial derivative of Z with respect to x by differentiating the result of step 1 as though y is constant.
   (b) $\partial^2 Z/\partial y\,\partial x$. Find the second partial derivative of Z with respect to x, then y, by differentiating the result of step 1 as though x is constant. This is called the second cross-partial derivative.
   (c) $\partial^2 Z/\partial y^2$. Find the second partial derivative of Z with respect to y by differentiating the result of step 2 as though x is constant.
   (d) $\partial^2 Z/\partial x\,\partial y$. This step is not necessary since the result will be the same as the result of step 4(b). In other words, $\partial^2 Z/\partial y\,\partial x = \partial^2 Z/\partial x\,\partial y$. However, $\partial^2 Z/\partial x\,\partial y$ is the second partial derivative of Z with respect to y, then x, and is obtained by differentiating the result of step 2 as though y is constant.
   (e) The extreme point is a maximum if

$$\frac{\partial^2 Z}{\partial x^2} < 0; \qquad \frac{\partial^2 Z}{\partial y^2} < 0 \qquad \text{and} \qquad \frac{\partial^2 Z}{\partial x^2}\cdot\frac{\partial^2 Z}{\partial y^2} - \left(\frac{\partial^2 Z}{\partial x\,\partial y}\right)^2 > 0$$

and is a minimum if

$$\frac{\partial^2 Z}{\partial x^2} > 0; \qquad \frac{\partial^2 Z}{\partial y^2} > 0 \qquad \text{and} \qquad \frac{\partial^2 Z}{\partial x^2}\cdot\frac{\partial^2 Z}{\partial y^2} - \left(\frac{\partial^2 Z}{\partial x\,\partial y}\right)^2 > 0$$

To illustrate the previous four steps, we may explore the function given by $Z = -3x^2 - 2y^2 + 68x + 52y - 4xy$. The objective is to determine the function's extreme points.

Step 1: $\dfrac{\partial Z}{\partial x} = -6x + 68 - 4y$

Step 2: $\dfrac{\partial Z}{\partial y} = -4y + 52 - 4x$

Step 3:
$$\begin{aligned}
-6x + 68 - 4y &= 0 \\
-4x + 52 - 4y &= 0 \\
\hline
-2x + 16 \qquad\ \ &= 0 \\
x &= 8 \\
y &= 5
\end{aligned}$$

Step 4: (a) $\dfrac{\partial^2 Z}{\partial x^2} = -6$

(b) $\dfrac{\partial^2 Z}{\partial y\,\partial x} = -4$

(c) $\dfrac{\partial^2 Z}{\partial y^2} = -4$

(d) $\dfrac{\partial^2 Z}{\partial x\, \partial y} = -4$. This step will not be necessary in subsequent

problems. However, it is useful at this stage in assuring the student that

$$\frac{\partial^2 Z}{\partial y\, \partial x} = \frac{\partial^2 Z}{\partial x\, \partial y}$$

(e) Since

$$\frac{\partial^2 Z}{\partial x^2} = -6 < 0$$

and

$$\frac{\partial^2 Z}{\partial y^2} = -4 < 0$$

and

$$\frac{\partial^2 Z}{\partial x^2} \cdot \frac{\partial^2 Z}{\partial y^2} - \left(\frac{\partial^2 Z}{\partial x\, \partial y}\right)^2 = (-6)(-4) - (-4)^2 = 8 > 0$$

when $x = 8$ and $y = 5$, Z reaches a *maximum* value of 402.

$$Z = -3x^2 - 2y^2 + 68x + 5y - 4xy$$

$$= -3(8)^2 - 2(5)^2 + 68(8) + 52(5) - 4(8)(5)$$

$$= 402$$

Therefore, at the point in space $x = 8$, $y = 5$, $Z = 402$, the three-dimensional figure reaches a maximum height.

5.22   Business Applications Using Partial Differentiation

Example 1 : An expanding company has recently developed a new product that has assisted the firm in achieving improved utilization of its production and marketing resources. The firm's total cost of producing and marketing Q_1 units of the new product and Q_2 units of an older product is given by $TC = Q_1{}^2 + 2Q_1 Q_2 + 3Q_2{}^2$. Based on internal and external research, the demand relationships for the two products are

$$Q_1 = 12 - \tfrac{1}{3}P_1$$

$$Q_2 = 8 - \tfrac{1}{5}P_2$$

where p_1 and p_2 are the selling prices of the new and old products, respectively, and the Q values are given in thousands of units.

Determine the appropriate prices to set for each product in order to maximize overall profit for the firm.

Solution: Since TC is expressed in terms of Q_1 and Q_2, we may wish to express total revenue (TR) accordingly. Therefore, it will be appropriate to alter the demand equations so that quantity rather than price is the independent variable:

$$p_1 = 36 - 3Q_1$$

$$p_2 = 40 - 5Q_2$$

Overall total revenue of the firm (TR) may be expressed:

$$\begin{aligned} \text{TR} &= p_1 Q_1 + p_2 Q_2 \\ &= (36 - 3Q_1)Q_1 + (40 - 5Q_2)Q_2 \\ &= 36Q_1 - 3Q_1{}^2 + 40Q_2 - 5Q_2{}^2 \end{aligned}$$

Since profit (π) is TR $-$ TC,

$$\begin{aligned} \pi &= (36Q_1 - 3Q_1{}^2 + 40Q_2 - 5Q_2{}^2) - (Q_1{}^2 + 2Q_1 Q_2 + 3Q_2{}^2) \\ &= 36Q_1 - 4Q_1{}^2 + 40Q_2 - 8Q_2{}^2 - 2Q_1 Q_2 \end{aligned}$$

To find the maximum level of π, the first partial derivatives must be taken and set equal to zero:

$$\frac{\partial \pi}{\partial Q_1} = 36 - 8Q_1 - 2Q_2 = 0$$

$$\frac{\partial \pi}{\partial Q_2} = 40 - 16Q_2 - 2Q_1 = 0$$

Multiplying the second equation by 4 and subtracting,

$$\begin{aligned} -8Q_1 - 2Q_2 + 36 &= 0 \\ -8Q_1 - 64Q_2 + 160 &= 0 \\ \hline 62Q_2 - 124 &= 0 \\ Q_2 &= 2 \\ 36 - 8Q_1 - 2(2) &= 0 \\ Q_1 &= 4 \end{aligned}$$

We may now substitute the calculated values of Q_1 and Q_2 into the modified demand equations:

$$\begin{aligned} p_1 &= 36 - 3Q_1 \\ &= 36 - 3(4) = \$24 \end{aligned}$$

$$p_2 = 40 - 5Q_2$$
$$= 40 - 5(2) = \$30$$

Thus it appears that if the new product is priced at $24 and if the old product is priced at $30, profits will be maximized.

The two straight second partial derivatives are

$$\frac{\partial^2 \pi}{\partial Q_1^2} = -8 \qquad \frac{\partial^2 \pi}{\partial Q_2^2} = -16$$

and both are negative. The second cross-partial derivative is

$$\frac{\partial^2 \pi}{\partial Q_2 \partial Q_1} = -2$$

The step 4(e) condition therefore is met:

$$\frac{\partial^2 \pi}{\partial Q_1^2} \cdot \frac{\partial^2 \pi}{\partial Q_2^2} - \left(\frac{\partial^2 \pi}{\partial Q_1 \partial Q_2} \right)^2$$

$$(-8)(-16) - (-2)^2 = 124$$

The second derivative tests show that the calculated product prices produce profit maximization.

Example 2: The Blaine-Arnold Corp. does no advertising and has fixed production and marketing costs of $190,000 per month plus a variable cost of $10 per unit. Its demand schedule shown in Table 5–6 has already been established. The firm spends $8,100 monthly for advertising in one test market and $40,000 monthly for advertising in a second test market. In each test market the price is varied to study the effect upon demand. The test results are included in Table 5–6. The firm wishes to select a price–advertising combination that will maximize company profits.[19]

Solution: When advertising costs are added to the production and marketing costs the total cost equation becomes

$$TC = 190,000 + 10Q + A$$

The demand function *without* advertising may be derived as follows. The slope (m) of the demand curve may be found by selecting any two known points on the linear curve, i.e., ($p_1 = 40$, $Q_1 = 6,000$) and ($p_2 = 50$, $Q_2 = 5,000$):

$$m = \frac{p_1 - p_2}{Q_1 - Q_2} = \frac{40 - 50}{6,000 - 5,000} = -\frac{1}{100}$$

[19] This problem is a modification of one given by David B. Montgomery and Glen L. Urban, *Management Science in Marketing* (Englewood Cliffs, N.J.: Prentice-Hall, Inc., 1969), pp. 166–170.

TABLE 5-6. Price–Advertising–Demand
Relationships

Price ($)	Advertising ($)	Units Sold
40	0	6,000
50	0	5,000
60	0	4,000
70	0	3,000
40	8,100	6,450
50	8,100	5,450
60	8,100	4,450
70	8,100	3,450
40	40,000	7,000
50	40,000	6,000
60	40,000	5,000
70	40,000	4,000

Therefore,

$$-\frac{1}{100} = \frac{40 - p}{6,000 - Q}$$

$$-6,000 + Q = 4,000 - 100p$$

$$Q = 10,000 - 100p$$

It is noted that with a constant price of $40, the insertion of $8,100 in advertising in the first test market increases units sold from 6,000 to 6,450. With price remaining at $40 the advertising expenditure of $40,000 in the second test market increases sales from 6,000 to 7,000 units. Therefore, $8,100 in advertising generates 450 additional sales; $40,000 in advertising generates 1,000 additional sales. Consequently, the portion of demand generated by advertising, Q_A, is equal to $5\sqrt{A}$. The total demand equation thus becomes

$$Q = 10,000 - 100p + 5\sqrt{A}$$

Solving for p,

$$p = 100 + \frac{\sqrt{A}}{20} - \frac{Q}{100}$$

total revenue (TR) $= pQ$

$$TR = 100Q + \frac{Q\sqrt{A}}{20} - \frac{Q^2}{100}$$

profit (π) = TR − TC

$$\pi = 100Q + \frac{Q\sqrt{A}}{20} - \frac{Q^2}{100} - 190{,}000 - 10Q - A$$

$$= 90Q + \frac{Q\sqrt{A}}{20} - \frac{Q^2}{100} - 190{,}000 - A$$

Differentiating the above equation with respect to Q and A,

$$\frac{\partial \pi}{\partial A} = \frac{Q}{40\sqrt{A}} - 1$$

$$\frac{\partial \pi}{\partial Q} = 90 + \frac{\sqrt{A}}{20} - \frac{Q}{50}$$

Setting the partial derivatives equal to zero and rearranging terms,

(1) $Q - 40\sqrt{A} = 0$

(2) $-\dfrac{Q}{50} + \dfrac{1}{20}\sqrt{A} + 90 = 0$

Multiplying equation (1) by $\frac{1}{50}$, the Q terms are eliminated and

$$A = 14{,}400$$

$$Q = 4{,}800$$

Therefore,

$$p = 100 + \frac{\sqrt{A}}{20} - \frac{Q}{100}$$

$$= 100 + \frac{120}{20} - \frac{4{,}800}{100}$$

$$= \$58$$

Thus a price of \$58 and advertising expenditures of \$14,400 *may* maximize profits. Testing the sufficiency conditions,

$$\frac{\partial^2 \pi}{\partial A^2} = -\frac{1}{80}QA^{-3/2}$$

$$\frac{\partial^2 \pi}{\partial Q^2} = -\frac{1}{50}$$

$$\frac{\partial^2 \pi}{\partial Q\, \partial A} = \frac{1}{40\sqrt{A}}$$

$$\frac{\partial^2 \pi}{\partial A^2} \cdot \frac{\partial^2 \pi}{\partial Q^2} - \left(\frac{\partial^2 \pi}{\partial A\, \partial Q}\right)^2 = -\frac{Q}{80A^{3/2}} \cdot -\frac{1}{50} - \left(\frac{1}{40\sqrt{A}}\right)$$

$$= \frac{-4800}{80(14,400)^{3/2}} \cdot -\frac{1}{50} - \left(\frac{1}{40 \times 120}\right)^2$$

$$= \text{a decimal fraction greater than one}$$

Therefore, the second derivative tests are complete and the calculated price and advertising expenditures are optimal for profit maximization.

5.23   Exercises in Partial Differentiation

1. Find all first and second partial derivatives.
   (a) $y = 5x^2 + 14 + 8Z - 16x - 2xZ + 5Z^2$
   (b) $Z = 5\sqrt{x} + \dfrac{9}{\sqrt{y}}$
   (c) $Z = 3x^2 + 7xy + 2y^2$

2. Investigate each of the following for the existence of maxima or minima:
   (a) $R = 12 + 10A - 16Q + A^2 - 2QA + 2Q^2$
   (b) $\pi = 6QA - Q^3 - A^3 + 10$
   (c) $f(x, y) = 4x^2 + 6y^2 - 12xy + 20x - 18y + 30$

3. An encyclopedia company using a direct-to-home method of distribution finds that an average of 20 customers per month walk into the company's office and purchase a library without a salesman's call. In addition to these voluntary sales, an average of 4 sales per month is acquired by each commissioned door-to-door salesman on a cold canvass basis. When coupon response advertisements are run in the local newspaper, the sales force increases its production by one order for each 10 leads received. However, since some salesmen antagonize consumers who have sent in leads, unit sales are reduced by $M^2L/1,000$ units each month.

$$M = \text{average monthly sales-force size}$$

$$L = \text{average number of leads generated by newspaper ads}$$

The company has average fixed monthly expenses of \$600 and must pay out a commission of \$80 on each order acquired by salesmen. In addition, the firm must pay the newspaper \$10 for each direct response lead. The average price per encyclopedia is \$400. Calculate the optimal average monthly sales-force size and number of leads in order to maximize the monthly profits controllable by the sales department.

4. A small speciality store determines that its total monthly operating costs may be expressed by the equation

$$TC = W^2 - 2W - WR + 2R^2 + 2$$

where W = wages and R = rental in thousands of dollars. Find the amount of each expenditure which leads to the lowest total cost for the store.

5. A promotion-minded firm found that its monthly profits could be represented by the function

$$\pi = -10 - 2A^2 + 16A - 4S^2 + 24S - 4AS$$

where

A = advertising expenditures in thousands of dollars

S = number of sales offices

π = profit in thousands of dollars

What is the maximum profit obtainable by the firm?

6. A manufacturer of industrial transformers has only two customers, A and B. Firm A is located 100 miles due north of Chicago; firm B is located 500 miles due east of Chicago. Where should the manufacturer move its plant if it wishes to minimize the sum of the square of its distance to each customer?

REFERENCES

FOWLER, F. PARKER, and SANDBERG, E. W., *Basic Mathematics for Administration* (New York: John Wiley & Sons, Inc., 1967).

MCADAMS, A. K., *Mathematical Analysis for Management Decisions* (New York: The Macmillan Company, 1970).

STERN, MARK E., *Mathematics for Management* (Englewood Cliffs, N.J.: Prentice-Hall, Inc., 1963).

THEODORE, CHRIS A., *Applied Mathematics: An Introduction* (Homewood, Ill.: Richard D. Irwin, Inc., 1971).

Appendixes

Appendices

A. Binomial Distribution, Individual Terms

$$P(s|n, p) = \binom{n}{s} p^s q^{n-s}$$

Example: $P(5|10, .30) = .1029$

INDIVIDUAL TERMS, BINOMIAL DISTRIBUTION

n	S	.05	.10	.15	.20	.25	p .30	.35	.40	.45	.50
1	0	.9500	.9000	.8500	.8000	.7500	.7000	.6500	.6000	.5500	.5000
	1	.0500	.1000	.1500	.2000	.2500	.3000	.3500	.4000	.4500	.5000
2	0	.9025	.8100	.7225	.6400	.5625	.4900	.4225	.3600	.3025	.2500
	1	.0950	.1800	.2550	.3200	.3750	.4200	.4550	.4800	.4950	.5000
	2	.0025	.0100	.0225	.0400	.0625	.0900	.1225	.1600	.2025	.2500
3	0	.8574	.7290	.6141	.5120	.4219	.3430	.2746	.2160	.1664	.1250
	1	.1354	.2430	.3251	.3840	.4219	.4410	.4436	.4320	.4084	.3750
	2	.0071	.0270	.0574	.0960	.1406	.1890	.2389	.2880	.3341	.3750
	3	.0001	.0010	.0034	.0080	.0156	.0270	.0429	.0640	.0911	.1250
4	0	.8145	.6561	.5220	.4096	.3164	.2401	.1785	.1296	.0915	.0625
	1	.1715	.2916	.3685	.4096	.4219	.4116	.3845	.3456	.2995	.2500
	2	.0135	.0486	.0975	.1536	.2109	.2646	.3105	.3456	.3675	.3750
	3	.0005	.0036	.0115	.0256	.0469	.0756	.1115	.1536	.2005	.2500
	4	.0000	.0001	.0005	.0016	.0039	.0081	.0150	.0256	.0410	.0625
5	0	.7738	.5905	.4437	.3277	.2373	.1681	.1160	.0778	.0503	.0312
	1	.2036	.3280	.3915	.4096	.3955	.3602	.3124	.2592	.2059	.1562
	2	.0214	.0729	.1382	.2048	.2637	.3087	.3364	.3456	.3369	.3125
	3	.0011	.0081	.0244	.0512	.0879	.1323	.1811	.2304	.2757	.3125
	4	.0000	.0004	.0022	.0064	.0146	.0284	.0488	.0768	.1128	.1562
	5	.0000	.0000	.0001	.0003	.0010	.0024	.0053	.0102	.0185	.0312
6	0	.7351	.5314	.3771	.2621	.1780	.1176	.0754	.0467	.0277	.0156
	1	.2321	.3543	.3993	.3932	.3560	.3025	.2437	.1866	.1359	.0938
	2	.0305	.0984	.1762	.2458	.2966	.3241	.3280	.3110	.2780	.2344
	3	.0021	.0146	.0415	.0819	.1318	.1852	.2355	.2765	.3032	.3125
	4	.0001	.0012	.0055	.0154	.0330	.0595	.0951	.1382	.1861	.2344
	5	.0000	.0001	.0004	.0015	.0044	.0102	.0205	.0369	.0609	.0938
	6	.0000	.0000	.0000	.0001	.0002	.0007	.0018	.0041	.0083	.0156

INDIVIDUAL TERMS, BINOMIAL DISTRIBUTION (Continued)

n	S	.05	.10	.15	.20	.25	p .30	.35	.40	.45	.50
7	0	.6983	.4783	.3206	.2097	.1335	.0824	.0490	.0280	.0152	.0078
	1	.2573	.3720	.3960	.3670	.3115	.2471	.1848	.1306	.0872	.0547
	2	.0406	.1240	.2097	.2753	.3115	.3177	.2985	.2613	.2140	.1641
	3	.0036	.0230	.0617	.1147	.1730	.2269	.2679	.2903	.2918	.2734
	4	.0002	.0026	.0109	.0287	.0577	.0972	.1442	.1935	.2388	.2734
	5	.0000	.0002	.0012	.0043	.0115	.0250	.0466	.0774	.1172	.1641
	6	.0000	.0000	.0001	.0004	.0013	.0036	.0084	.0172	.0320	.0547
	7	.0000	.0000	.0000	.0000	.0001	.0002	.0006	.0016	.0037	.0078
8	0	.6634	.4305	.2725	.1678	.1001	.0576	.0319	.0168	.0084	.0039
	1	.2793	.3826	.3847	.3355	.2670	.1977	.1373	.0896	.0548	.0312
	2	.0515	.1488	.2376	.2936	.3115	.2965	.2587	.2090	.1569	.1094
	3	.0054	.0331	.0839	.1468	.2076	.2541	.2786	.2787	.2568	.2188
	4	.0004	.0046	.0185	.0459	.0865	.1361	.1875	.2322	.2627	.2734
	5	.0000	.0004	.0026	.0092	.0231	.0467	.0808	.1239	.1719	.2188
	6	.0000	.0000	.0002	.0011	.0038	.0100	.0217	.0413	.0703	.1094
	7	.0000	.0000	.0000	.0001	.0004	.0012	.0033	.0079	.0164	.0312
	8	.0000	.0000	.0000	.0000	.0000	.0001	.0002	.0007	.0017	.0039
9	0	.6302	.3874	.2316	.1342	.0751	.0404	.0207	.0101	.0046	.0020
	1	.2985	.3874	.3679	.3020	.2253	.1556	.1004	.0605	.0339	.0176
	2	.0629	.1722	.2597	.3020	.3003	.2668	.2162	.1612	.1110	.0703
	3	.0077	.0446	.1069	.1762	.2336	.2668	.2716	.2508	.2119	.1641
	4	.0006	.0074	.0283	.0661	.1168	.1715	.2194	.2508	.2600	.2461
	5	.0000	.0008	.0050	.0165	.0389	.0735	.1181	.1672	.2128	.2461
	6	.0000	.0001	.0006	.0028	.0087	.0210	.0424	.0743	.1160	.1641
	7	.0000	.0000	.0000	.0003	.0012	.0039	.0098	.0212	.0407	.0703
	8	.0000	.0000	.0000	.0000	.0001	.0004	.0013	.0035	.0083	.0176
	9	.0000	.0000	.0000	.0000	.0000	.0000	.0001	.0003	.0008	.0020
10	0	.5987	.3487	.1969	.1074	.0563	.0282	.0135	.0060	.0025	.0010
	1	.3151	.3874	.3474	.2684	.1877	.1211	.0725	.0403	.0207	.0098
	2	.0746	.1937	.2759	.3020	.2816	.2335	.1757	.1209	.0763	.0439
	3	.0105	.0574	.1298	.2013	.2503	.2668	.2522	.2150	.1665	.1172
	4	.0010	.0112	.0401	.0881	.1460	.2001	.2377	.2508	.2384	.2051
	5	.0001	.0015	.0085	.0264	.0584	.1029	.1536	.2007	.2340	.2461
	6	.0000	.0001	.0012	.0055	.0162	.0368	.0689	.1115	.1596	.2051
	7	.0000	.0000	.0001	.0008	.0031	.0090	.0212	.0425	.0746	.1172
	8	.0000	.0000	.0000	.0001	.0004	.0014	.0043	.0106	.0229	.0439
	9	.0000	.0000	.0000	.0000	.0000	.0001	.0005	.0016	.0042	.0098
	10	.0000	.0000	.0000	.0000	.0000	.0000	.0000	.0001	.0003	.0010

INDIVIDUAL TERMS, BINOMIAL DISTRIBUTION (Continued)

n	S	.05	.10	.15	.20	.25	*p* .30	.35	.40	.45	.50
11	0	.5688	.3138	.1673	.0859	.0422	.0198	.0088	.0036	.0014	.0005
	1	.3293	.3835	.3248	.2362	.1549	.0932	.0518	.0266	.0125	.0054
	2	.0867	.2131	.2866	.2953	.2581	.1998	.1395	.0087	.0513	.0269
	3	.0317	.0710	.1517	.2215	.2581	.2568	.2254	.1774	.1259	.0806
	4	.0014	.0158	.0536	.1107	.1721	.2201	.2428	.2365	.2060	.1611
	5	.0001	.0025	.0132	.0388	.0803	.1321	.1830	.2207	.2360	.2256
	6	.0000	.0003	.0023	.0097	.0268	.0566	.0985	.1471	.1931	.2256
	7	.0000	.0000	.0003	.0017	.0064	.0173	.0379	.0701	.1128	.1611
	8	.0000	.0000	.0000	.0002	.0011	.0037	.0102	.0234	.0462	.0806
	9	.0000	.0000	.0000	.0000	.0001	.0005	.0018	.0052	.0126	.0269
19	0	.3774	.1351	.0456	.0144	.0042	.0011	.0003	.0001	.0000	.0000
	1	.3774	.2852	.1529	.0685	.0268	.0093	.0029	.0008	.0002	.0000
	2	.1787	.2852	.2428	.1540	.0803	.0358	.0138	.0046	.0013	.0003
	3	.0533	.1796	.2428	.2182	.1517	.0869	.0422	.0175	.0062	.0018
	4	.0112	.0798	.1714	.2182	.2023	.1491	.0909	.0467	.0203	.0074
	5	.0018	.0266	.0907	.1636	.2023	.1916	.1468	.0933	.0497	.0222
	6	.0002	.0069	.0374	.0955	.1574	.1916	.1844	.1451	.0949	.0518
	7	.0000	.0014	.0122	.0443	.0974	.1525	.1844	.1797	.1443	.0961
	8	.0000	.0002	.0032	.0166	.0487	.0981	.1489	.1797	.1771	.1442
	9	.0000	.0000	.0007	.0051	.0198	.0514	.0980	.1464	.1771	.1762
	10	.0000	.0000	.0001	.0013	.0066	.0220	.0528	.0976	.1449	.1762
	11	.0000	.0000	.0000	.0003	.0018	.0077	.0233	.0532	.0970	.1442
	12	.0000	.0000	.0000	.0000	.0004	.0022	.0083	.0237	.0529	.0961
	13	.0000	.0000	.0000	.0000	.0001	.0005	.0024	.0085	.0233	.0518
	14	.0000	.0000	.0000	.0000	.0000	.0001	.0006	.0024	.0082	.0222
	15	.0000	.0000	.0000	.0000	.0000	.0000	.0001	.0005	.0022	.0074
	16	.0000	.0000	.0000	.0000	.0000	.0000	.0000	.0001	.0005	.0018
	17	.0000	.0000	.0000	.0000	.0000	.0000	.0000	.0000	.0001	.0003
	18	.0000	.0000	.0000	.0000	.0000	.0000	.0000	.0000	.0000	.0000
	19	.0000	.0000	.0000	.0000	.0000	.0000	.0000	.0000	.0000	.0000

INDIVIDUAL TERMS, BINOMIAL DISTRIBUTION (Continued)

n	S	.05	.10	.15	.20	.25	p .30	.35	.40	.45	.50
20	0	.3585	.1216	.0388	.1115	.0032	.0008	.0002	.0000	.0000	.0000
	1	.3774	.2702	.1368	.0576	.0211	.0068	.0020	.0005	.0001	.0000
	2	.1887	.2852	.2293	.1369	.0669	.0278	.0100	.0031	.0008	.0002
	3	.0596	.1901	.2428	.2054	.1339	.0716	.0323	.0123	.0040	.0011
	4	.0133	.0898	.1821	.2182	.1897	.1304	.0738	.0350	.0139	.0046
	5	.0022	.0319	.1028	.1746	.2023	.1789	.1272	.0746	.0365	.0148
	6	.0003	.0089	.0454	.1091	.1686	.1916	.1712	.1244	.0746	.0370
	7	.0000	.0020	.0160	.0545	.1124	.1643	.1844	.1659	.1221	.0739
	8	.0000	.0004	.0046	.0222	.0609	.1144	.1614	.1797	.1623	.1201
	9	.0000	.0001	.0011	.0074	.0271	.0654	.1158	.1597	.1771	.1602
	10	.0000	.0000	.0002	.0020	.0099	.0308	.0686	.1171	.1593	.1762
	11	.0000	.0000	.0000	.0005	.0030	.0120	.0336	.0710	.1185	.1602
	12	.0000	.0000	.0000	.0001	.0008	.0039	.0136	.0355	.0727	.1201
	13	.0000	.0000	.0000	.0000	.0002	.0010	.0045	.0146	.0366	.0739
	14	.0000	.0000	.0000	.0000	.0000	.0002	.0012	.0049	.0150	.0370
	15	.0000	.0000	.0000	.0000	.0000	.0000	.0003	.0013	.0049	.0148
	16	.0000	.0000	.0000	.0000	.0000	.0000	.0000	.0003	.0013	.0046
	17	.0000	.0000	.0000	.0000	.0000	.0000	.0000	.0000	.0002	.0011
	18	.0000	.0000	.0000	.0000	.0000	.0000	.0000	.0000	.0000	.0002
	19	.0000	.0000	.0000	.0000	.0000	.0000	.0000	.0000	.0000	.0000
	20	.0000	.0000	.0000	.0000	.0000	.0000	.0000	.0000	.0000	.0000

INDIVIDUAL TERMS, BINOMIAL DISTRIBUTION (Continued)

n	S	.05	.10	.15	.20	.25	p .30	.35	.40	.45	.50
25	0	.2774	.0718	.0172	.0038	.0008	.0001	.0000	.0000	.0000	.0000
	1	.3650	.1994	.0759	.0236	.0063	.0014	.0003	.0000	.0000	.0000
	2	.2305	.2659	.1607	.0708	.0251	.0074	.0018	.0004	.0001	.0000
	3	.0930	.2265	.2174	.1358	.0641	.0243	.0076	.0019	.0004	.0001
	4	.0269	.1384	.2110	.1867	.1175	.0572	.0224	.0071	.0018	.0004
	5	.0060	.0646	.1564	.1960	.1645	.1030	.0506	.0199	.0063	.0016
	6	.0010	.0239	.0920	.1633	.1828	.1472	.0908	.0442	.0172	.0053
	7	.0001	.0072	.0441	.1108	.1654	.1712	.1327	.0800	.0381	.0143
	8	.0000	.0018	.0175	.0623	.1241	.1651	.1607	.1200	.0701	.0322
	9	.0000	.0004	.0058	.0294	.0781	.1336	.1635	.1511	.1084	.0609
	10	.0000	.0001	.0016	.0118	.0417	.0916	.1409	.1612	.1419	.0974
	11	.0000	.0000	.0004	.0040	.0189	.0536	.1034	.1465	.1583	.1328
	12	.0000	.0000	.0001	.0012	.0074	.0268	.0650	.1140	.1511	.1550
	13	.0000	.0000	.0000	.0003	.0025	.0115	.0350	.0760	.1236	.1550
	14	.0000	.0000	.0000	.0001	.0007	.0042	.0161	.0434	.0867	.1328
	15	.0000	.0000	.0000	.0000	.0002	.0013	.0064	.0212	.0520	.0974
	16	.0000	.0000	.0000	.0000	.0000	.0004	.0021	.0088	.0266	.0609
	17	.0000	.0000	.0000	.0000	.0000	.0001	.0006	.0031	.0115	.0322
	18	.0000	.0000	.0000	.0000	.0000	.0000	.0001	.0009	.0042	.0143
	19	.0000	.0000	.0000	.0000	.0000	.0000	.0000	.0002	.0013	.0053
	20	.0000	.0000	.0000	.0000	.0000	.0000	.0000	.0000	.0003	.0016
	21	.0000	.0000	.0000	.0000	.0000	.0000	.0000	.0000	.0001	.0004
	22	.0000	.0000	.0000	.0000	.0000	.0000	.0000	.0000	.0000	.0001

INDIVIDUAL TERMS, BINOMIAL DISTRIBUTION (Continued)

n	S	.05	.10	.15	.20	.25	p .30	.35	.40	.45	.50
50	0	.0769	.0052	.0003	.0000	.0000	.0000	.0000	.0000	.0000	.0000
	1	.2025	.0286	.0026	.0002	.0000	.0000	.0000	.0000	.0000	.0000
	2	.2611	.0779	.0113	.0011	.0001	.0000	.0000	.0000	.0000	.0000
	3	.2199	.1386	.0319	.0044	.0004	.0000	.0000	.0000	.0000	.0000
	4	.1360	.1809	.0661	.0128	.0016	.0001	.0000	.0000	.0000	.0000
	5	.0658	.1849	.1072	.0295	.0049	.0006	.0000	.0000	.0000	.0000
	6	.0260	.1541	.1419	.0554	.0123	.0018	.0002	.0000	.0000	.0000
	7	.0086	.1076	.1575	.0870	.0259	.0048	.0006	.0000	.0000	.0000
	8	.0024	.0643	.1493	.1169	.0463	.0110	.0017	.0002	.0000	.0000
	9	.0006	.0333	.1230	.1364	.0721	.0220	.0042	.0005	.0000	.0000
	10	.0001	.0152	.0890	.1398	.0985	.0386	.0093	.0014	.0001	.0000
	11	.0000	.0061	.0571	.1271	.1194	.0602	.0182	.0035	.0004	.0000
	12	0	.0022	.0328	.1033	.1294	.0838	.0319	.0076	.0011	.0001
	13	0	.0007	.0169	.0755	.1261	.1050	.0502	.0147	.0027	.0003
	14	0	.0002	.0079	.0499	.1110	.1189	.0714	.0260	.0059	.0008
	15	0	.0001	.0033	.0299	.0888	.1223	.0923	.0415	.0116	.0020
	16	0	.0000	.0013	.0164	.0648	.1147	.1088	.0606	.0207	.0044
	17	0	0	.0005	.0082	.0432	.0983	.1171	.0808	.0339	.0087
	18	0	0	.0001	.0037	.0264	.0772	.1156	.0987	.0508	.0160
	19	0	0	.0000	.0016	.0148	.0558	.1048	.1109	.0700	.0270
	20	0	0	.0000	.0006	.0077	.0370	.0875	.1146	.0888	.0419

INDIVIDUAL TERMS, BINOMIAL DISTRIBUTION (Continued)

n	S	.05	.10	.15	.20	.25	p .30	.35	.40	.45	.50
100	0	.0059	.0000	.0000	.0000	0	0	0	0	0	0
	1	.0312	.0003	.0000	.0000	0	0	0	0	0	0
	2	.0812	.0016	.0000	.0000	0	0	0	0	0	0
	3	.1396	.0059	.0001	.0000	.0000	0	0	0	0	0
	4	.1781	.0159	.0003	.0000	.0000	0	0	0	0	0
	5	.1800	.0339	.0011	.0000	.0000	0	0	0	0	0
	6	.1500	.0596	.0031	.0001	.0000	0	0	0	0	0
	7	.1060	.0889	.0075	.0002	.0000	0	0	0	0	0
	8	.0649	.1148	.0154	.0006	.0000	0	0	0	0	0
	9	.0349	.1304	.0276	.0015	.0000	0	0	0	0	0
	10	.0167	.1319	.0444	.0034	.0001	.0000	0	0	0	0
	11	.0072	.1199	.0640	.0069	.0003	.0000	0	0	0	0
	12	.0028	.0988	.0838	.0128	.0006	.0000	0	0	0	0
	13	.0010	.0743	.1001	.0216	.0014	.0000	.0000	0	0	0
	14	.0003	.0513	.1098	.0335	.0030	.0001	.0000	0	0	0
	15	.0001	.0327	.1111	.0481	.0057	.0002	.0001	0	0	0
	16	.0000	.0193	.1041	.0638	.0100	.0006	.0003	0	0	0
	17	.0000	.0106	.0908	.0789	.0165	.0012	.0006	0	0	0
	18	.0000	.0054	.0739	.0909	.0254	.0024	.0013	0	0	0
	19	.0000	.0026	.0563	.0981	.0365	.0044	.0025	0	0	0
	20	.0000	.0012	.0402	.0993	.0493	.0076	.0046	0	0	0

B. Random Numbers

041	574	691	422	069	327	297	534	975	017
413	008	118	957	472	128	211	703	467	135
711	893	377	699	615	360	616	221	359	249
401	612	709	080	770	237	516	369	798	475
938	909	835	661	649	217	415	214	515	840
072	954	127	890	376	743	821	538	510	413
205	998	614	436	782	184	631	321	604	073
892	029	661	127	304	289	740	603	390	375
609	571	304	066	196	439	006	636	707	065
129	036	107	214	075	557	246	084	789	327
753	015	451	086	377	162	178	844	334	458
276	481	931	196	296	559	188	166	461	959
472	153	619	638	386	155	181	438	876	241
009	272	020	194	964	774	631	853	283	605
645	115	464	091	484	537	252	677	920	192
365	679	262	488	898	534	236	519	566	534
083	427	286	658	715	149	039	591	292	393
743	342	511	950	273	277	794	056	559	602
320	195	118	365	921	903	838	703	709	850
646	518	202	657	683	448	926	167	715	892

C. Values of $e^{-\mu}$ (Poisson Distribution)

μ	$e^{-\mu}$	μ	$e^{-\mu}$	μ	$e^{-\mu}$	μ	$e^{-\mu}$
0.0	1.000	2.5	.082	5.0	.0067	7.5	.00055
0.1	.905	2.6	.074	5.1	.0061	7.6	.00050
0.2	.819	2.7	.067	5.2	.0055	7.7	.00045
0.3	.741	2.8	.061	5.3	.0050	7.8	.00041
0.4	.670	2.9	.055	5.4	.0045	7.9	.00037
0.5	.607	3.0	.050	5.5	.0041	8.0	.00034
0.6	.549	3.1	.045	5.6	.0037	8.1	.00030
0.7	.497	3.2	.041	5.7	.0033	8.2	.00028
0.8	.449	3.3	.037	5.8	.0030	8.3	.00025
0.9	.407	3.4	.033	5.9	.0027	8.4	.00023
1.0	.368	3.5	.030	6.0	.0025	8.5	.00020
1.1	.333	3.6	.027	6.1	.0022	8.6	.00018
1.2	.301	3.7	.025	6.2	.0020	8.7	.00017
1.3	.273	3.8	.022	6.3	.0018	8.8	.00015
1.4	.247	3.9	.020	6.4	.0017	8.9	.00014
1.5	.223	4.0	.018	6.5	.0015	9.0	.00012
1.6	.202	4.1	.017	6.6	.0014	9.1	.00011
1.7	.183	4.2	.015	6.7	.0012	9.2	.00010
1.8	.165	4.3	.014	6.8	.0011	9.3	.00009
1.9	.150	4.4	.012	6.9	.0010	9.4	.00008
2.0	.135	4.5	.011	7.0	.0009	9.5	.00008
2.1	.122	4.6	.010	7.1	.0008	9.6	.00007
2.2	.111	4.7	.009	7.2	.0007	9.7	.00006
2.3	.100	4.8	.008	7.3	.0007	9.8	.00006
2.4	.091	4.9	.007	7.4	.0006	9.9	.00005

D. Answers to Selected Exercises

CHAPTER 1

6. Pessimism, S_2
Regret, S_1
Rationality, S_1
Optimism, S_1
Maximax, S_1

8. p (success) $= \frac{1}{2}$

10. (a) Select S_2
(b) $p(N_1) \geq .6$

12. Test market, $+128$
Produce and market, $+113$
Sell patent, $+30$

CHAPTER 2

4. (a) $3:2$ against a victory
(b) Dry field
(c) .38

6.

p	$p(p \mid d = 7, n = 50)$
.30	.058
.05	.942

7.

	Posterior
Brown	.113
Black	.701
Green	.186

9. The firm should not take the survey and should use S_1. The fee is critical since the net expected incremental profit following the survey is $265,000.

10. (a) Using prior analysis, he should not inspect. EV $=$ $130.00.
(b) Using posterior analysis ($N = 3$), he should inspect. EV $=$ $136.90.
(c) Using posterior analysis ($N = 100$), he should not inspect. EV $=$ $131.60.

12. (b)

	Survey Result	Expected	Optimal Strategy
No survey	None	1.32	S_3
Informal survey,	Z_1		S_3
60% reliable	Z_2	1.29	S_3
	Z_3		S_3

	First Stage	Second Stage		Optimal Strategy
Two-stage formal survey,	Z_1	Cancel		S_3
80% and 90%	Z_2	Z_1		S_3
reliable	Z_2	Z_2		S_1
	Z_2	Z_3	1.34	S_1
	Z_3	Z_1		S_3
	Z_3	Z_2		S_1
	Z_3	Z_3		S_1

CHAPTER 3

1.
$$\begin{pmatrix} 342 & 408 & 703 \\ 43 & 42 & 56 \\ 172 & 168 & 224 \\ 188 & 132 & 65 \end{pmatrix}$$

2. $X = 4$
$Y = 5$
$Z = 2$

3. The market shares at equilibrium are
$X = 35\%$
$Y = 45\%$
$Z = 20\%$

7. The market shares at the end of period 1 are
$A = 39\%$
$B = 40\%$
$C = 21\%$

8. By 8 P.M., 360 fans could be serviced and a waiting line of 360 would have developed.

10. The firm would be approximately 25 days (25.2) behind schedule.

11. The probability of two arrivals is .2509. The probability of less than two arrivals is .5575.

12. The November market share for store G is 52.5 per cent.

CHAPTER 4

1. Maximization occurs when $A = 12$ and $B = 0$, resulting in a maximum value of $120.

3. Mail out 12,000 type A and 5,200 type B. The profit contribution will be $39,600.

4. $X = 2.73$, $Y = 2.18$, resulting in a maximum value of $14.18.

5. $A = 6.86$, $B = 1.71$, resulting in a minimum value of $65.14.

9. Nine packages of Gruyère and eight package of Swiss would result in a minimum total cost of $4.32.

10. Six packages of Gruyère and 12 packages of Swiss. Such a basket would cost $5.28.

11. Six vanilla-fudge cookies and 10 lemon creme cookies would cost 22 cents.

CHAPTER 5

Section 5.7

5. $f'(x) = 2(x + 1)$

6. $y' = 1 - 2/x^2$

9. $\dfrac{dTC}{dQ} = -\dfrac{DS}{Q^2} + \dfrac{pI}{2}$

Section 5.11

3. maximum at $(0, 5)$
minimum at $(2, 1)$

4. minimum at $(2, \frac{2}{3})$
maximum at $(1, \frac{5}{6})$
inflection point at $(\frac{3}{2}, \frac{3}{4})$

Section 5.14

1. $a = 20$ inches; $b = 40$ inches; volume $= 16,000$ cubic inches

3. $73.00 per season ticket

4. (a) $C = $69,000
(b) $t = 34$ months

Section 5.16

2. (c) Earnings will be equal in 1976.

3. When the firm sells 125,000 units, profits will be maximized at $30,050.

6. Maximum profit is $25.

7. Duty rate should be $75.

Section 5.19

3. $e = -200/1,568$

Section 5.23

2. (a) Point $(R = -22, Q = 3, A = -2)$ is a minimum.

4. $R = \$286$ per month
$W = \$1142$ per month

5. The maximum profit obtainable is $30,000.

Index of Authors Cited

Subject Index